math 7

for Christian Schools®

Bob Jones University Press, Greenville, South Carolina 29614
Textbook Division

Carl D. Herbster, Ed.D.

Consultants:
Robert R. Taylor, B.S., M.A., Ph.D.
Ruth Ella Dennison, B.A.
Marilyn H. Elmer, B.S., M.S.
Bonney Rudd Block, B.S.

Designed by Joyce Landis
Illustrated by James Harris
Brian Johnson
Kathleen Pflug
Daniel Smith

MATH for Christian Schools ®: Book 7

Produced in cooperation with the Bob Jones University Department of Mathematics of the College of Arts and Science, the School of Education, and Bob Jones Junior High School.

ISBN 0-89084-181-0

Printed in the United States of America

20 19 18 17 16 15 14 13 12 11 10

Contents

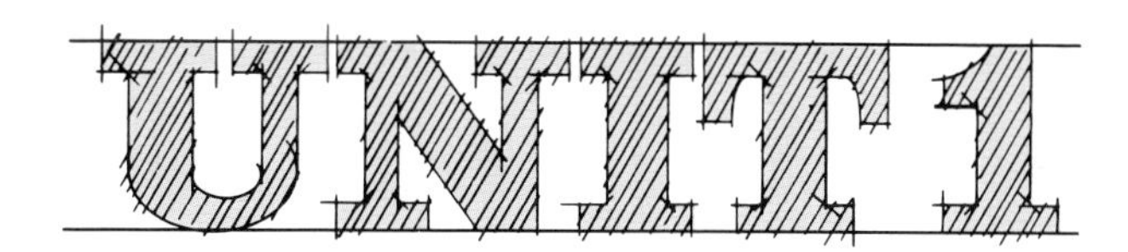

Grain Farmer

The sun was already setting in the western sky when Mr. Petrocelli set his weary body down in a comfortable chair. He had had a long, hard day in the fields, but at last the harvesting was finished. All year long he had worked in his fields, tilling the soil, planting the seeds, and spraying his plants with herbicides and pesticides to keep them free of weeds and insects.

Mr. Petrocelli is a successful farmer—successful because he works hard and plans ahead. Last year he planted these fields with corn; this year he planted them with soybeans. He rotates his crops yearly to make the best possible use of the soil. He planted soybeans this year because they replenish the soil's nitrogen, which was depleted by last year's corn crop. To avoid waste, he calculates the exact amount of seed he needs to plant. He keeps his disks, harrows, cultivators, planter, and combine in good condition so that the farm work need not be slowed down for repairs.

Of course, Mr. Petrocelli cannot do all the work by himself. He employs others to help him. He delegates responsibilities to men he can trust. Richard Barnett supervises the harvest work in the fields. Mickey Jaworski tends to the storage of the grain. Stewart Hausmann prepares the freshly harvested fields for the sowing of winter wheat. All have a part in the daily care of the crops.

Delegation of major responsibilities allows Mr. Petrocelli to watch the market and sell his soybeans at the right time. He plans thoughtfully, purchases quality seed, and gives the crops daily care and proper nourishment. He knows that unless he exercises care and foresight he cannot expect a good harvest. God carefully planned His field and prepared a special job for each worker. Daily nourishment in His Word will replenish us spiritually and enable us to yield a bountiful harvest for Christ. If we commune daily with God, we will rejoice with Him in the day of harvest, knowing that He has reaped what He has sown.

Sets

SEPTEMBER						
S	M	T	W	Th	F	S
					1	2
3	4	5	6	7	8	9
10	11	12	13	14	15	16
17	18	19	20	21	22	23
24	25	26	27	28	29	30

A description of the set

{the days of the week}

A list of the members of the set

{Sunday, Monday, Tuesday,
Wednesday, Thursday,
Friday, Saturday}

What do you think?

List the names of the months of the year.
Is September one of the names you listed?
Is Sunday one of the names you listed?
How many names did you list?
Does the order in which you listed the names matter? Why or why not?

Keys to Understanding

A *set* is a group or collection of objects.
A set is often named with a capital letter (set A).

The objects in a set are called *members* or *elements*.
The symbol $\in$ means "is an element of."
The symbol $\notin$ means "is not an element of."

The symbols { } mean "the set whose members are."
These symbols are called set braces.

A set with no members is called the *empty set*.
The symbols $\varnothing$ or { } mean "the empty set" or "the null set."

Sets may be described or listed.

described: A = {the four gospels in the New Testament}

listed: A = {Matthew, Mark, Luke, John}

Is Mark a member of set A?

We write it this way: Mark $\in$ A

Is Michael a member of set A?

We write it this way: Michael $\notin$ A

described: X = {the biblical characters living on earth today}

How many are in set X?

listed: X = { } or $\varnothing$

For a set to be useful, it must be *well defined*. That is, it must be easy to determine exactly what members belong to the set.

Example: {days of the week} is a well-defined set.

Example: {all pretty days} is not well defined.

Practice

List the members of each set.

1. L = {the letters in the word *large*}

2. E = {the letters in the word *happy*}

3. Y = {the first two of the Ten Commandments}

4. T = {the odd numbers less than 10}

5. D = {the red, white, and blue hippos}

6. F = {the three persons in the Godhead}

7. S = {the teachers in this school}

8. K = {letters in the word *Mississippi*}

Using the sets above, tell whether each statement is true or false.

9. a $\in$ L

10. a $\in$ K

11. 11 $\in$ T

12. Exodus $\notin$ F

13. Matthew $\in$ D

14. 5 $\in$ S

15. h $\notin$ E

16. p $\in$ E and K

Determine whether or not each of the following sets is well defined.

17. B = {boys in this classroom}

18. V = {good music}

19. C = {pretty girls in this school}

20. J = {months of the year}

Subsets

Is every book in the Bible a book of the New Testament?
Is every book in the New Testament a book of the Bible?

B = {the books in the Bible}
T = {the books in the New Testament}

Every member of set T is a member of set B; therefore T is a *subset* of B.
Is B a subset of T? Why or why not?

Keys to Understanding

Set D is a *subset* of set E if all the members of set D are also members of set E.

We write it this way: $D \subseteq E$
The symbol $\subseteq$ means "is a subset of."

The empty set is a subset of every set.
Every set is a subset of itself.

Set F is not a subset of set G if not all the members of set F are members of set G.
We write it this way: $F \not\subseteq G$
The symbol $\not\subseteq$ means "is not a subset of."

"Venn diagrams" are used to show relationships among two or more sets.

Are the basic vowels a subset of the letters of the alphabet?
What other set of letters is a subset of the alphabet?

A = {the letters of the alphabet}
V = {the basic vowels}

Express the relationship between A and V.

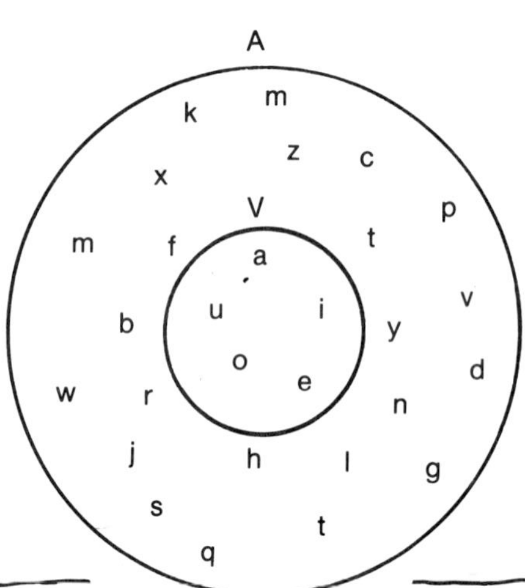

Practice

For each set on the left, state the letter naming the set of which it is a subset.

1. {2, 4, 6, 8}
2. {Indiana}
3. {r, s}
4. {Joseph}
5. {fall, winter}
6. {peaches, pears}
7. {o, s}
8. {math, English}
9. {trees, flowers}
10. {Peter}

A = {the seasons of the year}
B = {the subjects I am taking in school}
C = {the plants}
D = {the countries in North America}
E = {the disciples of Jesus}
F = {the letters in the word *girls*}
G = {the even numbers between 0 and 10}
H = {the fruit we eat}
I = {the states in the United States}
J = {the presidents of the U.S.A.}
K = {the sons of Jacob}
L = {the letters in the word *so*}

Tell whether statements 11-20 are true or false.

A = {2, 4, 6, 8, 10}
B = {a, b, c, d, e}
C = {2, 4, 6}
D = {b, e, d}
E = {4, 10}
F = {e, d}

11. $F \subseteq D$
12. $C \subseteq E$
13. $D \nsubseteq B$
14. $\varnothing \subseteq A$
15. $A \subseteq F$
16. $E \nsubseteq C$
17. $C \subseteq A$
18. $F \subseteq E$
19. $E \subseteq A$
20. $\varnothing \nsubseteq B$

Union of Sets

When you add, you combine two sets of objects to make a third set. Michelle and Linda combined these two sets (X and Y) and counted to see how many objects there were altogether (set Z). This was an example of the *union* of two sets. We write "$X \cup Y = Z$."

Keys to Understanding

The *union* of two sets is the set found by combining the members of both sets. Each of the members of the union is a member of at least one of the beginning sets.

The symbol $\cup$ means "union."

Description of sets B and C

B = {the letters in the word *basketball*}
C = {the letters in the word *cheerleader*}

Listing of sets B and C

B = {b, a, s, k, e, t, l}
C = {c, h, e, r, l, a, d}

Why was it not necessary to list the same letter twice?

Venn Diagram

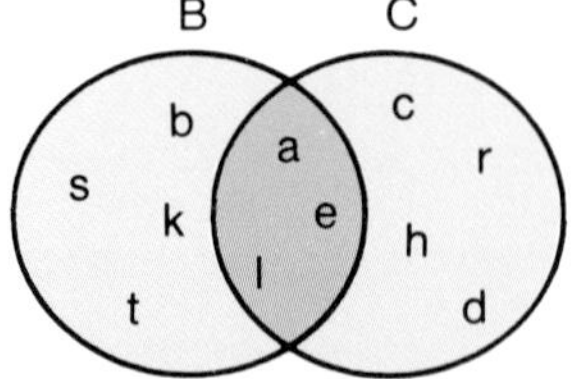

$B \cup C$ = shaded area

Description of the union of sets B and C

$B \cup C$ = {the letters in either the word *basketball* or the word *cheerleader*}

Listing of the union of sets B and C

$B \cup C = \{b, a, s, k, e, t, l, c, h, r, d\}$

Practice

Describe the set formed by the union of each of these pairs of sets.

1. B = {the male students in our class}
G = {the female students in our class}
$B \cup G = ?$

2. T = {the even numbers between 0 and 10}
S = {the odd numbers between 0 and 10}
$T \cup S = ?$

3. K = {the students in our school who are 16 years old}
H = {the students in our school who are 12 years old}
$K \cup H = ?$

4. V = {the men mentioned in the Old Testament}
M = {the men mentioned in the New Testament}
$V \cup M = ?$

5. C = {the students in our school with a C average or above}
G = {the students in our school with an A average}
$C \cup G = ?$

Use set notation to write the unions for numbers 6-15.

$A = \{1, 3, 5, 7, 9\}$
$B = \{a, e, i, o, u\}$
$C = \varnothing$
$D = \{2, 4, 6, 8\}$
$E = \{x, y, z\}$
$F = \{d, e, b, i\}$

Remember, do the work in the parentheses first!

6. $A \cup F =$

7. $B \cup E =$

8. $C \cup D =$

9. $F \cup B =$

10. $A \cup C =$

11. $B \cup D =$

12. $E \cup A =$

13. $(A \cup C) \cup D =$

14. $B \cup (D \cup F) =$

15. $(B \cup E) \cup F =$

Intersection of Sets

Two girls were asked, "What do you like to do?"
Their responses are in the following chart:

Susan

Shop
Read books
Roller-skate
Play badminton
Play the piano

Carolyn

Shop
Play the piano
Grow flowers
Play softball
Bake

What interests are common to both girls?

S = {Susan's interests} and C = {Carolyn's interests}

The intersection of sets S and C is
{the common interests of Susan and Carolyn}
or
{shopping, playing the piano}

Keys to Understanding

The *intersection* of two sets is a set whose members are members of both of the original sets.

The symbol ∩ means "intersection." Sets whose intersection is the empty set are called *disjoint sets.*

Venn Diagram

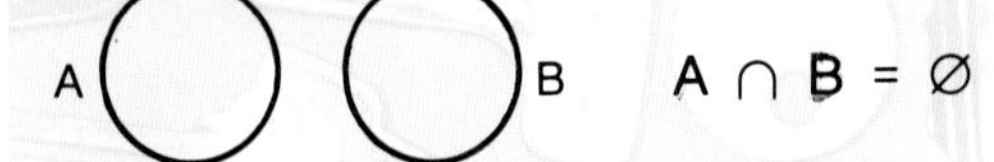

$A \cap B = \varnothing$

Think about the two sets used in our last lesson.

B = {b, a, s, k, e, t, l} = {the letters in the word *basketball*}
C = {c, h, e, r, l, a, d} = {the letters in the word *cheerleader*}

The intersection of the two sets is
$B \cap C$ = {the letters in both the word *basketball* and the word *cheerleader*}
or
$B \cap C$ = {a, e, l}

Venn Diagram

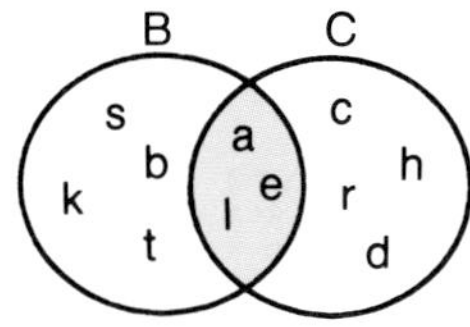

$B \cap C$ = shaded area

Practice

Describe the intersection of each of these pairs of sets.

1. D = {the letters in the word *freshman*}
E = {the letters in the word *senior*}
$D \cap E$ = ?

2. X = {the authors of the books in the New Testament}
Y = {the disciples of Jesus}
$X \cap Y$ = ?

3. O = {the students in our class who wear glasses}
P = {the students in our class who are male}
$O \cap P$ = ?

4. T = {the basic vowels in the alphabet}
V = {the first ten letters in the alphabet}
$T \cap V$ = ?

5. A = {the teachers in our school}
B = {the students in our class}
$A \cap B$ = ?

Use set notation to write the intersections for numbers 6-15.

X = {u, n, i, o}
Y = {a, e, i, o, u}
Z = {b, a, y}

P = {i, n, t, e, r, s, c, o}
Q = {s, u, b, e, t}
R = {m, e, b, r, s}

6. $X \cap Y$ =
7. $R \cap P$ =
8. $Y \cap R$ =
9. $Z \cap Y$ =
10. $R \cap X$ =
11. $Q \cap X$ =
12. $Y \cap P$ =
13. $R \cap Z$ =
14. $(P \cap Q) \cap Y$ =
15. $(Q \cap R) \cap Z$ =

Finite and Infinite Sets

Numbers are used to communicate.

DON'T WORRY, I'M AS CONFUSED AS YOU ARE.

Did you ever think how hard it would be to communicate without numbers? We would be at a loss for words, as is this young man, if we did not have numbers.

Numbers are used to count.

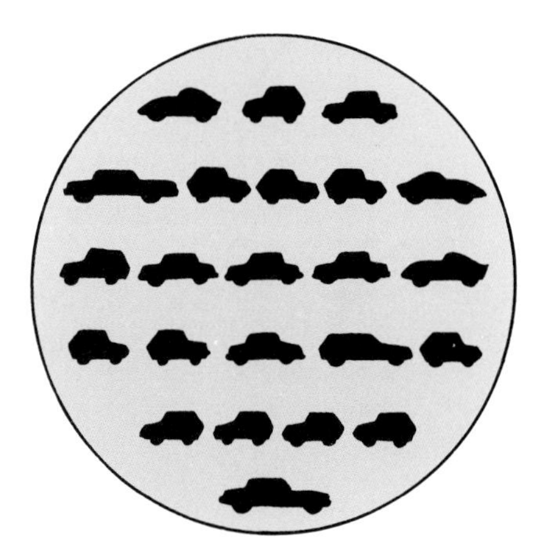

How many cars are in this group?
How did you find the answer?
Of course, you counted.
The numbers you used to count are called the set of natural numbers N.

N = {1, 2, 3, 4, 5 . . .}

N is an *infinite* set.

The union of the set N and the set {0} is called the set of whole numbers W.

W = {0, 1, 2, 3, 4 . . .}

W is an *infinite* set.

The set {0} is a *finite set*.

The three dots indicate that the elements in the set continue in like manner. The dots mean "and so on." Sometimes we also use three dots to shorten a long list of numbers in a finite set.

Example: {the whole numbers less than 20}

or

{0, 1, 2, 3 . . . 18, 19}

Keys to Understanding

A *finite set* is a set in which the members can be counted or listed.

Example: {5, 1, 3, 7, 2, 8, 10}

This set is a finite set because its members can be counted.

{5, 1, 3, 7, 2, 8, 10}
↑ ↑ ↑ ↑ ↑ ↑ ↑
1, 2, 3, 4, 5, 6, 7

An *infinite set* is a set that is not finite.

Example: {1, 2, 3, 4, 5, . . .}

Practice

Tell whether the following sets are finite or infinite.

1. {the men of the Bible}
2. {the numbers greater than 20}
3. {the students named Jim}
4. {the whole numbers multiplied by 2}
5. {the people with two faces}
6. {the grains of sand on the earth}
7. {the natural numbers greater than 11}
8. {the days God has lived}
9. {the hairs of your head}
10. {the days in your earthly life}
11-12. Give descriptions of two finite sets.
13-14. Give descriptions of two infinite sets.

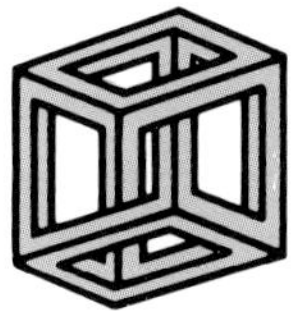

MIND BOGGLER

Give the next three numbers in each of these sets.

{1, 2, 4, 7, 11, __, __, __, . . .}
{1, 3, 7, 15, 31, __, __, __, . . .}

Math in Action

1. Mr. Petrocelli's soybean plants average 15 pods per plant. Each pod contains three beans. He planted an average of 637,120 plants per acre. How many soybeans can Mr. Petrocelli expect to harvest from each acre?
2. If it takes 155 pounds of seed to sow an acre, how many pounds will it take to sow 75 acres?
3. A one-acre lot on Mr. Petrocelli's farm measures 208.7 feet on each of its four sides. Mr. Petrocelli plants his soybeans in rows that are 30 inches apart. How many rows of soybeans will he be able to plant per acre of land?
4. Mr. Petrocelli's neighbor plants corn. He plants each of his rows 24 inches apart. How many rows of corn can he plant per acre of land? How many more rows per acre can he plant than Mr. Petrocelli can?
5. Mr. Petrocelli's combine gets an average of 9 miles per gallon. The gas tank holds 20 gallons. Mr. Petrocelli always fills his tank when it is one-quarter full. How many miles can he drive before he needs to fill the tank?

God is Infinite.

"Before the mountains were brought forth, or ever thou hadst formed the earth and the world, even from everlasting to everlasting, thou art God." Psalm 90:2

"I am Alpha and Omega, the beginning and the ending, saith the Lord, which is, and which was, and which is to come, the Almighty." Revelation 1:8

Man is finite.

"Whereas ye know not what shall be on the morrow. For what is your life? It is even a vapour, that appeareth for a little time, and then vanisheth away." James 4:14

"For all flesh is as grass, and all the glory of man as the flower of grass. The grass withereth, and the flower thereof falleth away." I Peter 1:24

Number Sets

Numbers are used to calculate.

You and a friend go to the nearest fast-food restaurant. You have $5 to spend. Do you have enough money for each of you to buy a hamburger, french fries, shake, and apple pie?

Numbers are used to compare.

The game of football illustrates a need to understand numbers *opposite* the whole numbers on the number line. This set of numbers is called the *negative integers.*

The progress of the Cougars on a series of plays

Down	Play	Result	Number line representation (0 represents line of scrimmage)
1st down	off tackle	gained 2 yards	0 +2
2nd down	QB sacked	lost 7 yards	-7 0
3rd down	complete pass	gained 8 yards	0 +8
4th down	end around	lost 4 yards	-4 0

What was the Cougars' total yardage for the four plays?

What do you think?

Many common ideas require measurements in opposite directions. What is the opposite of

temperatures above zero?
business gains?
five miles north?
taxes cut $500 a year?
loss of $2,000 in the stock market?
twenty-yard gain in football?

Keys to Understanding

The set of *natural numbers* N = {1, 2, 3, 4, 5, . . .}
The set of *whole numbers* W = {0, 1, 2, 3, 4, . . .}
The set of *integers* I = {. . .-3, -2, -1, 0, 1, 2, 3, . . .}

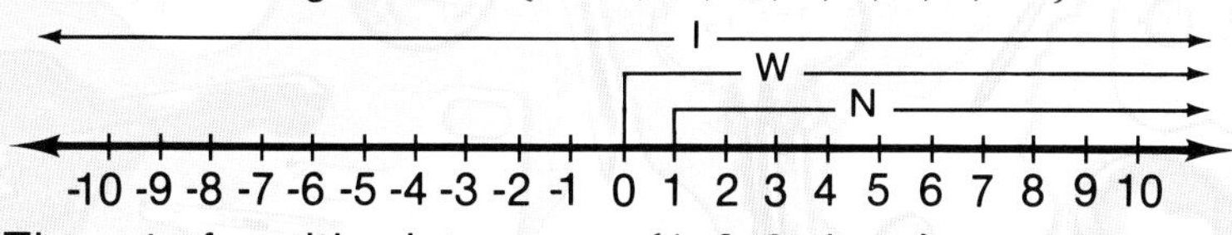

The set of positive integers = {1, 2, 3, 4, . . .}
The set of negative integers = {. . .-4, -3, -2, -1}

Practice

Use set notation ($\in$ or $\notin$) to tell whether the following numbers are members of the set of integers I.

1. 2.6 **4.** 0 **7.** -1
2. 6 **5.** -3 **8.** 80
3. $\frac{-5}{2}$ **6.** -86.3 **9.** $-7\frac{1}{2}$

Use set notation ($\in$ or $\notin$) to tell whether these same numbers are members of the set of whole numbers W.

10. 2.6 **13.** 0 **16.** -1
11. 6 **14.** -3 **17.** 80
12. $\frac{-5}{2}$ **15.** -86.3 **18.** $-7\frac{1}{2}$

Give the opposite of each of these numbers.

19. -191 **21.** -50 **23.** $2\frac{1}{2}$
20. 15 **22.** -6.8 **24.** 1,250

Exponents

When we express products with like factors, we use exponents.

Factored Form	Exponent Form	Word Form
$9 \cdot 9$ (two factors of 9)	9^2	9 to the second power (or 9 squared)
$5 \cdot 5 \cdot 5$ (three factors of 5)	5^3	5 to the third power (or 5 cubed)
$3 \cdot 3 \cdot 3 \cdot 3$ (four factors of 3)	3^4	3 to the fourth power
$12 \cdot 12 \cdot 12 \cdot 12 \cdot 12$ (five factors of 12)	12^5	12 to the fifth power

In the *exponential notation* 4^6, 4 is the *base* and 6 is the *exponent.* The exponent tells how many times the base is used as a factor of a product.
$4^6 = 4 \cdot 4 \cdot 4 \cdot 4 \cdot 4 \cdot 4 = 4{,}096$ (standard numeral)

Remember,
the dot (·) means
to multiply.

This exercise will help you understand how exponents work.

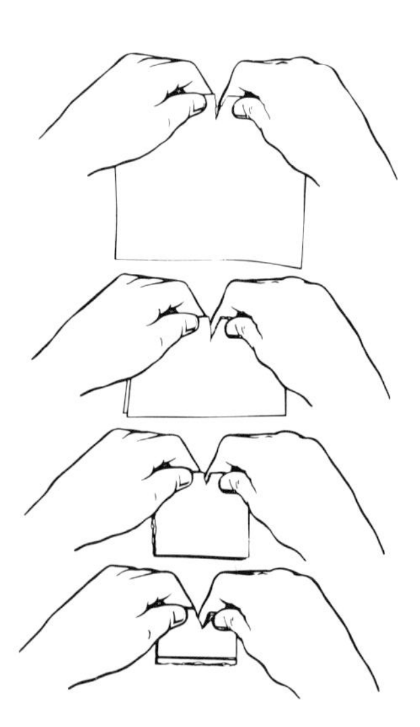

Take a sheet of paper
and tear it in half.
Stack the pieces together
and then tear them in half again.
Do this four times and
then fill in the chart.

Number of tears	Number of pieces	Exponential notation	Standard numeral
0		$2^0 =$	?
1		$2^1 =$	?
2		$2^2 =$	4
3		$2^3 =$	8
4		$2^4 =$	16

The exponent and the number of tears are equal.
How many pieces are there after zero tears? one tear?
What do you expect the standard numeral to be for the exponential notation 2^0? 2^1?

Keys to Understanding

An *exponent* tells how many times the base number n is used as a factor of a number. ($n^5 = n \cdot n \cdot n \cdot n \cdot n$)

Whenever a base number n other than zero is written with the exponent zero, its value is 1. ($n^0 = 1$ where $n \neq 0$)

Whenever a base number n is written with the exponent 1, its value is the base number. ($n^1 = n$)

Practice

Write each number in factored form.

Example: $5^4 = 5 \cdot 5 \cdot 5 \cdot 5$

1. 7^3 **3.** 10^4 **5.** 3^6 **7.** 2^5 **9.** 12^2

2. 5^5 **4.** 8^2 **6.** 4^3 **8.** 10^3 **10.** 13^1

Write these factors in exponent form.

Example: $2 \cdot 2 \cdot 2 = 2^3$

11. $2 \cdot 2 \cdot 2 \cdot 2$ **13.** $7 \cdot 7 \cdot 7 \cdot 7 \cdot 7$ **15.** $8 \cdot 8 \cdot 8 \cdot 8 \cdot 8 \cdot 8$

12. $5 \cdot 5 \cdot 5$ **14.** $10 \cdot 10$ **16.** 12

Write each as a standard numeral.

Example: $5^2 = 25$

17. 2^4 **19.** 3^3 **21.** 10^2 **23.** 0^8 **25.** 6^2

18. 5^3 **20.** 11^0 **22.** 8^1 **24.** 4^2 **26.** 8^0

Write each product in exponential notation.

Example: $(5 \cdot 5 \cdot 5) \cdot (7 \cdot 7 \cdot 7 \cdot 7) = 5^3 \cdot 7^4$

27. $(3 \cdot 3 \cdot 3) \cdot (2 \cdot 2 \cdot 2 \cdot 2 \cdot 2) =$

28. $(10 \cdot 10 \cdot 10 \cdot 10) \cdot (4 \cdot 4 \cdot 4 \cdot 4 \cdot 4) =$

29. $(6 \cdot 6 \cdot 6 \cdot 6 \cdot 6 \cdot 6 \cdot 6 \cdot 6 \cdot 6) \cdot (5 \cdot 5 \cdot 5) =$

30. $(7 \cdot 7 \cdot 7 \cdot 7) \cdot (11 \cdot 11 \cdot 11 \cdot 11 \cdot 11 \cdot 11 \cdot 11 \cdot 11) =$

Exponents in Base 10

A googol is the number 10,000, 000, 000, 000, 000, 000, 000, 000, 000, 000, 000, 000, 000, 000, 000, 000, 000, 000, 000, 000, 000, 000, 000, 000, 000, 000, 000, 000, 000, 000, 000, 000, 000.

A simpler way to write a googol is to use exponents in base 10.

a googol = 10^{100}

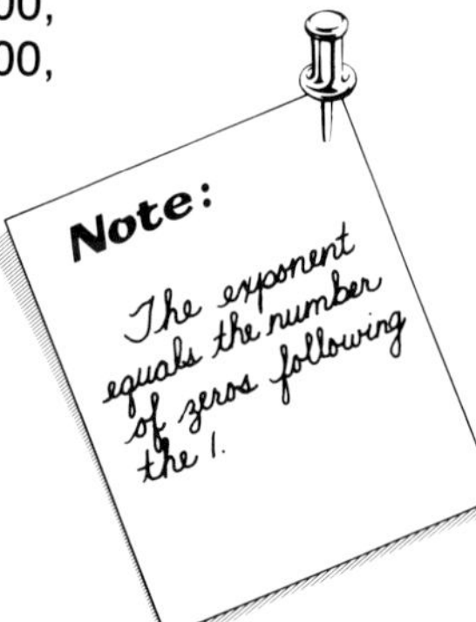

We can write very large numbers by using exponents in base 10.
One billion = 1,000,000,000 = 10^9

A googolplex = 10^{googol}

What do you think?

Do you think there is such a number?
How would you write it?
Could you write it as a standard numeral in your lifetime?
Is this number the largest in the world?

We can also write very small numbers by using exponents in base 10.

one-billionth = $\frac{1}{1,000,000,000} = \frac{1}{10^9}$

one-tenth = $\frac{1}{10} = 0.1 = \frac{1}{10^1}$

one-thousandth = $\frac{1}{1,000} = 0.001 = \frac{1}{10^3}$

Remember, numbers less than 1 can be written as common fractions or as decimals.

The number of zeros following the 1 in the denominator equals the number of digits to the right of the decimal point.

The exponent of 10 in the denominator also equals the number of digits to the right of the decimal point.

Practice

Write each as a standard numeral.

1. 10^3 **2.** 10^5 **3.** 10^8 **4.** 10^2 **5.** 10^0

Write each as a common fraction and a decimal fraction, using standard form.

6. $\frac{1}{10^2}$ **7.** $\frac{1}{10^4}$ **8.** $\frac{1}{10^6}$ **9.** $\frac{1}{10^1}$ **10.** $\frac{1}{10^5}$

Write each of the following numbers, using exponential notation.

11. $10 \cdot 10 \cdot 10 \cdot 10 \cdot 10$

12. $10 \cdot 10 \cdot 10$

13. $10 \cdot 10 \cdot 10 \cdot 10 \cdot 10 \cdot 10 \cdot 10$

14. $\frac{1}{10 \cdot 10 \cdot 10}$

15. $\frac{1}{10}$

16. 10,000

17. 100,000,000

18. 0.0001

19. $\frac{1}{100,000,000}$

20. 10,000,000,000

Fill in the blanks, using exponential notation.

21. $4,000 = 4 \cdot 1,000 = 4 \cdot$ ____

22. $70,000 = 7 \cdot 10,000 = 7 \cdot$ ____

23. $500 = 5 \cdot 100 = 5 \cdot$ ____

24. $0.009 = 9 \cdot 0.001 = 9 \cdot$ ____

25. $0.06 = 6 \cdot 0.01 = 6 \cdot$ ____

Place-Value Chart

	10^6	10^5	10^4	10^3	10^2	10^1	10^0	$\frac{1}{10^1}$	$\frac{1}{10^2}$	$\frac{1}{10^3}$	$\frac{1}{10^4}$	$\frac{1}{10^5}$	$\frac{1}{10^6}$
Place Value	1,000,000	100,000	10,000	1,000	100	10	1	0.1	0.01	0.001	0.0001	0.00001	0.000001
Place Name	millions	hundred-thousands	ten-thousands	thousands	hundreds	tens	ones	tenths	hundredths	thousandths	ten-thousandths	hundred-thousandths	millionths

How can you find the value of each digit in a numeral?

How do you know what place a digit is in?

Remember what the decimal point is for.

Keys to Understanding

Digits are symbols used to write numbers in standard form.
There are ten members in the set of digits.
The set of digits = {0, 1, 2, 3, 4, 5, 6, 7, 8, 9}

The value of each digit depends on the position of the digit in the numeral.

Each place value in a numeral is a power of 10.
The value of a digit equals the digit times the value of the place it occupies.
For example, in the numeral 213, the value of the digit 2 = $2 \cdot 10^2 = 200$.

Practice

What place does the digit 9 occupy in each of these numerals?

1. 592
2. 392,104
3. 19.81
4. 0.19
5. 0.72396
6. 19,280
7. 65.98
8. 918
9. 8.019
10. 9.001

Using the numeral 4,586.039, tell which digit is in each of the following places.

11. thousands
12. tenths
13. ones
14. thousandths
15. hundreds

What is the value of the digit 5 in each of these numerals?

16. 456
17. 12.5
18. 51,226
19. 0.005
20. 1,582

Write the word names for these numerals.

21. 263
22. 1,560
23. 48.1
24. 2.36
25. 0.0416
26. 118.01
27. 0.13
28. 11.801

Remember that the decimal point is read "and."

Write the following in standard-numeral form.

29. fourteen ten-thousandths
30. five hundred eighty and five-tenths
31. eleven thousand six hundred ten and three-hundredths
32. ten and four hundred-thousandths
33. eight million ten thousand fifty-two
34. one millionth
35. eleven and one hundred eleven thousandths
36. twelve thousand thirteen
37. six hundred eighty-two ten-thousandths
38. two hundred one and thirty-three hundredths
39. five thousand sixty-eight and five-tenths
40. twenty-seven and five-thousandths

Expanded Notation

Keys to Understanding

The value of a digit equals the digit times its place value.
The value of a numeral equals the sum of the values of its digits.
This sum can be expressed in *expanded form*.

Standard-form numeral

678.12

Expanded form using names

six hundred seventy-eight and twelve-hundredths

Expanded form using place values

$(6 \cdot 100) + (7 \cdot 10) + (8 \cdot 1) + (1 \cdot 0.1) + (2 \cdot 0.01)$

Expanded form using exponential notation

$(6 \cdot 10^2) + (7 \cdot 10^1) + (8 \cdot 10^0) + (1 \cdot \frac{1}{10^1}) + (2 \cdot \frac{1}{10^2})$

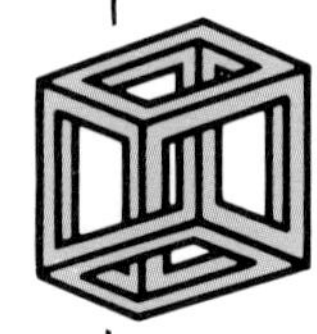

MIND BOGGLER

Arrange the eight digits below so that you have a numeral in which the 1s are separated by one digit, the 2s by two digits, the 3s by three digits, and the 4s by four digits.
1, 1, 2, 2, 3, 3, 4, 4

Practice

Write the following as expanded numerals, using exponential notation.

1. 572 **3.** 4,563.28 **5.** 7.013 **7.** 43.7 **9.** 120,643.4

2. 6.12 **4.** 27,012,514 **6.** 4.0102 **8.** 8 **10.** 4.00002

Write the following as standard-form numerals.

11. $(9 \cdot 10^5) + (8 \cdot 10^4) + (0 \cdot 10^3) + (1 \cdot 10^2) + (0 \cdot 10^1) + (4 \cdot 10^0)$

12. $(6 \cdot 10^4) + (2 \cdot 10^3) + (3 \cdot 10^2) + (5 \cdot 10^1) + (1 \cdot 10^0)$

13. $(5 \cdot 10^2) + (3 \cdot 10^1) + (0 \cdot 10^0) + (6 \cdot \frac{1}{10^1}) + (8 \cdot \frac{1}{10^2}) + (1 \cdot \frac{1}{10^3})$

14. $(0 \cdot 10^0) + (5 \cdot \frac{1}{10^1}) + (2 \cdot \frac{1}{10^2}) + (0 \cdot \frac{1}{10^3}) + (9 \cdot \frac{1}{10^4}) + (4 \cdot \frac{1}{10^5})$

15. $(2 \cdot 10^1) + (4 \cdot 10^0) + (5 \cdot \frac{1}{10^1}) + (3 \cdot \frac{1}{10^2}) + (8 \cdot \frac{1}{10^3})$

Write the word names for these numerals.

16. 15.003 **17.** 0.058 **18.** 1,053.81 **19.** 101.101 **20.** 401,532

Tell which number is greater.

21. $3 \cdot 10^8$ or 30,000,000

22. 0.000004 or $4 \cdot \frac{1}{10^5}$

23. $7 \cdot 10^{16}$ or $8 \cdot 10^{16}$

24. $(4 \cdot 10^4) + (8 \cdot 10^3) + (0 \cdot 10^2) + (2 \cdot 10^1) + (9 \cdot 10^0)$ or 40,000

25. one hundred-thousandth or $1 \cdot \frac{1}{10^2}$

Comparing Numbers

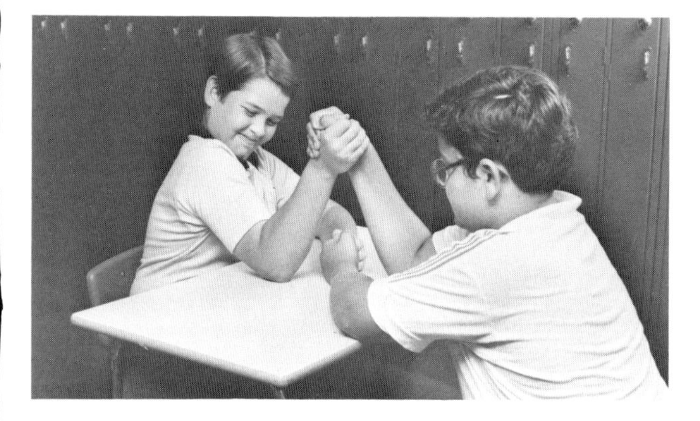

Who is going to win this
test of strength—Brad or Terry?

What are the possible outcomes?

What do you think?

What relationships are possible when two numbers are being compared?
What signs do we use to represent these relationships?
How do we determine how two numbers compare?

One way to compare numbers is to locate them on the number line. The numbers to the left on the number line are smaller than the numbers to the right. Locate the numbers 5 and 4 on the number line.

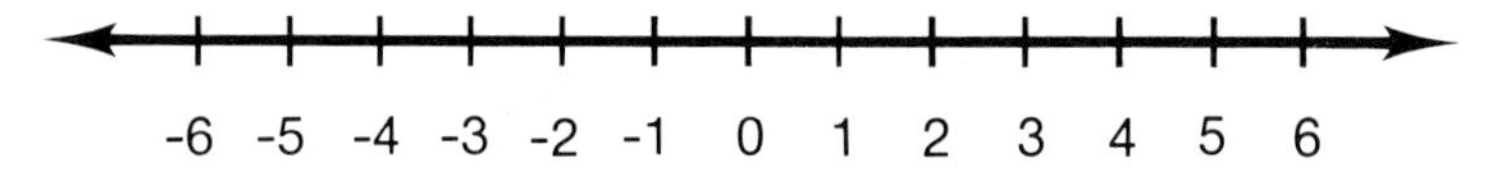

Since 4 is to the left of 5, $4 < 5$.

Locate the numbers -3 and 0.

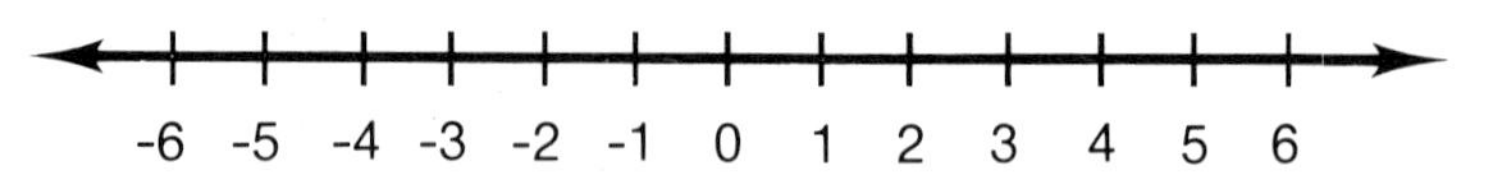

Since 0 is to the right of -3, $0 > -3$.

Keys to Understanding

The symbol $<$ means "is less than."
The symbol $>$ means "is greater than."
The symbol $=$ means "is equal to."

For any two numbers x and y, one and only one of the following mathematical statements is true:

$x < y$
$x = y$
$x > y$

Practice

Locate these decimals on a number line, and then compare them, using the appropriate sign ($<$, $>$).

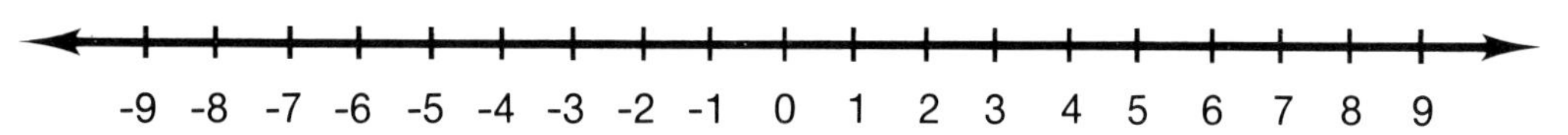

1. 3 and 5
2. -5 and 5
3. -7 and -9
4. -4 and 2
5. 1 and -1
6. 2 and -3
7. 7 and -8
8. 6 and 3
9. $-7\frac{1}{2}$ and -7
10. $3\frac{1}{2}$ and 4

Compare these numbers, using the appropriate sign ($<$, $>$, $=$).

11. 8 and 10
12. -6 and -4
13. -3 and 3
14. 1 and 0 **1**
15. -11 and 0
16. $2 \cdot 10^4$ and 20,000
17. $4 \cdot \frac{1}{10^5}$ and $4 \cdot \frac{1}{10^4}$
18. $3 \cdot 10^2$ and $3 \cdot \frac{1}{10^2}$
19. $6 \cdot \frac{1}{10^4}$ and 0.0006
20. 0.000005 and $5 \cdot \frac{1}{10^5}$

Unit Review

Write in words what the following expressions mean.
Example: $a = b$
answer: a equals b

1. $A \cup B$
2. $X \in H$
3. $a < b$
4. x^2
5. $E \subseteq F$
6. $A = \{1, 2, 3\}$
7. $b > a$
8. $T = \emptyset$
9. $A \cap B$
10. $A = \{1, 2, 3, \ldots\}$

Tell whether statements 11-20 are true or false.

$A = \{2, 4, 6, 8, \ldots\}$
$B = \{1, 2, 3, 4, \ldots\}$
$C = \{3, 5, 8, 9\}$
$D = \{1, 5, 7, 9\}$
$E = \{8, 9, 10, 11\}$
$F = \{1, 3, 5, 7, \ldots\}$

11. $A \subseteq B$
12. $C \subseteq F$
13. $(D \cup F) \subseteq B$
14. $E \subseteq B$
15. $28 \notin A$
16. $A \cup E = \{2, 4, 6, 9, 10, 11\}$
17. $A \cap C = \{8\}$
18. $D \cap E = \{9, 11\}$
19. $B = \{\text{the whole numbers}\}$
20. $F \cup B = B$

Write the following in expanded form, using exponential notation.

21. 12,683 **22.** 5,812.01 **23.** 0.00315 **24.** 917.093 **25.** 4,315,287

Write the word names for these numerals.

26. 853.4 **27.** 0.0105 **28.** 243,106.13 **29.** 91.5083 **30.** 1,061.05

Compare these numbers, using the appropriate sign ($<$, $>$, $=$).

31. $(3 \cdot 10^3) + (2 \cdot 10^2) + (8 \cdot 10^1) + (7 \cdot 10^0) + (4 \cdot \frac{1}{10^1})$ and 328.74

32. $(6 \cdot 10^2) + (3 \cdot 10^1) + (5 \cdot 10^0) + (8 \cdot \frac{1}{10^1}) + (0 \cdot \frac{1}{10^2})$ and 634.804

33. $(1 \cdot 10^6) + (4 \cdot 10^5) + (7 \cdot 10^4) + (2 \cdot 10^3) + (5 \cdot 10^2) + (1 \cdot 10^1) + (9 \cdot 10^0)$ and 1,492,579

34. $(2 \cdot 10^0) + (1 \cdot \frac{1}{10^1}) + (7 \cdot \frac{1}{10^2}) + (5 \cdot \frac{1}{10^3}) + (4 \cdot \frac{1}{10^4}) + (4 \cdot \frac{1}{10^5})$ and 2.17544

35. $(5 \cdot 10^1) + (3 \cdot 10^0) + (6 \cdot \frac{1}{10^1}) + (8 \cdot \frac{1}{10^2}) + (5 \cdot \frac{1}{10^3})$ and 5.3685

36. five thousand two hundred eighty and $(5 \cdot 10^2) + (2 \cdot 10^1) + (8 \cdot 10^0)$

37. 1.9 and 19

38. 0.056 and 0.56

39. 5,680.3 and 568.3

40. 0.0001 and 0.00021

Match the following.
Give the letter for each number.

41. 4^0	**a.** 1	**46.** $\frac{1}{a^2}$	**a.** 32
42. a^2	**b.** 16	**47.** 100^1	**b.** 6
43. 4^2	**c.** $a \cdot a$	**48.** 10^3	**c.** 100
44. $\frac{1}{10^2}$	**d.** 8	**49.** 2^5	**d.** 1,000
45. 2^3	**e.** 0.01	**50.** $10^0 \cdot 6$	**e.** 0.001
	f. $2 \cdot a$		**f.** $\frac{1}{a \cdot a}$

MIND BOGGLER

Find the answers, using each number of set X exactly once so that the sum of the numbers in each of the sets A, B, and C equals 22.

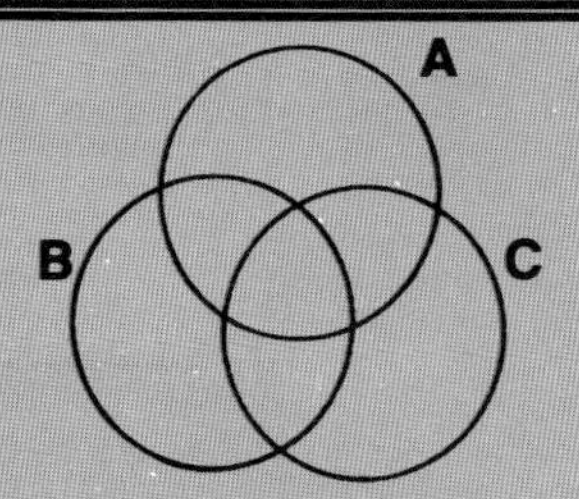

What is—

1. set A
2. set B
3. set C
4. $A \cap B$
5. $B \cap C$
6. $A \cap (C \cap B)$

$X = A \cup B \cup C$

$X = \{1, 2, 3, 4, 5, 6, 7, 8, 9, 10\}$

Skills Checkup

1. 5,898 + 1,473 + 9,602 + 7,948
2. 5,371 + 8,684 + 79 + 328
3. 96,987 + 37,146 + 53,428 + 78,969 + 89,575
4. 557 + 94,785 + 73,699 + 8,667 + 89,694

5. 709 - 562
6. 8,400 - 758
7. 91,568 - 56,375
8. 40,905 - 33,558
9. $9{,}768 \cdot 70$
10. $1{,}809 \cdot 54$
11. $9{,}300 \cdot 367$
12. $2{,}734 \cdot 852$
13. $317 \div 6$
14. $9{,}610 \div 3$
15. $34{,}389 \div 49$
16. $4{,}875 \div 15$
17. $\frac{5}{8} + \frac{1}{3}$
18. $\frac{3}{8} + \frac{5}{6}$
19. $4\frac{4}{5} + 5\frac{2}{5}$
20. $3\frac{5}{9} + 5\frac{2}{3}$
21. $10\frac{5}{7} - 3\frac{2}{3}$
22. $\frac{9}{16} - \frac{3}{8}$
23. $17 - 1\frac{5}{12}$
24. $7\frac{8}{9} - 4\frac{1}{4}$
25. $\frac{1}{2} \cdot \frac{3}{4}$

26. Four boys went on a camping trip. The expenses of the trip were as follows: food, $54.18; camping equipment, $18.58; transportation, $25.69; other expenses, $16.27. What was the total cost of the camping trip?
27. If the four boys divided the cost equally, how much did each pay?

1. 6,257 + 3,963 + 5,108 + 7,788
2. 4,919 + 85 + 472 + 2,867
3. 9,944 + 5,872 + 61,977 + 94,587
4. 83,474 + 62,968 + 55,667

5. 609 - 264
6. 7,300 - 521
7. 98,333 - 57,445
8. 30,701 - 25,622
9. 5,863 · 90
10. 7,090 · 74
11. 8,200 · 53
12. 4,178 · 689
13. 315 ÷ 7
14. 8,100 ÷ 8
15. 42,736 ÷ 53

16. $\frac{7}{10} + \frac{4}{5}$
17. $4\frac{3}{10} + 1\frac{1}{2}$
18. $2\frac{5}{6} + 3\frac{3}{8}$
19. $7\frac{2}{3} + 2\frac{3}{4}$
20. $\frac{11}{16} - \frac{1}{4}$
21. $3\frac{1}{6} - 2\frac{3}{4}$
22. $7\frac{5}{8} - \frac{5}{12}$
23. $4\frac{1}{2} - 1\frac{4}{5}$

24. If a can of corn costs $.37, how much would five cans cost?
25. If your grocery bill came to $17.39 and you gave the clerk a $20 bill, how much would your change be?

FILAMENT

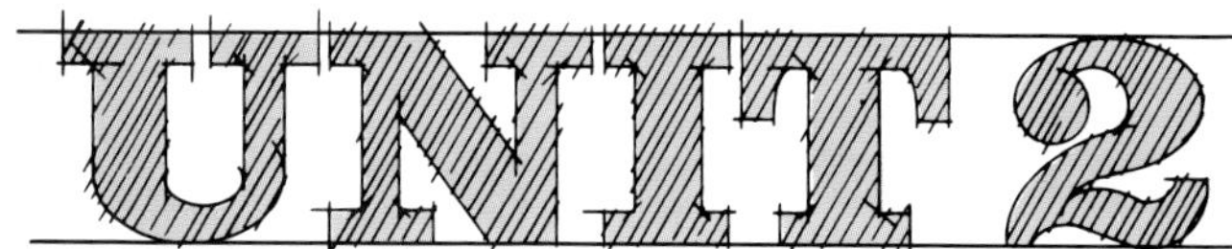

Radio Engineer

"Five, four, three, two, one, cue. You're on the air."

"Good afternoon, and welcome to our discussion with Willy Asten. Today he will be discussing . . ."

"Bob, be sure to have those telephones hooked up with the delay system for the call-in question-and-answer period at the end of this program."

"They're all set, sir," replied the engineer, "and Carol is standing by to switch us back to auto when the program is over. The discussion should end four minutes before the hour. The dead roll will play three minutes and forty-three seconds of music, followed by a fifteen-second station break. The news report from Washington has been recorded and is being fed into the computer. Everything seems to be following the program log."

"It looks as though you can follow the rest of the cues by yourself. I'm glad you've taken the initiative to do these jobs as early as possible. This is the final live program for the day. As soon as it's over, switch the programming to automatic and leave it there for the rest of the evening. Be sure to check the time tape. We had a little difficulty with it yesterday, but I think it's working now. I'm going to the music library to see how Louise is coming with the music modules."

When Mr. Thompson entered the music library, he found Louise, stopwatch in hand, timing selections of classical music. She was organizing the music into a matched-flow format, four segments of 11½-12½-minute modules. "Unless you have any questions," Mr. Thompson interrupted, "I'll let you continue timing while I make my way to the other departments."

"Thanks for stopping by, Mr. Thompson. I've almost finished classifying and matching these tapes in preparation for broadcasting. I'll be sure to let you know when I'm finished."

Radio station personnel must be ready to act when their cue is given. Failure to do so may result in a delay of programming. As Christians, we must act when God "cues" us. "Behold, now is the accepted time; behold, now is the day of salvation" (II Corinthians 6:2b). Now. Salvation is not something that we can put off until later. Christ died for our sins to prepare the way for us to enter His kingdom. We must accept as a free gift His work on the cross.

Mathematical Properties

A binary operation is the combining of two numbers mathematically. Examples: $4 + 3$, $3 \cdot 6$, $7 - 5$, $9 \div 3$

Binary operations have been used since the beginning of recorded history. One of the first mentions of the use of a binary operation is in Genesis 4:15. When Cain killed his brother Abel, the Lord punished Cain, but said that whoever killed Cain would be revenged "sevenfold." This meant that whoever killed Cain would receive *7 times the punishment* that Cain received for killing Abel.

What do you think?

What are four basic binary operations used in mathematics?
What are mathematical properties?
What are the basic mathematical properties of binary operations?
How do we use mathematical properties?
What are biblical principles?
What are some basic biblical principles?
What is the similarity between mathematical properties and biblical principles?

> Happy is the man that findeth wisdom, and the man that getteth understanding. Proverbs 3:13

Practice

Give the principle or truth found in each one of the following Scripture passages. Tell how you could apply each of the principles in your own life.

1. Proverbs 3:5-6
2. Matthew 7:7
3. Galatians 6:9
4. Hebrews 13:17
5. I John 2:15-17
6. I Corinthians 6:19
7. James 1:5
8. Colossians 3:23
9. I Timothy 6:8
10. Proverbs 14:29

11-15. Give five more biblical principles with a Scripture reference for each one.

Commutative Property

What do you think?

Does it matter in which order you do these things?

1. Pick up the telephone; dial the number
2. Brush your teeth; comb your hair
3. $A \cup B$

If the order in which we perform a binary operation does not affect the result, the operation possesses the commutative property. If the order does have an effect on the result, the operation is not commutative.

Is situation number 1 above commutative?

Is situation number 2 above commutative?

Is situation number 3 above commutative?

Keys to Understanding

Commutative Property of Addition

For any two numbers *a* and *b*,

$a + b = b + a$

Commutative Property of Multiplication

For any two numbers *a* and *b*,

$a \cdot b = b \cdot a$

Practice

Do the following operations. Write only the answers.

1. $863 + 32 =$
   $32 + 863 =$
2. $112 + 347 =$
   $347 + 112 =$
3. $498 + 101 =$
   $101 + 498 =$
4. $82 \cdot 4 =$
   $4 \cdot 82 =$
5. $10 \cdot 12 =$
   $12 \cdot 10 =$
6. $8 \cdot 21 =$
   $21 \cdot 8 =$
7. Does it matter in which order we add two numbers?
8. Does the commutative property apply to the addition operation?
9. Does it matter in which order we multiply two numbers?
10. Does the commutative property apply to the multiplication operation?

Do the following operations. Write only the answers.

11. $25 - 20 =$
    $20 - 25 =$
12. $583 - 72 =$
    $72 - 583 =$
13. $101 - 276 =$
    $276 - 101 =$
14. $20 \div 5 =$
    $5 \div 20 =$
15. $81 \div 9 =$
    $9 \div 81 =$
16. $210 \div 30 =$
    $30 \div 210 =$
17. Does it matter in which order we subtract two numbers?
18. Does the commutative property apply to the subtraction operation?
19. Does it matter in which order we divide two numbers?
20. Does the commutative property apply to the division operation?

Associative Property

Which way should Sally mix the cake?

Should she mix the cake mix and water together and then mix in the eggs, or mix the cake mix into a mixture of the eggs and water?

Does the way in which Sally combines the ingredients affect the result?

This illustrates the associative property.

If the way in which numbers are grouped in binary operations has no effect on the result, the operation possesses the associative property. If the grouping does have an effect on the result, the operation is not associative.

Keys to Understanding

Associative Property of Addition

For any numbers a, b, and c,
$(a + b) + c = a + (b + c)$

Associative Property of Multiplication

For any numbers a, b, and c,
$(a \cdot b) \cdot c = a \cdot (b \cdot c)$

Practice

Do the following operations. Write only the answers.

1. $(10 + 5) + 20 =$
2. $10 + (5 + 20) =$
3. $(7 + 8) + 12 =$
4. $7 + (8 + 12) =$
5. $9 + (8 + 3) =$
6. $(9 + 8) + 3 =$

Remember, do the work in the parentheses first.

7. Does it matter how we group numbers when we add?
8. Does the associative property apply to the addition operation?

9. $(25 - 10) - 5 =$
10. $25 - (10 - 5) =$
11. $8 - (4 - 3) =$
12. $(8 - 4) - 3 =$
13. $(20 - 8) - 4 =$
14. $20 - (8 - 4) =$

15. Does it matter how we group numbers when we subtract?
16. Does the associative property apply to the subtraction operation?

17. $(8 \cdot 3) \cdot 2 =$
18. $8 \cdot (3 \cdot 2) =$
19. $(5 \cdot 2) \cdot 3 =$
20. $5 \cdot (2 \cdot 3) =$
21. $10 \cdot (10 \cdot 4) =$
22. $(10 \cdot 10) \cdot 4 =$

23. Does it matter how we group numbers when we multiply?
24. Does the associative property apply to the multiplication operation?

25. $(20 \div 10) \div 5 =$
26. $20 \div (10 \div 5) =$
27. $16 \div (8 \div 4) =$
28. $(16 \div 8) \div 4 =$
29. $(27 \div 9) \div 3 =$
30. $27 \div (9 \div 3) =$

31. Does it matter how we group numbers when we divide?
32. Does the associative property apply to the division operation?

Distributive Property

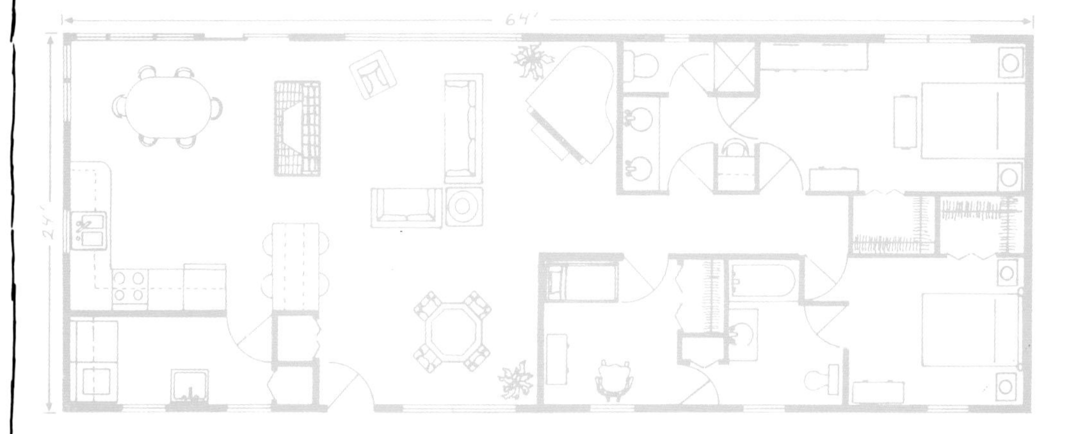

Find the perimeter of (distance around) this rectangle.

How did you proceed?

Did you add the length and width together and then double the sum to get the perimeter?

$P = 2 \cdot (l + w) = 2 \cdot (64 + 24) = 2 \cdot 88 = 176$

Or did you add twice the length and twice the width together to get the perimeter?

$P = (2 \cdot l) + (2 \cdot w) = (2 \cdot 64) + (2 \cdot 24) = 128 + 48 = 176$

Did your result depend on which of the two procedures you used to find the perimeter?

Therefore either procedure will give you the same result.

$P = 2 \cdot (l + w) = (2 \cdot l) + (2 \cdot w)$

This illustrates the *distributive property* of multiplication over addition.

Keys to Understanding

Distributive Property over Addition

For any numbers a, b, and c,

$$a \cdot (b + c) = (a \cdot b) + (a \cdot c)$$

Distributive Property over Subtraction

For any numbers a, b, and c,

$$a \cdot (b - c) = (a \cdot b) - (a \cdot c)$$

The distributive property can also be written this way:

$$a(b + c) = (a \cdot b) + (a \cdot c)$$

(We need not use the multiplication sign before the parentheses.)

Practice

Do the following operations.

1. $5 \cdot (4 + 2) =$
2. $(5 \cdot 4) + (5 \cdot 2) =$
3. $8 \cdot (4 + 1) =$
4. $(8 \cdot 4) + (8 \cdot 1) =$
5. $4 \cdot (7 + 5) =$
6. $(4 \cdot 7) + (4 \cdot 5) =$
7. $9 \cdot (6 - 3) =$
8. $(9 \cdot 6) - (9 \cdot 3) =$
9. $3 \cdot (8 - 6) =$
10. $(3 \cdot 8) - (3 \cdot 6) =$

We can use the distributive property over subtraction to solve multiplication problems.

$$7 \cdot 49 = 7 \cdot (50 - 1) = (7 \cdot 50) - (7 \cdot 1) = 350 - 7 = 343$$

This procedure can help us solve multiplication problems mentally.

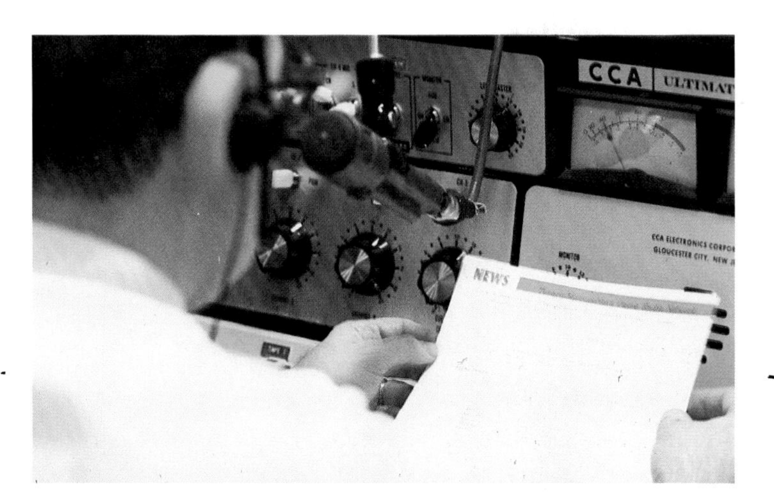

Using Mathematical Properties

Mathematical properties are very useful. They help us solve math problems just as biblical principles help us solve life's problems. Being able to use principles and properties to solve problems is very practical. Here is an example of how math properties are used.

We use the distributive property over addition every time we multiply numbers with more than one digit.

Example:

$$\begin{aligned} 8 \cdot 12 &= 8 \cdot (10 + 2) \\ &= (8 \cdot 10) + (8 \cdot 2) \\ &= 80 + 16 \\ &= 96 \end{aligned}$$

or

$$\begin{array}{r} 12 \\ \times\ 8 \\ \hline 8 \cdot 2 = 16 \\ 8 \cdot 10 = \underline{80} \\ 96 \end{array}$$

$$\begin{aligned} 12 \cdot 18 &= (10 + 2) \cdot (10 + 8) \\ &= (10 + 2) \cdot 10 + (10 + 2) \cdot 8 \\ &= (10 \cdot 10) + (10 \cdot 2) + (10 \cdot 8) + (2 \cdot 8) \\ &= 100 + 20 + 80 + 16 \\ &= 216 \end{aligned}$$

or

$$\begin{array}{r} 18 \\ \times\ 12 \\ \hline (2 \cdot 8) = 16 \\ (2 \cdot 10) = 20 \\ (10 \cdot 8) = 80 \\ (10 \cdot 10) = \underline{100} \\ = 216 \end{array}$$

Practice

State the property that each of the following illustrates.

1. $10 \cdot (8 \cdot 2) = (10 \cdot 8) \cdot 2$
2. $16 + 25 = 25 + 16$
3. $8 \cdot 43 = (8 \cdot 40) + (8 \cdot 3)$
4. $52 \cdot 6 = 6 \cdot 52$
5. $9(5 - 3) = (9 \cdot 5) - (9 \cdot 3)$
6. $11 + (6 + 12) = (11 + 6) + 12$
7. $x(4 + 3) = 4x + 3x$
8. $(3 + 4) + (2 + 5) = (2 + 5) + (3 + 4)$
9. $5 \cdot 29 = (5 \cdot 30) - (5 \cdot 1)$
10. $(2x + 3x) + 4x = 2x + (3x + 4x)$

Tell whether each of the following is true or false. (Avoid computation.)

11. $6(4 + 2) = (6 \cdot 4) + (6 \cdot 2)$
12. $3(5 + 1) = (3 \cdot 5) + 1$
13. $8(4 - 2) = (8 \cdot 4) + (8 \cdot 2)$
14. $(3 + 4) + 6 = 3(4 + 6)$
15. $9 \cdot 8 = (4 + 5) \cdot (3 + 5)$
16. $(5 \cdot 2) + (6 \cdot 3) = (3 \cdot 6) + (2 \cdot 5)$
17. $(41 \cdot 38) + (41 \cdot 62) = 4{,}100$
18. $(8 \cdot 7) + 3 = 8(7 + 3)$
19. $3 \cdot 69 = (3 \cdot 70) - (3 \cdot 1)$
20. $8 \cdot 32 = (8 \cdot 3) + (8 \cdot 2)$

21-30. For each one you marked true, tell which property it illustrates.

Math in Action

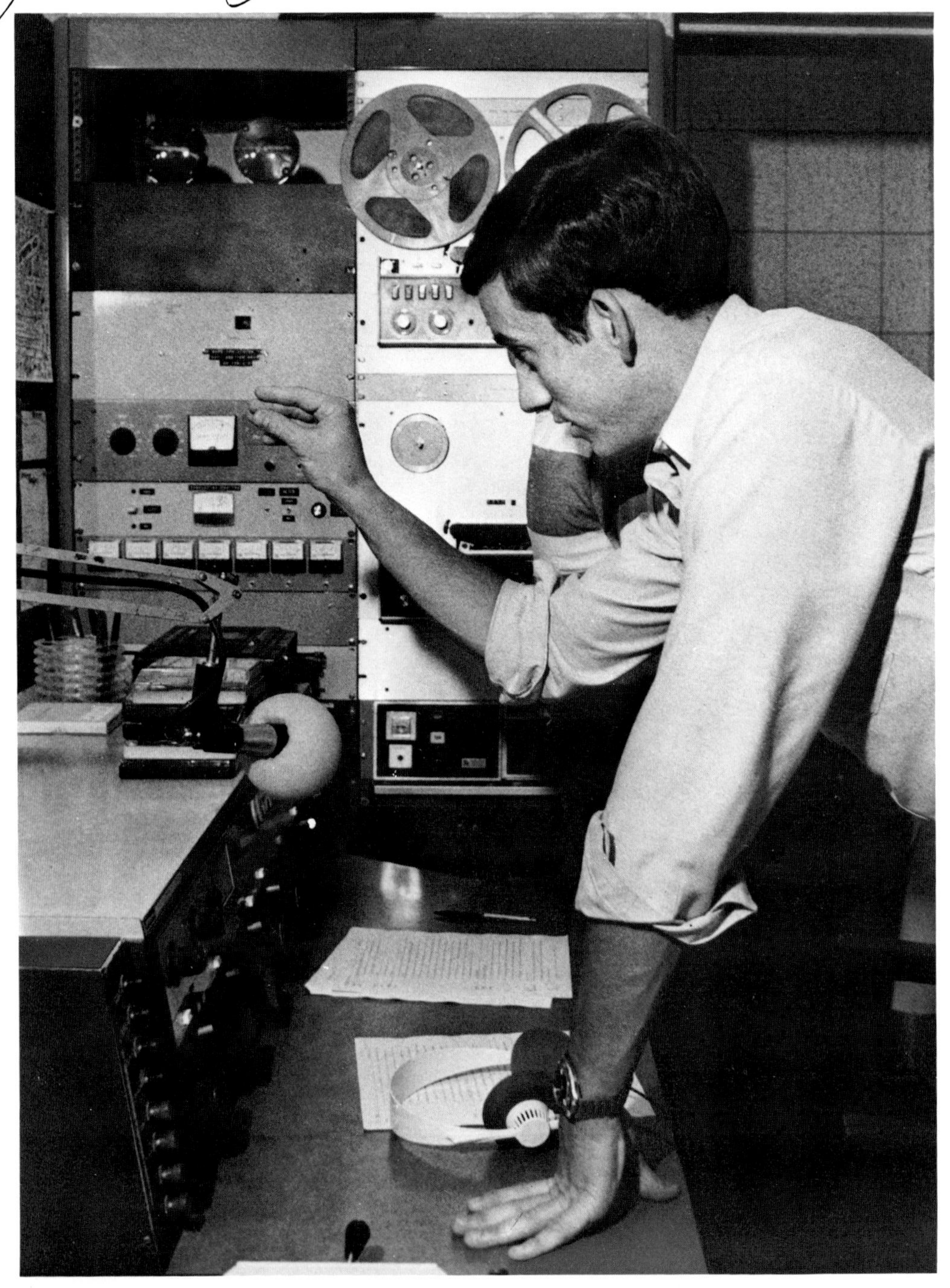

1. If a radio station were to play four $11\frac{1}{2}$-minute music modules in one hour, how many minutes would be left for other programming?
2. Mr. Thompson scheduled two $12\frac{1}{2}$-minute modules, three 30-second station breaks, one 14-minute interview, and three 45-second commercials to be aired in one hour. How much time can he allot to the news?
3. Louise has 3 hours and 35 minutes' worth of music to classify into $12\frac{1}{2}$-minute modules. How many modules will she be able to make? (Remember that you cannot have parts of a module.)
4. Commercial radio stations may operate at 100,000 watts. If a station is operating at 75,000 watts, at what fraction of capacity is it operating?
5. It takes Mr. Thompson 4 hours and 35 minutes to plan a program log. A computer can do the same job in $9\frac{3}{5}$ minutes. How much time will the station save by having the computer plan the program?

Properties of 0 and 1

Choose any number and add 0 to it. What is the result?

$$4 + 0 = 4$$
$$275 + 0 = 275$$

Any number plus 0 equals that same, or identical, number. Why? Because 0 is the *identity element* for addition.

Choose any number and multiply it by 1.

$$4 \cdot 1 = 4$$
$$275 \cdot 1 = 275$$

Any number multiplied by 1 equals that same, or identical, number. Why? Because 1 is the *identity element* for multiplication.

Keys to Understanding

Identity Element for Addition

For any number n,
$n + 0 = n$ and $0 + n = n$

Identity Element for Multiplication

For any number n,
$n \cdot 1 = n$ and $1 \cdot n = n$

Mr. Sams went to his hen house to gather eggs to take to the farmers' market. If he came out with two empty baskets, how many eggs had he gathered?

2 baskets · 0 eggs per basket = 0 eggs total

$$2 \cdot 0 = 0$$

If Mr. Sams had *ten* baskets with no eggs in each basket, then how many eggs did he have?

10 baskets · 0 eggs per basket = 0 eggs total

If Mr. Sams continued to bring empty baskets out of the hen house, would he ever have any eggs?

n baskets · 0 eggs = 0 eggs total

$$n \cdot 0 = 0$$

(n = any number)

Keys to Understanding

Multiplicative Property of 0

For any number n,

$n \times 0 = 0$ and $0 \times n = 0$

Division Property of 0

For any number n,

$0 \div n = 0$ or $\frac{0}{n} = 0$

We never divide a number by 0. Division by 0 is not possible, because for any number n the expressions $n \div 0$ or $\frac{n}{0}$ do not represent a number.

If Mr. Sams had two baskets containing a total of 0 eggs, how many eggs were in each basket?

0 eggs ÷ 2 baskets = 0 eggs per basket

$$0 \div 2 = 0$$

If he had ten baskets containing a total of 0 eggs, how many eggs were in each basket?

0 eggs ÷ 10 baskets = 0 eggs per basket

$$0 \div 10 = 0$$

Note: *Division by 0 is not possible.*

Does it matter how many baskets he had?

0 eggs ÷ n baskets = 0 eggs per basket

$$0 \div n = 0$$

(n = any number)

Could you determine how many baskets Mr. Sams brought out if you knew that there were 0 eggs in the hen house and 0 eggs in each basket?

0 eggs ÷ 0 eggs per basket = how many baskets?

Who knows?

Practice

Do the indicated operations.

1. $8 \cdot 1 =$
2. $2.76 + 0 =$
3. $3.16 \cdot 1 =$
4. $2.3\,(4 - 3) =$
5. $(0 + 6.3) + 0 =$
6. $\frac{5}{8} \cdot 1 =$
7. $(0.015 \cdot 1) \cdot 1 =$
8. $0 + (1 \cdot 13) =$
9. $1 \cdot (0 + 3.8) =$
10. What is the identity element for addition? for multiplication?

Complete each of the following computations.

11. $2.8 \cdot 0 =$
12. $4 - \frac{0}{16} =$
13. $(3 - 3) \cdot (8 - 7) =$
14. $4.75(10 - 9) =$
15. $\frac{(8 - 8)}{42} =$
16. $\frac{9.6}{(6 - 5)} =$
17. $(5 + 6) + (8 - 8) =$
18. $\frac{1{,}368}{(13 - 12)} =$
19. $16.5 - (81 - 81) =$
20. $8 \cdot 0 \cdot 4 \cdot 9 \cdot 7 =$

Find the value of n.
Example: If $83 + n = 83$, then $n = 0$.

21. $n + 35 = 35$
22. $48 \cdot n = 48$
23. $\frac{n}{6.7} = 0$
24. $n + n = 0$
25. $516 + (n - 8) = 516$
26. $n(n + 1) = 0$
27. $\frac{(n - 12)}{n} = 0$
28. $13\,(n - 3) = 13$
29. $3.1 \cdot n \cdot 6.4 \cdot 5 = 0$
30. $n(n + 1) = n$

Addition of Large Numbers

Addition done the long way.

Addition done the easier and shorter way.

Practice

Use the easy, quick method to solve these problems.

1. 502 + 264	**2.** 4,975 + 2,684	**3.** 36,538 + 25,642	**4.** 517 + 238
5. 3,862 + 2,381	**6.** 84,902 + 17,818	**7.** 123 + 789	**8.** 8,019 + 3,197
9. 598,316 + 44,509	**10.** 1,678 + 543	**11.** 28,175 + 5,761	**12.** 612,557 + 528,725
13. $ 10.18 22.36 15.83 + 7.25	**14.** $ 56.75 23.48 18.63 + 73.26	**15.** 1,386 25,917 248,738 454 + 96,115	**16.** 2,709 34,213 728 60,017 + 569,805

A census (population count) is taken every ten years in the United States.

Lake County Census

City	Population
Lakeville	2,863
Rivertown	23,516
Bay City	112,749
Crooked Creek	316
Pondville	7,037
Oceanside	386,958

1. How many people make their homes in either Bay City or Oceanside?
2. How many people of Lake County live in cities with populations less than that of Rivertown?
3. How many people of Lake County live in a city with a population of more than one thousand?
4. **What is the total population of the cities in Lake County?**
5. How many people of Lake County live somewhere other than Oceanside?

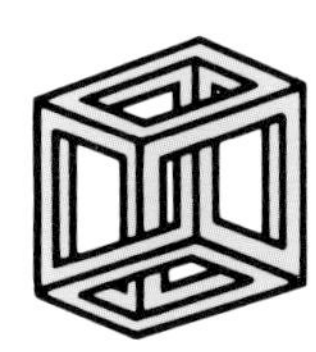

MIND BOGGLER

These three utility plants furnish water, gas, and electricity to these three houses. A pipeline must be laid from each plant to each house, but no two pipelines should cross. How can this be done?

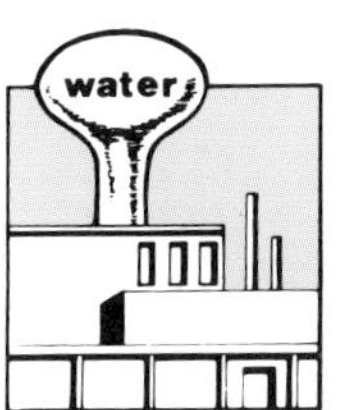

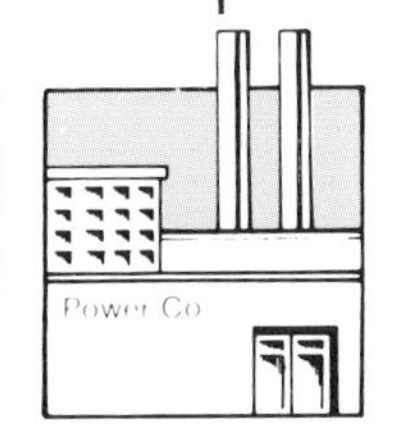

Subtraction of Large Numbers

Subtraction done the long way.

Subtraction done the easier and shorter way.

Note: *You can do the renaming mentally.*

Practice

Solve these problems.

1. 486 − 327	**2.** 628 − 236	**3.** 8,013 − 5,364	**4.** 632 − 386
5. 834 − 487	**6.** 11,312 − 8,775	**7.** 502 − 167	**8.** 137 − 99
9. $ 12.50 − 7.75	**10.** 916 − 838	**11.** 834 − 99	**12.** $56.12 − 28.55
13. 128,560 − 86,435	**14.** 368,316 − 175,083	**15.** $50,580.45 − 23,775.69	**16.** 9,801 − 7,973

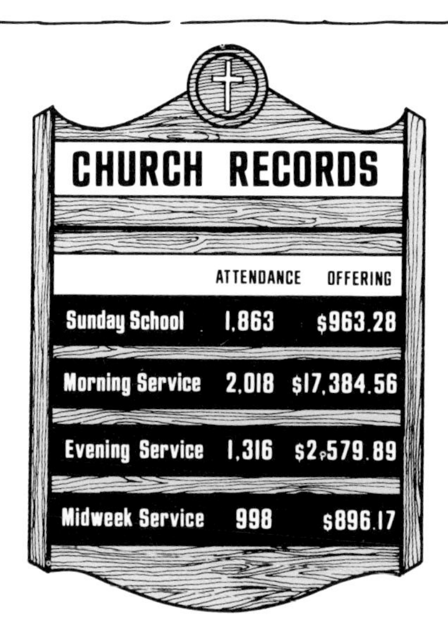

CHURCH RECORDS

	ATTENDANCE	OFFERING
Sunday School	1,863	$963.28
Morning Service	2,018	$17,384.56
Evening Service	1,316	$2,579.89
Midweek Service	998	$896.17

1. How many more people attended the morning service than Sunday school? than the evening service?
2. How much more money was given during the morning service than during the evening service? than during the midweek service?
3. What is the difference between the highest attendance and the lowest attendance?
4. What is the difference between the giving in Sunday school and in the midweek service?
5. How much money did the church receive during the week?

Multiplying by Powers of 10

Multiplication also can be done using an easy way, especially when the multiplier is a power of 10 or has terminal zeros.

What do you notice about the product when the multiplier is a power of 10 or has terminal zeros?

Practice

At least how many zeros will terminate these products?

1. 1,000 × any number

2. 500 × any number

3. (7×10^7) × any number

4. 1,000,000 × any number

Solve these problems.

5. 496 × 10	**6.** 32,718 × 100	**7.** 6,881 × 2,000	**8.** 7,280 × 5,000
9. 618 × 100	**10.** 2,903 × 500	**11.** 2,635 × 1,000	**12.** 28,146 × 10,000
13. 327 × 200	**14.** 1,476 × 3,000	**15.** 18,363 × 700	**16.** 19,487 × 700
17. 100 × 30	**18.** 10,000 × 841	**19.** 168,472 × 40,000	**20.** 927,866 × 200,000

When multiplying large numbers, you can multiply from right to left or from left to right.
The easier way seems to be from right to left.

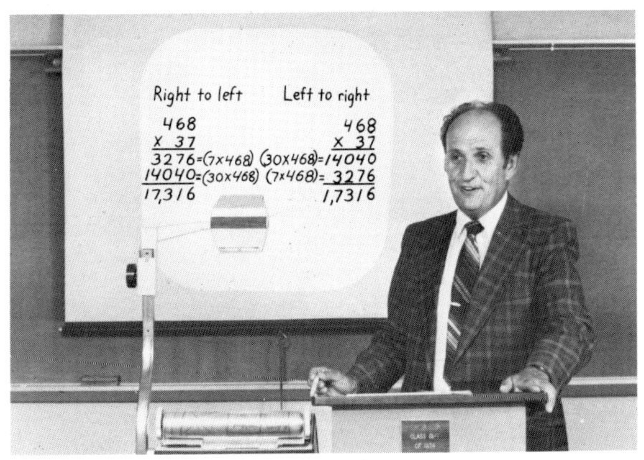

When multiplying, ending zeros may be put in or left out.

put in	left out
326	326
× 248	× 248
2608	2608
13040	1304
65200	652
80,848	80,848

Practice

Solve these problems, using *your* favorite method.

1. 327 × 26	**2.** 718 × 84	**3.** 2,903 × 56	**4.** $14.76 × 120	**5.** 476 × 52
6. 243 ×171	**7.** 1,554 × 83	**8.** 4,371 × 257	**9.** 280 × 78	**10.** 561 × 404
11. $8.28 × 25	**12.** 6,381 × 2,345	**13.** 903 × 43	**14.** 833 × 256	**15.** $10.50 × 48

Problem Solving

The seventy-six seniors of Community Christian High School are going to a local steak house for a banquet.

What will be the total cost of the banquet if each senior orders the following? (Be sure to show *all* your work.)

1. A T-bone steak and a drink
2. A sirloin steak, a salad, and a drink
3. A chopped sirloin, a dessert, and a drink
4. A steak sandwich, a salad, a dessert, and a drink

The school has decided to pay for the banquet and allows each senior to have his choice of one of two meals.

5. What will the school's bill be if the seniors ordered as follows? (Be sure to show your work.)

Meal	Number ordered
Sirloin steak and drink	34
Chopped sirloin, salad, dessert, and drink	42

If you were a waiter or waitress, you would need to be proficient at figuring up bills. Using the prices of the steak house, add up these bills. (Show *all* your work.)

TB = T-bone
Sir = Sirloin steak
CS = Chopped sirloin
SS = Steak sandwich
Sa = Salad
Dr = Drink
Ds = Dessert

6.

Family of three
2 Sir—
1 SS—
2 Sa—
2 Ds—
3 Dr—

Total = ?

7.

Family of seven
2 TB—
3 CS—
2 SS—
7 Sa—
7 Ds—
7 Dr—

Total = ?

8.

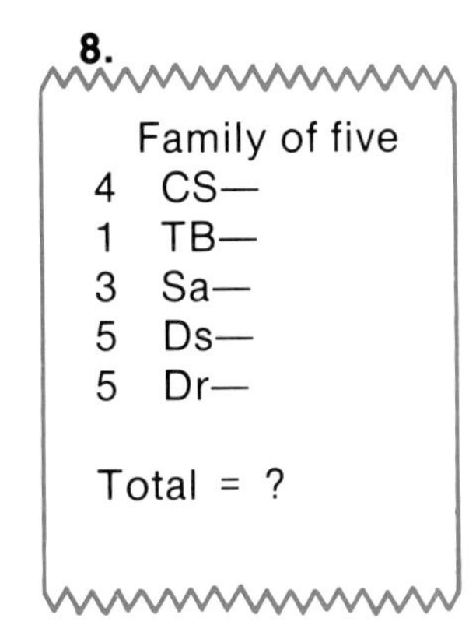

Family of five
4 CS—
1 TB—
3 Sa—
5 Ds—
5 Dr—

Total = ?

9. What is the difference between feeding the family of seven and the family of three?

10. How much money did the steak house receive from these three families?

Dividing Large Numbers

Note: *When you have a remainder, you can express it as a fraction of the divisor.* $2\overline{)9}$ = $4\frac{1}{2}$

Division also can be done the easier, shorter way. This way will work with problems with or without a remainder.

Practice

Solve these problems. If there is a remainder, express it as a fraction.

1. 63)693	**2.** 25)5,075	**3.** 21)7,255	**4.** 37)9,435
5. 59)5,075	**6.** 76)8,132	**7.** 45)2,977	**8.** 18)2,443
9. 13)1,001	**10.** 74)7,489	**11.** 88)30,536	**12.** 27)83,421
13. 66)4,356	**14.** 23)30,038	**15.** 73)53,606	**16.** 20)32,448
17. 63)12,601	**18.** 57)12,711	**19.** 91)13,688	**20.** 528)32,837

145 girls and 152 boys are attending
Sky Trail Camp in the mountains.

1. How many campers must sit at each table if there are thirty-three tables in the dining hall?
2. How many cabins are needed for the boys if each cabin sleeps twelve campers?
3. All the campers went canoeing at the same time. Each canoe will hold three people. How many canoes must the camp have for all the campers to canoe together?
4. The girls are going on a hike in groups. If they want fifteen in each group, how many group leaders will they need?
5. The campers have been divided into twenty-seven Bible-study groups. How many campers are in each group?

Checking by Inverse Operations

To check addition → subtract.

```
   3,186      5,747
 + 2,561    - 2,561
   -----      -----
   5,747      3,186
```

To check subtraction → add.

```
   7,315      2,594
 - 4,721    + 4,721
   -----      -----
   2,594      7,315
```

To check multiplication → divide.

```
     476            476
   ×  28       ________
   -----     28)13,328
    3808        11 2
    9520        ----
  ------         2 12
  13,328         1 96
                 ----
                  168
                  168
                  ---
                    0
```

To check division → multiply.

```
          323       323
     ________     ×  46
  46)14,858       -----
     13 8          1938
     ----         12920
      1 05       ------
        92       14,858
      ----
       138
       138
       ---
         0
```

To check division with a remainder, multiply and add the remainder.

```
       13        13
     ____      × 11
  11)145       ----
     11          13
     --         13
      35        ---
      33        143
      --      +   2
       2        ---
                145
```

Practice

Add and check your answers.

1. $\begin{array}{r} 583 \\ +\ 439 \\ \hline \end{array}$ 2. $\begin{array}{r} 3{,}014 \\ +\ 687 \\ \hline \end{array}$ 3. $\begin{array}{r} \$28.17 \\ +\ 43.92 \\ \hline \end{array}$ 4. $\begin{array}{r} 134{,}947 \\ +\ 58{,}623 \\ \hline \end{array}$

Subtract and check your answers.

5. $\begin{array}{r} 453 \\ -\ 269 \\ \hline \end{array}$ 6. $\begin{array}{r} 1{,}863 \\ -\ 555 \\ \hline \end{array}$ 7. $\begin{array}{r} \$56.79 \\ -\ 48.65 \\ \hline \end{array}$ 8. $\begin{array}{r} 253{,}112 \\ -\ 149{,}581 \\ \hline \end{array}$

Multiply and check your answers.

9. $\begin{array}{r} 238 \\ \times\ 40 \\ \hline \end{array}$ 10. $\begin{array}{r} 693 \\ \times\ 74 \\ \hline \end{array}$ 11. $\begin{array}{r} \$29.37 \\ \times\ 58 \\ \hline \end{array}$ 12. $\begin{array}{r} 1{,}987 \\ \times\ 274 \\ \hline \end{array}$

Divide and check your answers.

13. $59\overline{)708}$ 14. $78\overline{)1{,}482}$ 15. $45\overline{)7{,}230}$ 16. $274\overline{)189{,}882}$

This is part of a school's hardware bill. Find the prices that should be in the blanks.

HARRY'S HARDWARE

Invoice No.
22033

Quantity	Item	Unit Price	Total Price
124	Light bulbs	49¢	17. ____
16	Gallons of Paint	18. ____	$207.20
19. ____	Trash cans	$4.77	$57.24
35	Paint brushes	$2.43	20. ____

Rounding and Estimating

Ten-speed bikes were on sale for $147.95 each. If the department store sold twenty-two bikes during the sale, about how much money did they take in?
Did you estimate to solve this problem?

Careful estimating is helpful in daily life.
About how much did you study last night?
About how many came to the last school program?
About how far do you live from your church?
About how much will it cost for you to attend school this year?
About how much ice cream can you eat?

Careful estimating is also helpful in checking math computations to see if they are reasonable.

$$\begin{array}{r} 916 \\ \times\ 42 \\ \hline 16{,}438 \end{array} \quad \text{This is not reasonable, because} \quad \begin{array}{r} 900 \\ \times\ 40 \\ \hline 36{,}000 \end{array}$$

In order to estimate, you must be able to use *round* numbers.

Steps in Rounding Numbers

1. Mentally point out the place (named place) to which you are going to round the number.
2. Now look at the digit to the right of the named place.
   a. If it is equal to or greater than 5, increase the digit in the named place by 1. (rounding up)
   b. If it is less than 5, the named place is not changed. (rounding down)
3. Each digit to the right of the named place should then be replaced with a 0.

Round to the nearest

ten thousand	18,052.462 $\doteq$ 20,000
hundred	18,052.462 $\doteq$ 18,100
one	18,052.462 $\doteq$ 18,052
tenth	18,052.462 $\doteq$ 18,052.5
hundredth	18,052.462 $\doteq$ 18,052.46

Practice

Round the following numbers to the nearest thousand.

1. 8,752 **2.** 9,356.3 **3.** 74,873.12 **4.** 14,320 **5.** 1,613.5

Round the following numbers to the nearest ten.

6. 49.6 **7.** 153.7 **8.** 171.48 **9.** 289.5 **10.** 12,483

Round the following numbers to the nearest tenth.

11. 0.83 **12.** 2.432 **13.** 15.165 **14.** 0.0561 **15.** 216.483

Estimate the following answers by rounding the numbers before calculating.

16. 384 + 465

17. 77 × 32

18. 629 - 179

19. \$12.85 × 28

20. 69)2,139

21. 7,892 - 569

22. 688 × 71

23. 89 × 63

24. \$104.12 + 17.96

25. 23)1,311

Unit Review

State the math property that each of the following represents.

1. $a + (b + c) = (a + b) + c$
2. $10 \cdot 12 = (10 \cdot 2) + (10 \cdot 10)$
3. $a \cdot 1 = a$
4. $(6 \cdot 4) \cdot 0 = 0$
5. $a + b = b + a$
6. $a(b + c) = (a \cdot b) + (a \cdot c)$
7. $(26 - 12) + 0 = (26 - 12)$
8. $a \cdot b = b \cdot a$
9. $6 \cdot 49 = (6 \cdot 50) - (6 \cdot 1)$
10. $a(b \cdot c) = (a \cdot b) \cdot c$

Give a numerical example of each of the following properties.

11. Associative for addition
12. Associative for multiplication
13. Commutative for addition
14. Commutative for multiplication
15. Multiplicative of zero
16. Distributive over addition
17. Distributive over subtraction
18. Division of zero
19. Identity for addition
20. Identity for multiplication

Complete each of the following computations.

21. $3.58 + (4 - 4) =$
22. $4{,}862\,(12 - 11) =$
23. $12 \cdot 13 \cdot 11 \cdot 0 \cdot 22 =$
24. $\frac{16 - 16}{2} =$
25. $\frac{1{,}480}{(8 - 8)} =$
26. $16.2 - (6 - 6) =$

Solve these problems.

27. $386 + 179$
28. $5{,}001 - 988$
29. $36\overline{)4{,}732}$
30. 356×26
31. $281 - 163$
32. $12\overline{)516}$
33. 218×139
34. 278×43
35. $9{,}573{,}187 + 2{,}468{,}329$

Round the following numbers as indicated.

36. 3.214 (nearest hundredth)

37. 5,783.4 (nearest ten)

38. 8.91 (nearest one)

39. 628.35 (nearest tenth)

40. 1,587,321 (nearest million)

41. 0.0187 (nearest thousandth)

42. 2,004.58 (nearest thousand)

43. 0.5886 (nearest hundredth)

44. 256,560 (nearest ten thousand)

45. 4.3895 (nearest one)

Solve these problems. Check your answers.

46. Debbie wants to buy her mother a new watch. The one she wants costs $53.95. She has saved $17.50 from baby-sitting jobs. How much more money does she need?

47. The junior high students at Bethel Christian School are collecting money to help send a missionary to Brazil. The seventh grade has collected $167.54 and the eighth grade has collected $238.47. How much money have the students collected altogether?

48. The school needs new songbooks for chapel. The songbooks can be bought for $2.55 each. What will 250 songbooks cost?

49. The Taylor family traveled 1,976 miles on their vacation. If their average speed on the trip was 52 miles per hour, how many hours did they spend driving?

50. If the youth group can canvass 250 homes in a day, how many could they canvass in 17 days?

MIND BOGGLER

$a + b = 56$
$a - b = 18$

What numbers do *a* and *b* represent?

Skills Checkup

1. 9,295 + 9,124 + 724 + 491
2. 2,581 + 2,222 + 145 + 87
3. 11 + 22 + 33 + 44 + 55 + 66
4. 723,567 + 214,789 + 8,987
5. 123 + 321 + 456 + 654 + 545
6. 12 + 34 + 543 + 879 + 345
7. 23 + 34 + 456 + 5,678 + 67,890
8. 123,458 + 987,674 + 473 + 97
9. 1,135 + 124 + 3,333 + 1,234
10. 12,061 + 4,597 + 11,294 + 35

11. 1,259 - 117
12. 173,203 - 989
13. 302 - 209
14. 2,265 - 1,234
15. 60,398 - 5,909
16. 56,013 - 9,214
17. 1,312 - 615
18. 72,892 - 29,907
19. 72,792 - 12,546
20. 896 - 379
21. 496 × 327
22. 19,763 × 234
23. 38 × 130
24. 3,459 × 837
25. 25 × 34,876
26. 19 × 357
27. 9 × 345,672
28. 3 × 20,207
29. 4 × 234,469
30. 35 × 2,813
31. 2,934 ÷ 9
32. 4,128 ÷ 12
33. 148 ÷ 4
34. 4,125 ÷ 11
35. 2,260 ÷ 5
36. 9,918 ÷ 29
37. 1,404 ÷ 6
38. 8,704 ÷ 256
39. 1,965 ÷ 5
40. 11,778 ÷ 906

1. 4,525 + 3,791 + 3,642
2. 700 - 497
3. 91,789 + 42,298 + 12,378
4. 87,032 - 77,290
5. 34 + 546 + 98,783 + 125
6. 36,042 - 12,385
7. 82 × 69
8. 736 × 845
9. 952 × 224
10. 12,368 × 35
11. 715 ÷ 5
12. 39,473 ÷ 78
13. 135 ÷ 27
14. 39,664 ÷ 67
15. $2\frac{8}{9} + 5\frac{4}{9}$
16. $\frac{4}{5} + \frac{1}{3}$
17. $2\frac{1}{2} + 3\frac{1}{6}$
18. $7\frac{2}{3} + 5\frac{1}{5}$
19. $11\frac{1}{2} - 5$
20. $17 - 12\frac{3}{10}$
21. $\frac{4}{5} - \frac{1}{4}$
22. $34\frac{11}{12} - 29\frac{5}{6}$
23. $\frac{3}{5} \times \frac{3}{7}$
24. $\frac{5}{9} \times \frac{1}{3}$
25. $\frac{7}{12} \times \frac{4}{7}$
26. $\frac{1}{2} \times \frac{9}{10}$
27. $\frac{3}{10} \div \frac{5}{6}$
28. $\frac{3}{8} \div \frac{1}{2}$
29. $12 \div 4\frac{2}{3}$
30. $\frac{8}{9} \div 6$

31. Because he wants to buy a new bicycle, Carlos saves $4 of each $15 that he earns doing yard work. He earned $75 last month. How much was he able to put into his savings account toward the bicycle?
32. If the earth travels about 600,000,000 miles a year, how far have you traveled in your lifetime?
33. Cassandra wants to purchase some art equipment and supplies that cost $64.35. She is able to save $1.65 every week. How long will it take her to save the money she needs?
34. Three pieces of pipe weigh 9.2 kilograms, 14.9 kilograms, and 41.7 kilograms. What is their total weight?

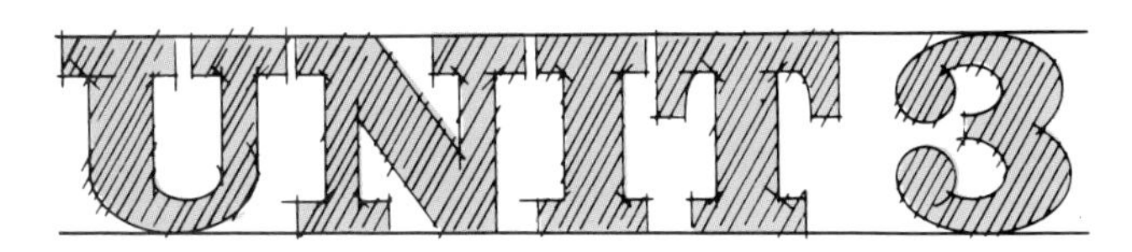

Pastor

"Now if you'll look at line 7 under 'Missions,' you'll notice that we have increased the Pattersons' support for this quarter. They're planning to get to the field sometime this month, and you'll remember that we voted to increase their support for six months to help pay shipping costs and meet other miscellaneous needs they'll have in going to Japan."

Pastor Bell listened closely as the church treasurer read the quarterly financial report. His thoughts wandered briefly. "It's amazing to see how God has blessed this ministry over the last few years. I remember when I first came to this town with my dream of planting a church. Jana and I did *everything* in those early days. We had to make decisions we never imagined we'd face. Once we'd established a fair-sized congregation, we had to find a building to suit our needs. The people thought I was a little too optimistic at first when I suggested we move to a site that would allow for expansion. In only five years we were knocking out walls, adding on to the Sunday school building, and expanding our parking lot.

"Our missions budget, though, is what I marvel over. Being faithful there has brought blessing in other areas. It seems that the greater percentage of our offerings we give to missions, the more God blesses in attendance and membership and in the lives of the people.

"Being a pastor had been rewarding in many ways. It has taught me spiritual lessons that enable me to help my people. It's amazing how many other things I've learned as well. Being able to claim tax deductions for library, church-related mileage, and housing and utility expenses has given Jana and me more flexibility to invest in God's work. Giving an accurate account of those things takes a little bookkeeping time, but the result is well worth the effort. It's really just a part of being faithful over what God has entrusted to me."

Few occupations demand the practical wisdom, careful decision making, and complete devotion required of a pastor. He needs to know many things—even "nonreligious" things—in order to serve the Lord well in his special calling. Everything that he does, whether it be preaching to his congregation or changing the oil in his car, is a part of his spiritual work. Likewise, we all have a special calling from God. As a pastor uses all his talents and knowledge to help lead his people, so a Christian businessman uses his talents to witness for Christ, and a Christian student applies himself so that he can be used by the Lord wherever he may serve. "Whether therefore ye eat, or drink, or whatsoever ye do, do all to the glory of God" (I Corinthians 10:31).

Mathematical Phrases

An interpreter changes words and phrases from one language into another so that they can be understood.

In a similar way, we must change word phrases into math phrases in order to solve math problems.

Word phrases can be represented by math symbols.

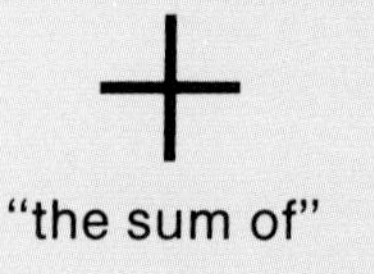

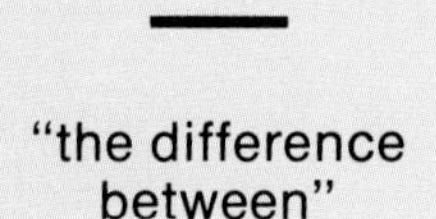

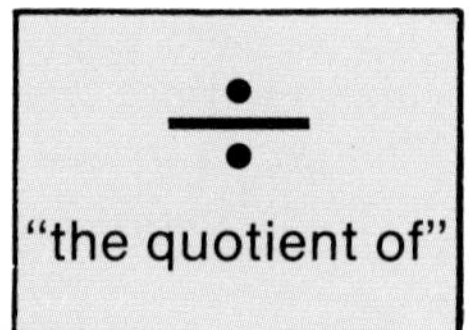

Word Phrase	Math Phrase
the sum of 3 and 6	$3 + 6$
the difference between 3 and 6	$6 - 3$
the product of 3 and 6	6×3, or $6 \cdot 3$
the quotient of 6 divided by 3	$6 \div 3$, or $3\overline{)6}$, or $\frac{6}{3}$

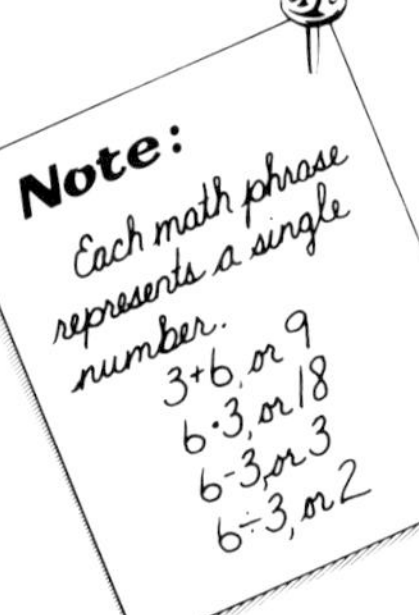

The word phrase "the quantity" indicates parentheses in the corresponding math phrase.

Word Phrase	Math Phrase
the sum of 6 and the quantity 3 times 5	$6 + (3 \cdot 5)$
3 less than the quantity 5 plus 6	$(5 + 6) - 3$
3 divided by the quantity 6 minus 5	$\frac{3}{(6-5)}$
6 times the quantity 5 added to 3	$6(3 + 5)$

Remember, the number next to the parentheses is to be multiplied.

Practice

Give the symbol that represents each word or phrase. (+ , - , · , ÷)

1. subtracted from
2. more than
3. divided by
4. difference between
5. product of
6. less than
7. added to
8. quotient of
9. times
10. plus
11. minus
12. fraction of
13. increased by
14. decreased by
15. sum of

Write a math phrase for each of the following word phrases.

16. 16 decreased by 7
17. $\frac{1}{4}$ of 20
18. the sum of 10 and 5
19. 8 less than 25
20. 36 divided by 9
21. the quantity 3 plus 2, times 4
22. 3 times the quantity 7 minus 3
23. the difference between 8 and 20
24. 12 increased by 31
25. the product of the quantity 5 increased by 2 and the quantity 8 divided by 2

Write a word phrase for each math phrase.

26. 28 + 13
27. 116 - 82
28. 8(4 - 1)
29. $\frac{(21-7)}{2}$
30. 9 - (4 + 3)

Mathematical Sentences

Word Sentences to Math Sentences

Word sentence: Five less than 8 *is equal to* the sum of 1 and 2.
Math equation: $8 - 5 = 1 + 2$
Word sentence: Eight multiplied by 3 *is greater than* 11 plus the quantity 2 times 5.
Math inequality: $8 \cdot 3 > 11 + (2 \cdot 5)$

The symbols $>$ and $<$ tell more about the relationship of the numbers in the sentence than the symbol $\neq$ tells.

Remember the easy way to tell $<$ and $>$ apart.

Keys to Understanding

A mathematical sentence is used to show a relationship between numbers.

Two General Relationships

1. A math sentence that states an equality relationship is called an *equation*.
   The symbol $=$ means "is equal to."
2. A math sentence that is not an equation is called an *inequality.*
   There are three inequality symbols.
   The symbol $>$ means "is greater than."
   The symbol $<$ means "is less than."
   The symbol $\neq$ means "is not equal to."

Practice

Tell whether each math sentence is true or false.

1. $8 + 12 = 20$
2. $6 - 3 > 2 + 2$
3. $12 \cdot 2 \neq (3 \cdot 10) - 6$
4. $(3 \cdot 2) + 6 < 15$
5. $(42 \div 7) = (6 \cdot 6) \div 6$
6. $3(9 - 3) = 3 \cdot 3$
7. $18 - 7 > 2(6 + 1)$
8. $2 + (6 \cdot 8) \neq (4 \cdot 12) + 2$
9. $(a + b) + c = a + (b + c)$

Write a math sentence for each of the following word sentences.

10. Ten decreased by 5 is equal to 3 plus 2.
11. Eight increased by 10 is greater than 2 multiplied by 7.
12. The quantity 2 plus 3 times 4 is equal to 40 divided by 2.
13. The sum of 17 and 15 is equal to the product of 4 and 8.
14. Seven is less than 10, which is less than 13.
15. The quantity 9 times 2 divided by 6 is equal to $\frac{1}{2}$ of 6.
16. Five times the quantity 12 minus 11 is not equal to 10.
17. Three added to 4 added to the quantity 3 times 4 is equal to 19.
18. The difference between 20 and 3 is greater than 2 times 8.
19. The product of the quantity 7 minus 2 and the quantity 9 divided by 3 is equal to 7 more than 8.

Write a word sentence for each of the following math sentences.

20. $43 > 6 \cdot 7$
21. $3 + 8 = 11$
22. $2 \cdot 8 = 4 \cdot 4$
23. $\frac{3 - 1}{5} \neq \frac{1}{2}$
24. $(3 \cdot 10) + 6 < \frac{4 \cdot 20}{2}$
25. $4(21 \div 7) = (20 - 8)(9 - 8)$

Open Sentences

Jennifer wants Chad to tell whether the open sentence $n + 10 = 22$ is true or false.
Chad decided that he needed more information before he could tell whether the sentence is true or false. Right now it is neither. He figured out that the sentence will be true if n equals 12. The sentence will be false if n equals any number besides 12. Therefore 12 is the solution of $n + 10 = 22$.

Keys to Understanding

A math sentence that is neither true nor false until more information is given is called an *open sentence.*

An open sentence contains at least one variable.

A letter of the alphabet that represents a number is called a *variable.*

A number that replaces the variable in a sentence so as to make the sentence true is called a *solution.*

The set of all possible solutions to a given sentence is called the *solution set.*

What do you think?

What type of sentence is $n + 3 > 11$?
Is the sentence an open sentence? Why or why not?
Is there a solution for this sentence?
How many solutions are there for $n + 3 > 11$?
What notation would you use to write the solution?

Note: When multiplying a number times a variable, write the number to the left of the variable: $5n$

Practice

Tell whether each sentence is true, false, or open.

1. $n - 6 = 9$

2. $2(3 + 2) = 10$

3. $\frac{10}{2} < \frac{(9 - 6)}{3}$

4. $8(r + 2) - 5(10 - 3) = 13$

5. $6a + 3 > 15$

6. $(31 - 5) \div 13 = 2$

7. $10(b - 6) = 6 + 4$

8. $6(8 + 7) > 55$

9. $a^2 + 2ab + b^2 = 4$

Using n as the variable, write an open math sentence for each word sentence.

10. A number increased by 7 is equal to 20.

11. Sixteen minus a number is equal to 15 divided by 3.

12. A number multiplied by 8 is equal to 24.

13. Twelve is less than the sum of a number and 10.

14. Twenty is equal to 5 times the quantity 6 plus a number.

15. A number divided by 7 is greater than 10 decreased by 2.

Write a word sentence for each of the following open sentences.

16. $n + 4 = 19$

17. $16 - 2n = 12$

18. $\frac{28}{n} = 8 - 4$

19. $\frac{(n - 9)}{2} = 1$

20. $3(10 - n) = \frac{18}{2}$

Math in Action

1. Below is a record of Pastor Burkholder's church-related mileage for one week. What is the total number of miles he traveled?

Sun.	Miles	Thurs.	Miles
Church	16	Prayer Breakfast	8
Mon.		Church	8
Church	8	Home visits	17
Pastors' meeting	99	Funeral service	66
Tues.		Fri.	
Hospital visits	20	Youth fellowship	20
Wed.		Sat.	
Church	8	Bus visits	15

If Pastor Burkholder's car gets 15 miles to the gallon, how many gallons of gas did he use last week?
If gasoline costs $1.35 per gallon, how much did he spend on gasoline for the week?

2. Pastor Wilcox needs to order Sunday school materials for his church. The attendance for last week was as follows:

Preschool	25	Senior High	31
Primary	41	College/Career	22
Junior	46	Adult	59
Junior High	26		

If he allows for 5 extra people in each department, how many items will he need for the entire Sunday school program?

3. The Kessler family is going to France as missionaries. They need $1,775 per month support on the field. If they have $981 pledged so far, how much more do they need?

4. Grace Bible Church is planning to expand its parking lot. It needs space for 50 more cars. If each car requires 96 square feet of space, how many square feet of parking space are needed?

5. The regular-fund offerings at Bethel Baptist Church over the past four weeks were as follows: $375.42; $251.75; $264.19; $229.92.
What was the total offering for the month?
What was the average weekly offering?

Solving Equations

$n + 6 = 14$

What is the solution? Or, what is n?

Try 0. $0 + 6 = 14$?
Try 1. $1 + 6 = 14$?
Try 2. $2 + 6 = 14$?
Try 3. $3 + 6 = 14$?
Try 4. $4 + 6 = 14$?

Can we find the solution without trying every number?

What do you think?

What number plus 6 equals 14? Think, $? + 6 = 14$.
What is the solution of $n + 6 = 14$? $n = ?$
Will any other number make the sentence true?
How many elements are in the solution set of $n + 6 = 14$?

$2n + 2 = 14$

What is n?
What number plus 2 equals 14?
Think, $? + 2 = 14$. $12 + 2 = 14$
Now, 2 times what number equals 12?
Think, $2 \cdot ? = 12$. $2 \cdot 6 = 12$
What is the solution of $2n + 2 = 14$?

To check the equation, replace the n with 6.

$(2 \cdot 6) + 2 = 14$
$12 + 2 = 14$
$14 = 14$

Does 6 make the sentence true?

Practice

Solve and *check* the following equations.

1. $n + 2 = 6$
2. $a + 7 = 7$
3. $n + 1 = 12$
4. $b - 5 = 2$
5. $n - 2 = 15$
6. $c - 6 = 0$
7. $2y = 10$
8. $4b = 12$
9. $3n = 3$
10. $\frac{a}{3} = 5$
11. $\frac{n}{6} = 1$
12. $\frac{h}{5} = 2$
13. $3a + 2 = 8$
14. $4n + 3 = 15$
15. $3b - 4 = 20$
16. $\frac{n}{5} + 2 = 6$
17. $\frac{a}{3} - 1 = 2$
18. $4y - 1 = 7$
19. $3b + 6 = 12$
20. $\frac{1}{2}n + 3 = 5$

Write a math sentence for each word sentence and give the solution.

21. Four more than a number is equal to 8.
22. Two less than a number is equal to 5.
23. A number divided by 2 is equal to 3.
24. Three times a number minus 5 is equal to 4.
25. Five plus 2 times a number is equal to 11.
26. One-half of a number increased by 10 is equal to 20.
27. The sum of a number and 3 is 12.
28. The product of 5 and a number is 15.
29. Ten times a number decreased by 5 is 5.
30. The quantity 2 plus a number divided by 3 is 4.

Solving Inequalities

$n + 6 < 14$

Try whole numbers to find a solution.

Try 0.	$0 + 6 < 14$?
Try 1.	$1 + 6 < 14$?
Try 2.	$2 + 6 < 14$?
Try 3.	$3 + 6 < 14$?
Try 4.	$4 + 6 < 14$?

LOOK, SHEERLUCK, STRANGE GREEK HIEROGLYPHICS!

All of these whole numbers make the sentence true. So what is the solution?

What do you think?

If $n + 6 < 14$ were an equation, what would the solution be?
Does any whole number more than 8 make the sentence true?
Does any whole number less than 8 make the sentence true?
What whole numbers would be in the solution set of the inequality?
How many numbers do you think would make the sentence true?
What are the numbers that will solve the inequality
$n + 6 \neq 14$?
How would you write a description of the solution set?

$3n + 6 > 12$

What whole numbers will be in the solution?
If $3n + 6 > 12$ were an equation, what would the solution be?
Since n would equal 2 if it were an equation, try a number one more and one less than 2 to see if they solve the inequality.

$(3 \cdot 3) + 6 > 12$?	$(3 \cdot 1) + 6 > 12$?
$9 + 6 > 12$?	$3 + 6 > 12$?
$15 > 12$? yes	$9 > 12$? no

The inequality works with 3 but not with 1. Therefore whole numbers greater than 2 are in the solution set.
The solution set can be written using set notation: $n = \{3, 4, 5, \ldots\}$

Practice

Using set notation, list the elements in the set of whole numbers that solve these inequalities.
Example: $c - 4 > 5$ {10,11,12, . . .}

1. $a + 1 > 9$
2. $n + 3 > 4$
3. $c + 6 < 10$
4. $2n + 1 > 11$
5. $\frac{a}{3} < 1$
6. $n + 3 > 7$
7. $4a + 1 < 13$
8. $b - 3 > 1$
9. $3y - 9 > 18$
10. $\frac{1}{2}n + 4 > 5$

Using set notation, write the description of the solution sets of these inequalities. Example: $2n > 12$ {numbers greater than 6}

11. $3n < 12$
12. $a + 6 > 10$
13. $c - 4 < 6$
14. $\frac{b}{4} \neq 2$
15. $\frac{1}{3}a > 1$
16. $2n - 6 < 12$
17. $8 + n \neq 10$
18. $5y - 6 > 14$

Tell which numbers listed after the inequalities are solutions.

inequalities	**possible solutions**
19. $n + 4 > 8$	0, 1, 4, 6, 8, 10
20. $n + 7 < 12$	2, 4, 6, 8, 10, 12
21. $n - 4 > 12$	5, 7, 9, 11, 13, 15
22. $3n + 2 < 17$	1, 3, 5, 7, 9, 11
23. $3n - 1 \neq 8$	0, 1, 2, 3, 4, 5
24. $12n \neq 0$	1, -1, 2, -2, 3, -3
25. $\frac{n}{5} + 1 > 3$	0, 5, 10, 15, 20, 25

Reading the Problem

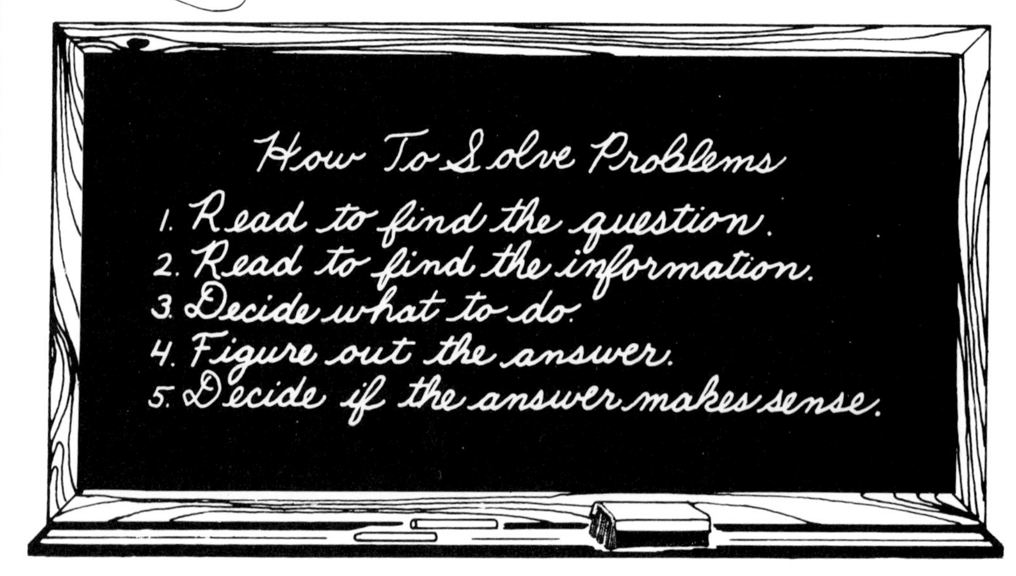

Practice

Read each problem and identify only the information needed to answer the question.

1. John earns $4 an hour mowing yards and has put $140 into his savings account. If he withdraws $60 from his account, how much money will he have left?
2. Mary baby-sits for the Hauperts two nights a week for three hours each night. The Hauperts pay her $2 an hour. If Mary has $20 already saved, how much money will she make in a week baby-sitting?
3. Roy has five coins that have a combined value of 29¢. What are the five coins if one of the coins is not a dime?
4. Nancy practices the piano ten hours a week. She has been playing the piano for fifteen years. If Nancy is twenty-four years old, how old was she when she started piano lessons?
5. The basketball team traveled 96 miles in the school bus to a game. The trip took two hours, and the bus used 16 gallons of gasoline. How many miles did the bus average on each gallon of gas?

Read each problem and tell what additional information is needed in order to answer the question.

6. The apple stand has 150 apples on it. All the apples are Red Delicious. How many apples could be bought for $1?
7. Karen is baking cookies on two rectangular cookie sheets. How many cookies can she bake at one time?
8. Glenn has weeded five rows of the garden. How many more rows must he weed before he is finished?
9. There were 546 people who attended both Sunday school and church on Sunday. How many people attended just Sunday school?
10. A plane traveled from New York to Chicago in four hours. What was the plane's average speed in miles per hour?
11. What is the age of Tim's brother if he is eight years older than Tim?
12. David scored a total of 412 points during the basketball season. What was his scoring average?

Deciding and Doing

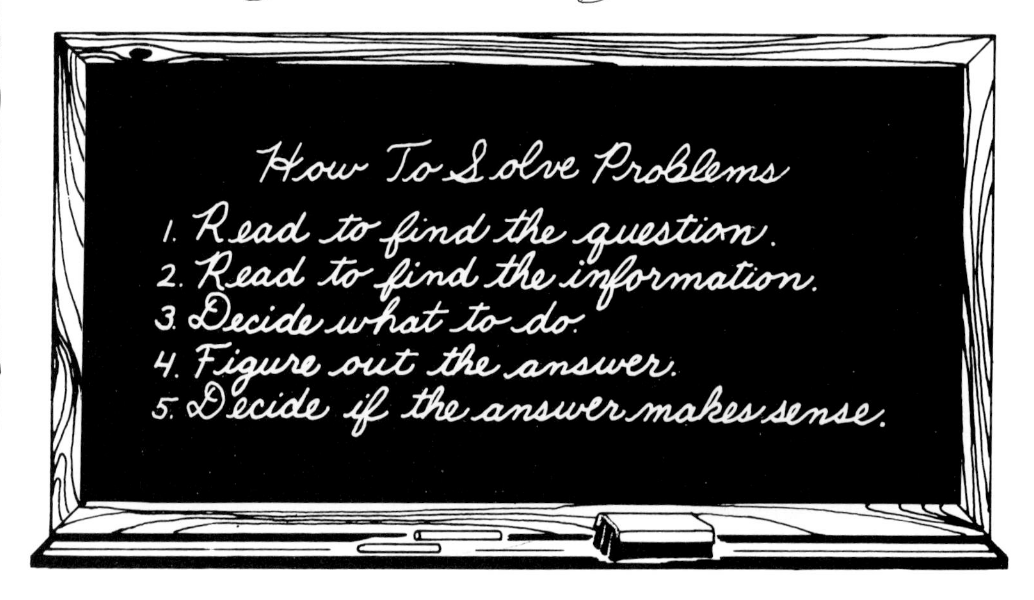

When deciding what to do, think of what operation you should use.

a. When do you add?
b. When do you subtract?
c. When do you multiply?
d. When do you divide?

Remember some of the *clue words* for +, -, ·, and ÷.

Practice

Decide what to do, and then solve the problems.

1. Brenda earns $35 a day working at a grocery store. She works six days a week. What is her total income each week?
2. Jack went fishing and caught twenty-eight fish altogether. He threw nineteen of the fish back because they were too small. How many fish did he keep?
3. Sandy wants to buy a new school outfit. The blouse costs $15, the skirt $25, and the shoes $38. How much money does she need to buy the clothes she wants?
4. At the hardware store light bulbs cost $.85. If Wesley has $9.50 to spend, how many light bulbs can he buy?

5. Rich rides three miles per day on his paper route. How many miles does he ride in twelve days?
6. The total annual payroll for the teachers at Heritage Christian School is $84,000. If there are eight teachers on the payroll, how much does each make per year?
7. Jeff has $55 and wants to buy a bicycle that costs $137. How much more money does he need?
8. It costs $965 to educate one student at Community High. The enrollment at the school is 168. How much money will it take to educate all the students?
9. Jill baked three dozen cookies on Thursday, two dozen on Friday, and five dozen on Saturday. How many cookies did she bake in all?
10. Roy bought his wife Carolyn a bottle of perfume for $9.50. Carolyn bought Roy a bottle of after-shave for $5.75. How much more money did Roy spend than Carolyn?

Read this chart.

11. Give the difference in age between the oldest and the youngest.
12. Find the sum of all their ages.
13. What is the average of their ages?
14. Arrange the men in order of youngest to oldest.
15. How much longer did Jared live than Enos?

Old Men of the Bible

Name	Age
Seth	912 years
Enos	905 years
Kenan	910 years
Mahalaleel	895 years
Jared	962 years
Methuselah	969 years

NOW, YOU HAVE ONE CHANCE TO BLOW OUT ALL YOUR CANDLES!

"What meaneth then this bleating of the sheep in mine ears, and the lowing of the oxen which I hear?" I Samuel 15:14

In mathematics it is not enough to know what to do; we must also be able to do it.

Even so, it is not enough to know what God wants us to do; we must do it. The Bible tells us that we should be "doers of the word, and not hearers only, deceiving your own selves" (James 1:22).

Saul knew that he was commanded to "go and smite Amalek, and utterly destroy all that they have, and spare them not; but slay both man and woman, infant and suckling, ox and sheep, camel and ass" (I Samuel 15:3). He did not do it, however, and consequently he lost his kingdom.

> "For rebellion is as the sin of witchcraft, and stubbornness is as iniquity and idolatry. Because thou hast rejected the word of the Lord, he hath also rejected thee from being king." I Samuel 15:23

Scripture teaches us that when we do not do what God wants us to do, we sin.

> "Therefore to him that knoweth to do good, and doeth it not, to him it is sin." James 4:17

Checking the Answers

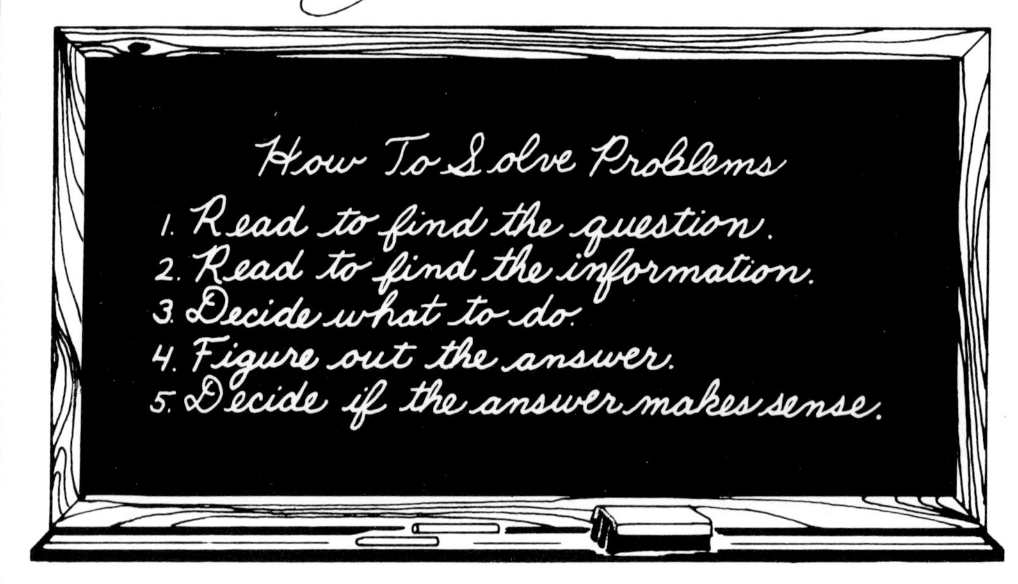

Practice

Give an estimated answer for each of these problems.

1. The 157 students of Grace Junior High collected 97,340 pounds of newspaper. What was the average number of pounds collected by each student?
2. If each of the 157 students at Grace Junior High gave \$1.50 to the mission project, how much money was given altogether?
3. The Hamiltons traveled 1,386 miles on their family vacation. On the first day they drove 498 miles. How far did they travel after the first day?
4. There are 29,400 soup labels in the school office. The school secretary will put 525 labels in a package. How many packages will there be when she completes the job?
5. Jim is collecting pennies. He has thirty-seven books of pennies with seventy-five pennies in each book. How many pennies does he have?

Remember how to *round* numbers.

6. If a junior high school has twenty-eight students in section 1, twenty-three students in section 2, thirty students in section 3, and twenty-nine students in section 4, how many students are there in the school?
7. A restaurant purchases 195 pounds of potatoes a day. How many pounds of potatoes will they buy in a week? in a year?
8. The boys on the assembly crew are setting up the chairs for a special program in the assembly room. They have 450 chairs. If there are to be fifteen rows, how many chairs should be on each row?
9. Denny saved $38.51 from jobs he had during the summer. Ken saved $51.25. How much more did Ken save than Denny did?
10. The junior high is purchasing songbooks. If the songbooks can be bought for $1.55 each, how much will 165 songbooks cost?
11. Todd and John were passing out tracts. Todd passed out 562 and John passed out 374. How many did they pass out altogether? How many more did Todd pass out?
12. Richard found a good deal on a car. However, after making a down payment, he still had to make twenty-four payments of $107.52. How much did Richard have to pay after the down payment?
13. Last month a store made a profit of $12,026.91. The three owners are going to divide the profit equally among themselves. How much will each receive?
14. Mike worked eight hours a day on his job. He earned $20 a day. What was his hourly wage?
15. Mr. Martin traveled at an average speed of 54 miles per hour on a trip. If he drove for 11 hours, how far did he travel? If his car gets 18 miles per gallon, how much gas did he use?

Multi-step Problems

A waiter is paid $3.75 an hour and averages $1.50 an hour in tips. How much money would he make in a forty-hour week?

When a problem involves two or more steps, solve one step at a time.

1. Find the total pay per hour.
   $\$3.75 + \$1.50 = \$5.25$
2. Find the total amount he made.
   $\$5.25 \cdot 40 = \$210$

   Does the answer $210 make sense?

Note:
The information given determines what you should do first.

Practice

Solve these problems.

1. How much will 156 eggs cost if the price per dozen is $.89?
2. Pat wants to buy a new formal for the school banquet. She has $20 and her dad has promised to give her $25. The dress she wants to buy costs $61. How much more money does she need to buy the dress?
3. Ken picks strawberries for a farmer who pays him $.20 for each quart he picks. He picked 42 quarts on Monday, 37 on Tuesday, and 53 on Wednesday. How much money did he make?
4. A school has decided to pay each of the eight bus drivers $840 per month. What will be the total cost for bus drivers in a nine-month school year?
5. Rob weighs 12 pounds more than Kevin, and Tim weighs 23 pounds more than Kevin. If Tim weighs 112 pounds, how much does Rob weigh?

Long-distance direct-dial rates within the United States

	Mon.	Tues.	Wed.	Thurs.	Fri.	Sat.	Sun.
8 A.M.-5 P.M.							
5 P.M.-11 P.M.							
11 P.M.-8 A.M.							

Weekdays		Evenings		Nights and Weekends	
First Minute	Each Additional Minute	First Minute	Each Additional Minute	First Minute	Each Additional Minute
$.75	$.50	$.50	$.35	$.35	$.25

6. Linda called a friend long distance one evening and talked for twenty-two minutes. How much did it cost to make the call?
7. At 7:00 A.M. Mrs. Watts called her son at college. The call cost her $1.35. How long did she and her son talk?
8. The athletic director made three long-distance calls to schedule games. They were all made on weekdays and lasted two minutes, four minutes, and six minutes. What was the total cost of the calls?
9. How much could you save by making a seven-minute call on the weekend instead of on a weekday?
10. Figure the total cost of the Weber's long-distance phone calls.

Saturday 6:00 P.M.	11 min.
Monday 10:00 A.M.	5 min.
Tuesday 7:00 P.M.	8 min.
Friday 7:00 A.M.	28 min.

Using Open Sentences

Mike weighs three times as much as his sister Jane. If Mike weighs 81 pounds, how much does Jane weigh?
What number are you trying to find?

How to Solve Problems Using Open Sentences

1. Read to find the information, both known and unknown.
2. Represent the unknown information with a variable.
3. Write a mathematical equation using the information.
4. Solve the equation by finding the value of the variable.
5. Check the answer by replacing the variable with the answer.

Information known	→	Mike's weight = 81 pounds
Information unknown	→	Jane's weight = w
Math equation	→	$3w = 81$
Equation solution	→	$w = 27$
Check	→	$3(27) = 81$
		$81 = 81$

Remember how to check answers.

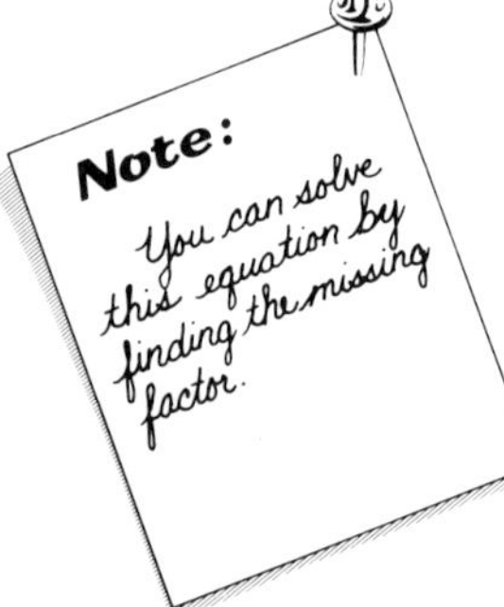

Practice

Solve these problems by using open sentences. Show all five steps.

1. The gas station received a delivery of thirty-six new tires. Now the station has fifty-two tires. How many tires did it have before the delivery?
2. There were 450 people at the school program. This was 45 fewer people than attended the last program. How many attended the last program?
3. What number divided by 3 is equal to 15?
4. Herb spent $2.25 on candy bars. Each candy bar he bought cost $.25. How many candy bars did he buy?
5. The school's basketball team has played nineteen ball games. If they have lost seven, how many have they won?
6. Andy is 6 feet tall. Ken is 6 inches shorter than Andy. How tall is Ken?
7. Mr. Taylor bought a new car for $8,200. The dealer gave him $1,800 in trade-in for his old car. How much did Mr. Taylor have to pay?
8. Mrs. Hawkins went to the store and bought three dozen eggs and one loaf of bread. Her total bill without tax was $3.50. The bread cost $.80. How much per dozen did the eggs cost?
9. George used a $20 bill to buy a calculator that cost $8. If he also paid $.32 tax, how much change did he get back?
10. Walt is half the age of his father. If Walt is eighteen, how old is his father?

Making Up Problems

The Crusader soccer team scored five goals in Saturday's game. They scored two goals in the first half. How many goals did they score in the second half?

Make up a problem for the equation $2 + n = 5$.

Practice

Make up a problem for each of the following equations.

1. $n + 12 = 60$

2. $a - 3 = 7$

3. $x - 11 = 4$

4. $b + 6 = 12$

5. $4n = 16$

6. $\frac{a}{3} = 12$

7. $6x = 18$

8. $2n + 1 = 11$

9. $5b - 6 = 7$

10. $\frac{1}{4}y = 5$

11-15. Make up five of your own story problems, using each of the four operations at least once. Write a math equation for each of these problems.

Statement of account with: Richard Stump

Central State Bank
Account number 411-4240-6

Date	Checks	Checks, cont'd.	Deposits	Balance
9-1				273.96
9-4	106.00		167.55	335.51
9-10	38.69	10.00		286.82
9-11	150.75	7.25		128.82
9-15	51.25		288.68	366.25
9-19	48.30	40.00		277.95
9-22	64.20	150.00	437.00	500.75
9-25	33.83	84.50		
	40.00	30.00		312.42
9-30	84.50	58.70	289.39	
	191.68			
				______

16. What was the total amount of deposits?

17. What will the final balance be?

18. If Richard makes three more deposits of $66 each and writes one check for $131, how much will his new balance be?

19-20. Make up two story problems using the bank statement shown above.

Unit Review

Tell whether each math sentence is true, false, or open.

1. $2 + 3 = 5 + 1$
2. $6 - 3 < 18$
3. $4(3 + 2) \neq 5 \cdot 4$
4. $\frac{6}{3} > (5 - 3) - 2$
5. $3(8 - 3) = 15$
6. $\frac{1}{2}(n) < 12 - 7$

Write a math sentence for each of the following word sentences.

7. Ten less than 12 is equal to 2.
8. Four times a number is greater than 9.
9. One-half of 10 is not equal to 4.
10. Two times the quantity 6 minus 1 is less than 20.
11. One hundred minus twice a number is equal to 70.
12. Sixteen divided by 2 is less than 10.
13. The quantity 6 plus a number divided by 3 is equal to 5.
14. The quantity 3 plus 2 times the quantity 7 minus 7 is equal to zero.
15. The quotient of a number divided by 3 is equal to 8 less than twice the number.

Find the solutions to these equations. Check your answers.

16. $n - 6 = 11$
17. $2b = 12$
18. $11 + n = 15$
19. $3x + 1 = 10$
20. $\frac{a}{4} = 7$
21. $\frac{1}{2}(n + 1) = 4$
22. $6 + (3 - x) = 8$
23. $9b = 81$
24. $5a - 2 = 23$
25. $\frac{3}{6}n = 2$

Give the set of whole numbers that solves each of these inequalities.

26. $2n > 6$

27. $n + 5 < 10$

28. $2n + 3 \neq 13$

29. $6n - 2 > 20$

Solve these problems.

30. A car is traveling at 50 miles per hour. How far will the car travel in 7 hours?

31. Dennis sold 35 papers Monday, 40 on Tuesday, and 30 on Wednesday. If each paper costs $.20, how much money did he collect?

32. Marilyn earned $6.00 baby-sitting. She bought a notebook for $2.50 and two pens at $.60 each. How much of her baby-sitting money did she have left?

Solve these problems, using open sentences.

33. The junior high school has an enrollment of 178 students. Today 34 of the students are absent. How many are present?

34. Doug has saved four times as much money as Ken. Doug has $112 in the bank. How much has Ken saved?

35. Bill thought of a number and multiplied it by 5. Then he added 11 to the product. The answer he got was 41. What was the number?

MIND BOGGLER

Ron bought a phonograph record that has a total diameter of 12 inches. The recording has an outer edge of $\frac{1}{4}$ inch, and the unused center has a diameter of $2\frac{1}{4}$ inches. There is an average of 100 grooves per inch. What is the area of the playing surface of the record?

Skills Checkup

1. 123 + 3,786 + 94 + 78
2. 34,398 + 578 + 23 + 359
3. 193 + 387 + 83 + 118
4. 546 + 23,489 + 5,621 + 17
5. 1,234 + 5,678 + 3,578 + 765
6. 4 + 53 + 302 + 9,546
7. 3 + 9 + 39 + 393 + 3,939
8. 2,592 + 2,345 + 456 + 45
9. 58 + 580 + 5,800 + 85 + 850
10. 125 + 487 + 56 + 15,573

11. 4,591 - 3,989
12. 30,000 - 18,986
13. 137,042 - 91,489
14. 1,359 - 1,297
15. 14 × 389
16. 824 × 87
17. 402 × 359
18. 2,458 × 7
19. 9,204 ÷ 354
20. 8,055 ÷ 179
21. 3,425 ÷ 25
22. 2,136 ÷ 89

23. $5\frac{1}{3} + 1\frac{3}{8}$
24. $2\frac{2}{5} + 1\frac{1}{6}$
25. $\frac{3}{4} + \frac{5}{6}$
26. $3\frac{1}{5} + 3\frac{1}{4}$
27. $\frac{4}{5} + \frac{1}{2}$
28. $\frac{2}{3} - \frac{5}{8}$
29. $\frac{7}{9} - \frac{1}{3}$
30. $\frac{7}{8} - \frac{1}{4}$
31. $\frac{7}{8} - \frac{1}{9}$
32. $\frac{5}{6} - \frac{3}{8}$

33. Terry works $3\frac{1}{4}$ hours per day, five days a week, at a neighborhood supermarket. How many hours does he work in a week? in four weeks? in one year?
34. It takes 30 minutes per pound to bake a turkey. How long will it take to bake a turkey weighing $7\frac{1}{2}$ pounds?
35. If the turkey is to be served to dinner guests at 7 P.M., at what time should it be put into the oven?

1. 23 + 49 + 19 + 78 + 54 + 17
2. 356 + 304 + 879 + 391 + 392
3. 3,907 + 897 + 907 + 328 + 23
4. 17,571 - 8,297
5. 18,234 - 8,888
6. 12 × 2,029
7. 24 × 4,051
8. 44 × 2,193
9. 2,136 ÷ 90
10. 3,425 ÷ 25
11. $\frac{3}{4} + \frac{1}{4}$
12. $\frac{7}{8} + \frac{3}{8}$
13. $\frac{3}{4} + \frac{3}{10}$
14. $\frac{2}{3} + \frac{5}{8}$
15. $\frac{2}{5} + \frac{4}{5}$
16. $\frac{11}{16} - \frac{3}{16}$
17. $\frac{5}{8} - \frac{3}{10}$
18. $\frac{8}{9} - \frac{1}{6}$
19. $\frac{1}{2} - \frac{1}{3}$
20. $\frac{3}{4} - \frac{1}{7}$
21. $\frac{2}{3} \times \frac{3}{5}$
22. $\frac{3}{10} \times \frac{4}{5}$
23. $\frac{5}{9} \times \frac{1}{3}$
24. $\frac{4}{7} \times \frac{3}{8}$
25. $\frac{9}{10} \times \frac{5}{6}$
26. $\frac{4}{9} \div \frac{2}{3}$
27. $\frac{7}{9} \div \frac{3}{4}$
28. $\frac{3}{4} \div 1\frac{1}{2}$
29. $2\frac{1}{2} \div 3\frac{1}{3}$
30. $3\frac{2}{3} \div 4\frac{2}{5}$
31. A government bulletin stated that an average American family wastes approximately 400 pounds of food in a year. What fractional part of a ton of food is wasted per family per year?
32. In Luena County there are 147 miles of county roads. About $\frac{2}{3}$ of these miles of road have a gravel surface. About how many miles of road in Luena County have a gravel surface?
33. In an election in the town of Leland, Kentucky, there were 2,340 votes cast. How many of the 3,678 eligible voters did not exercise their privilege to vote?
34. Mrs. Lander bought three packages of beef that weighed $3\frac{1}{2}$ pounds, $1\frac{3}{4}$ pounds, and $1\frac{5}{6}$ pounds. What is the total weight of beef she purchased?
35. Valerie weighs $6\frac{1}{2}$ pounds more than Pam. If Pam weighs $94\frac{3}{4}$ pounds, how much does Valerie weigh?

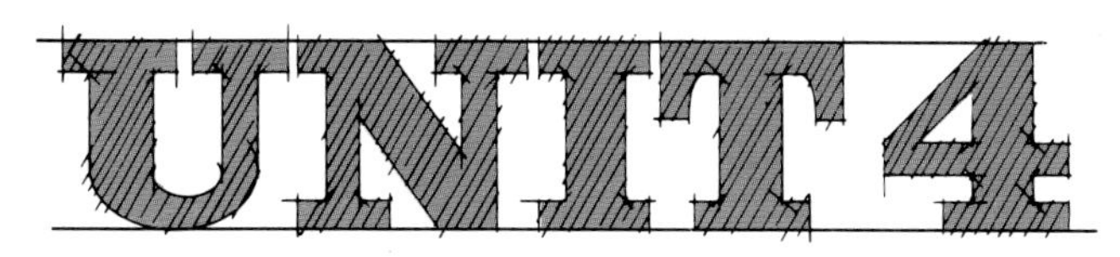

Textile Worker

Textiles affect you every day. They mean the difference between gently massaging your face in the morning with a soft washcloth or chafing it with a scratchy one. They mean the difference between staying cool in 98° weather in a cotton shirt or "burning up" in a polyester one. Textiles determine whether the first sensation your feet feel in the morning is plush and comforting or cold and startling; whether your shirts are still crisp and fresh at the end of a day or crumpled by the time you get to school.

But there's much more to the textile industry than just the finished product. Behind the scenes are the people whose ideas and skills create that garment or fabric that catches your eye.

It all begins with the textile designer. He translates his ideas into patterns suitable for fabric. Patterns may be geometric, linear, or floral. The designer considers the size of the design, the eventual use of the product, and the color. Without his touch, our wardrobes and furnishings might be useful and comfortable, but they would hardly be attractive. Who can imagine Scotsmen without plaids, Hawaiians without bright floral patterns, or American pioneer women without gingham or calico?

The textile technician is the link between the design and the production of a fabric. He decides which type of fabric, machinery, and dyes will best present the designer's pattern. Calculating the number of yarns per inch or the number of yarns needed to create stripes or plaids are among his responsibilities.

Production is next. Textile machinery spins natural or man-made fibers into yarns, often blending two or more fibers to produce fabrics with different qualities. The machinery either weaves or knits yarns to produce fabrics; some are tightly woven, while others are loose. All of these variables—the blending of fibers, the spinning of the yarn, and the construction of the fabric—combine to give you the wide range of choices that you enjoy.

Did you ever have a dress or shirt that was just the right color and style but that wrinkled so badly that its positive qualities were lost in its shabby appearance? The type of fibers used and the way they are spun influence a fabric's strength and appearance. Of what quality of fiber is your life composed? Just as fibers are twisted to produce varying degrees of strength, God often puts us in stressful situations in order to produce strength of emotional, spiritual, or moral fiber in our lives. Quality takes time and effort. Let God do His work, that you "may be perfect and entire, wanting nothing" (James 1:4).

Basic Definitions

Geometry is "the study of points and the shapes they form."

If you look around carefully, you will see that God used many different shapes in creation. Can you imagine what the world would look like without these shapes? Each part of nature is one kind of geometric shape or another. We need to study these shapes to better understand the world God created for us.

A point and a line cannot be formally defined. However, everyone should have an *idea* of what each is.

Keys to Understanding

A point and a line are basic *ideas* in geometry.

A *point* is often represented by a dot and is named using capital letters.

$\overset{A}{\bullet}$ means "point A."

A *straight line* is represented by a set of points extending infinitely in opposite directions. A unique line is determined and named by any two points on the line.

A B $\overleftrightarrow{AB}$ means "line AB."

One line can have many names, using different points.

A B C $\overleftrightarrow{AB} = \overleftrightarrow{BC} = \overleftrightarrow{AC} = \overleftrightarrow{BA} = \overleftrightarrow{CB} = \overleftrightarrow{CA}$

The arrowheads indicate that the line goes on endlessly.

What do you think?

Which of these figures are a representation of a point or a set of points?

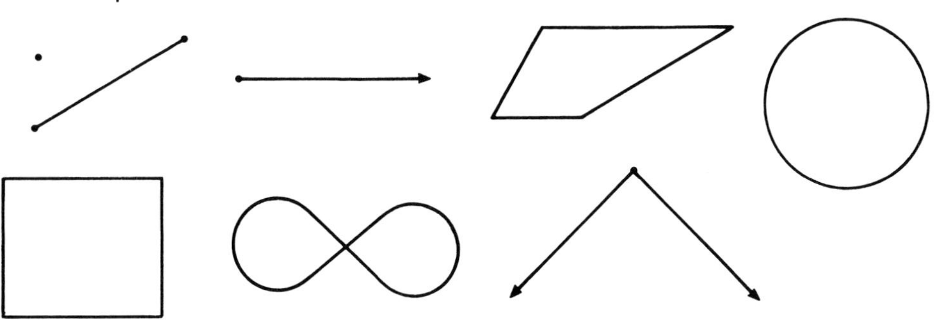

Is every geometric figure made up of a set of points?

Special Kinds of Points

If two lines cross, we call them *intersecting lines.* Intersecting lines have one and only one point in common, which is called the *point of intersection.*
(Point of Intersection P)

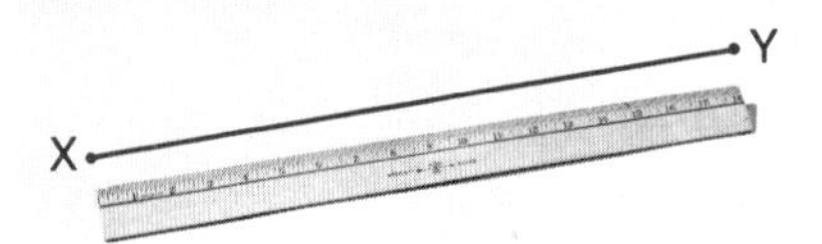

If only part of a line is being considered, we call it a *line segment.* A line segment has two *endpoints.*
(Endpoints X and Y)

If line segments form a geometric figure, we call each point of intersection in the figure a *vertex.*
(Vertices A, B, C, D)

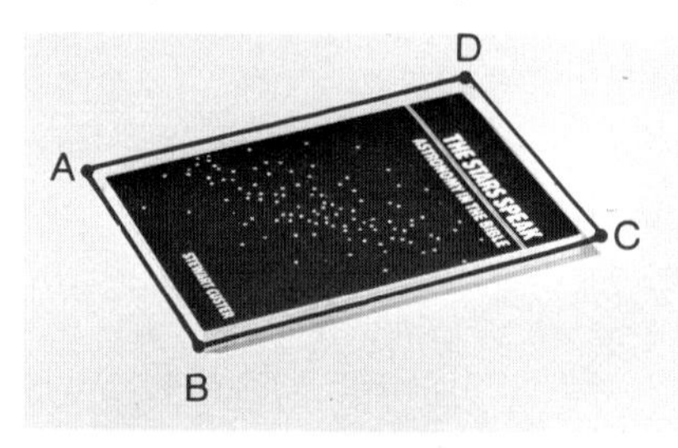

Keys to Understanding

A *line segment* is a part of a straight line consisting of an infinite set of points between two endpoints.

A B $\overline{AB}$ means "line segment AB."

A *ray* is a part of a straight line consisting of an infinite set of points extending from an endpoint endlessly in one direction.

A B $\overrightarrow{AB}$ means "ray AB."

Practice

1. What do we mean when we say the word *point*?
2. What is the difference between a dot and a point?
3. How many lines can be drawn through two points?
4. How many lines can be drawn through one point?
5. How many points are in a line segment? How many determine a line?

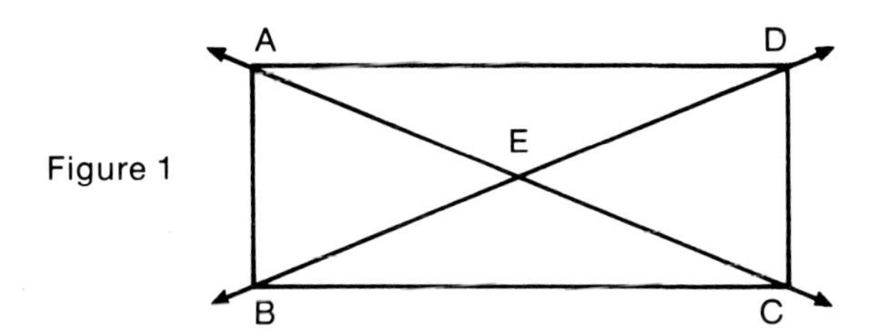

Figure 1

Refer to Figure 1 above.

6. How many points are in the figure?
7. Which points in the figure are named?
8. Name the ten line segments you can find.
9. Name all the lines you can find in this figure.
10. Name the four rays in the figure with endpoint E.
11. Name the four vertices of the rectangle.
12. Name the point of intersection of $\overline{AC}$ and $\overline{BD}$.

Refer to Figure 2 at the right.

13. Give another name for $\overleftrightarrow{AC}$.
14. Give another name for $\overleftrightarrow{AD}$.
15. Which points in the figure are named?
16. Which points in the figure are vertices?
17. Which lines intersect at point A?
18. Name all the lines you can find in this figure.
19. Do $\overleftrightarrow{DB}$ and $\overleftrightarrow{CE}$ have a point of intersection?
20. Are $\overrightarrow{AB}$ and $\overrightarrow{AC}$ the same? $\overrightarrow{AD}$ and $\overrightarrow{DE}$?

Figure 2

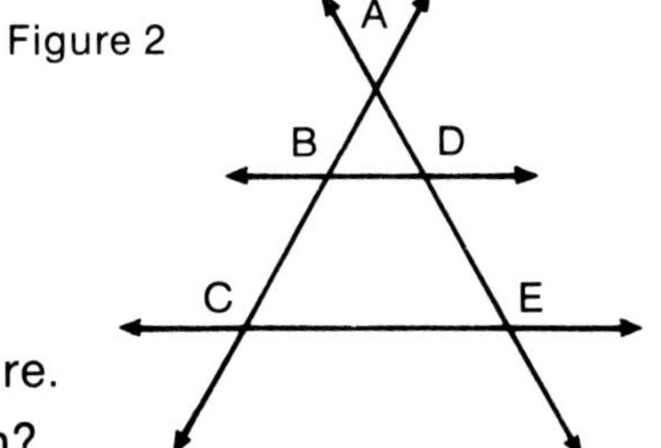

Planes and Angles

MISS SIZEMORE, I HAVE MY PROJECT ON PLANE GEOMETRY.

A *plane* cannot be formally defined, yet we have many ideas about what a plane looks like. In geometry, a plane is simply a flat surface made up of points.

Keys to Understanding

A *plane* is a basic *idea* in geometry.

A plane is represented by a set of points extending infinitely in all directions, forming a flat surface.

A plane is determined by any three points in the plane as long as they are not on the same line.

What do you think?

Will a line and a point not on the line determine a plane?
Will two intersecting lines determine a plane?
If two points of a line are in a plane, will all the points of the line be in the plane?
Does a plane have a boundary?
Name five objects in your classroom that represent a plane.

Most of us look at a clock several times a day, especially when it is near mealtime or time for class to be over. Every time we look, the hands of the clock are forming an angle.

Keys to Understanding

An *angle* is the union of two rays that have a common endpoint. The common endpoint is called the *vertex*.

∠B means "angle B."

∠ABC means "angle ABC."

∠CBA means "angle CBA."

∠1 means "angle 1."

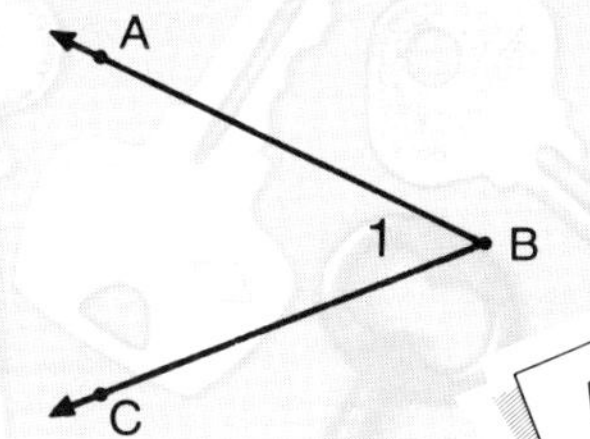

Note: When naming an angle, always put the vertex letter in the center.

Practice

Name each of these angles in three ways.

1.

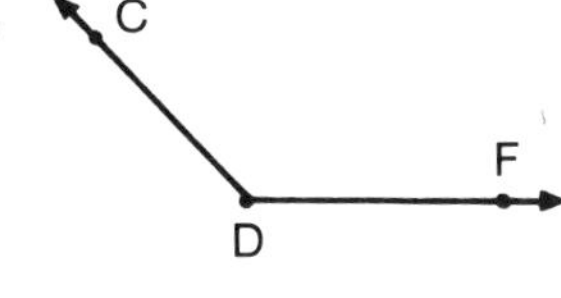

2.

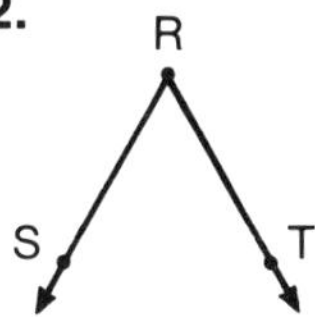

3.

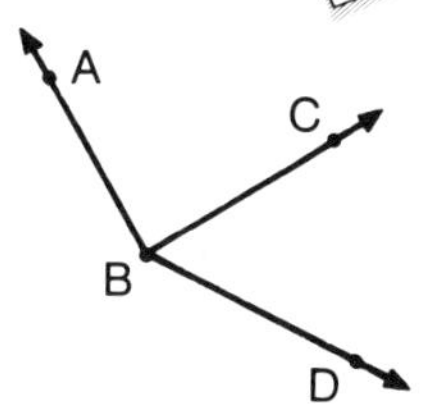

4.

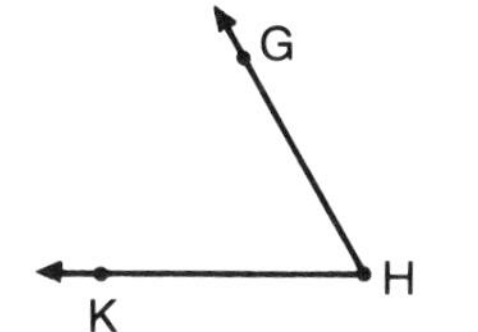

5.

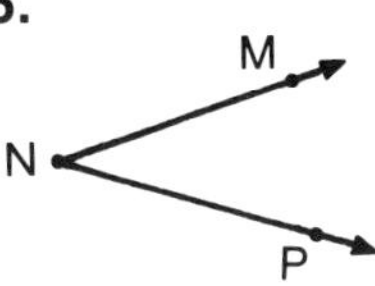

Give two different names for each of the three angles shown in number 3.

Measuring Angles

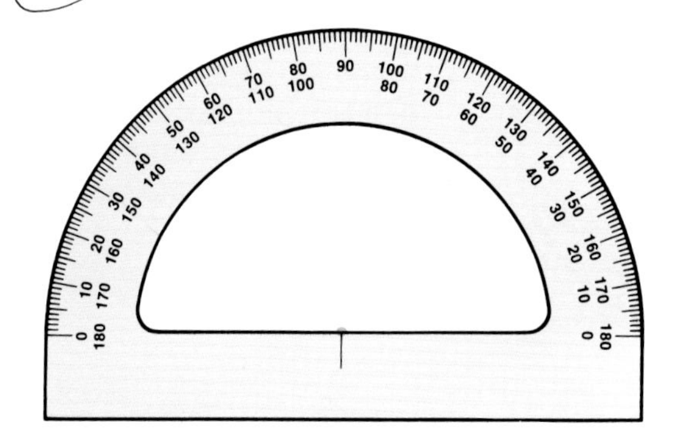

We use a protractor to measure angles. The unit used for measuring angles is the *degree.* The symbol ° means "degrees."
A protractor is one-half of a circle and contains 180 degrees.

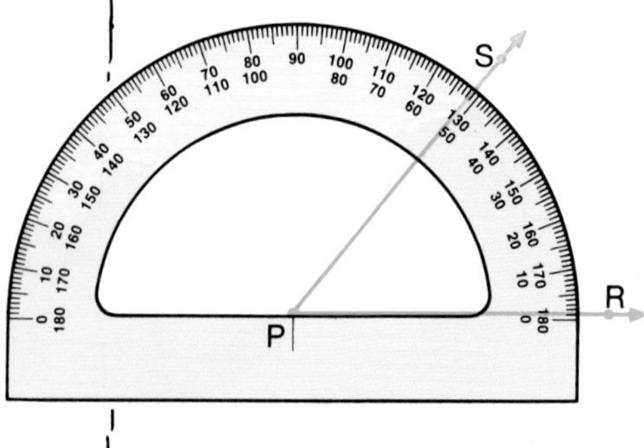

Follow these steps to measure ∠RPS:

1. Place the straight edge of the protractor on one of the rays of the angle (PR).
2. The middle mark must be placed on the vertex of the angle (∠RPS).
3. Starting at 0° on the right and moving around to the left, read the measurement where the second ray crosses the protractor (PS). This is the measure of the angle (50°).

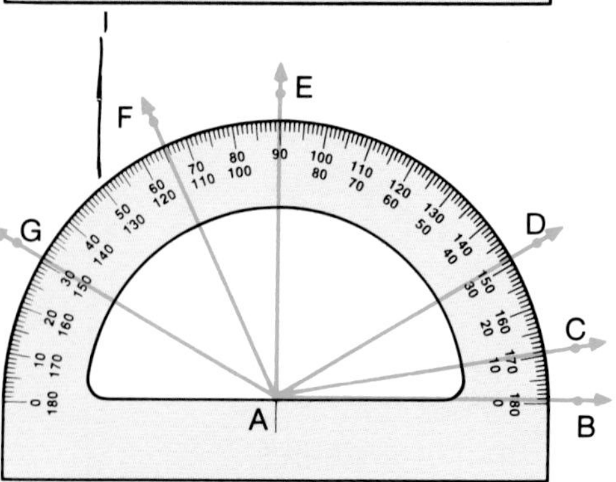

What are the measurements of these angles?

1. m∠BAC =
2. m∠DAB =
3. m∠BAE =
4. m∠BAG =
5. m∠FAB =

What is the difference between an angle and the measure of the angle?

We also can use a protractor to draw an angle with a given measurement.

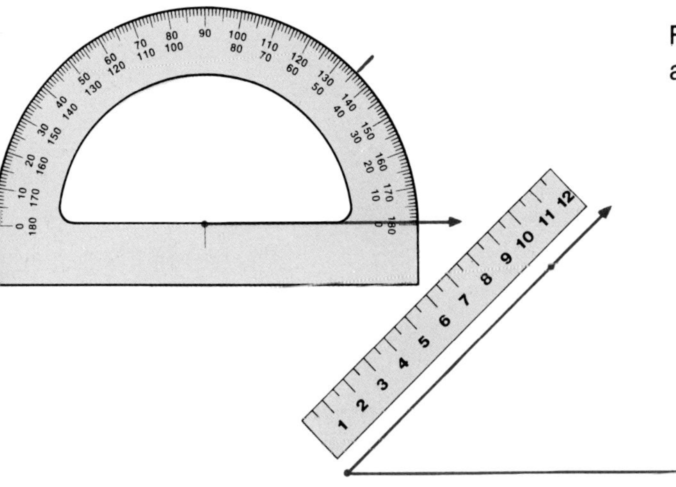

Follow these steps to draw a 45° angle:

1. Draw a ray and place the protractor on the ray so that the endpoint is on the center mark.
2. Look at the scale and put a mark at 45°.
3. Draw the ray between the two points, using a ruler.
4. Measure the angle to make sure that it is 45°.

Practice

Measure these angles.

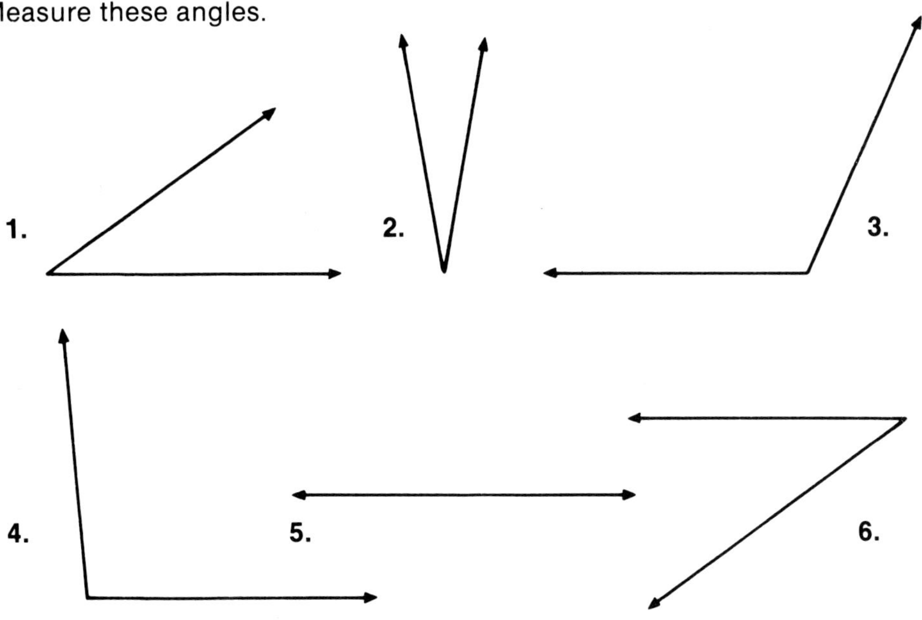

Draw these angles.

7. 60°
8. 125°
9. 15°
10. 160°

Types of Angles

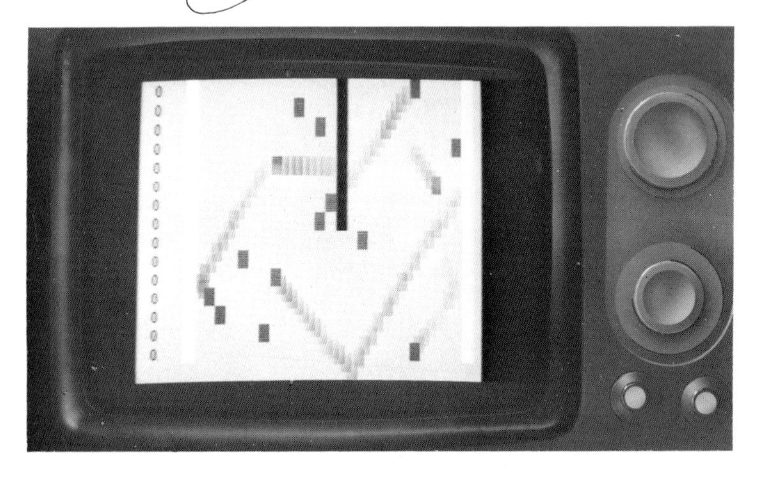

When you play an electronic game, you see many different kinds of angles. Angles are named according to their size. Notice the angles below and their names.

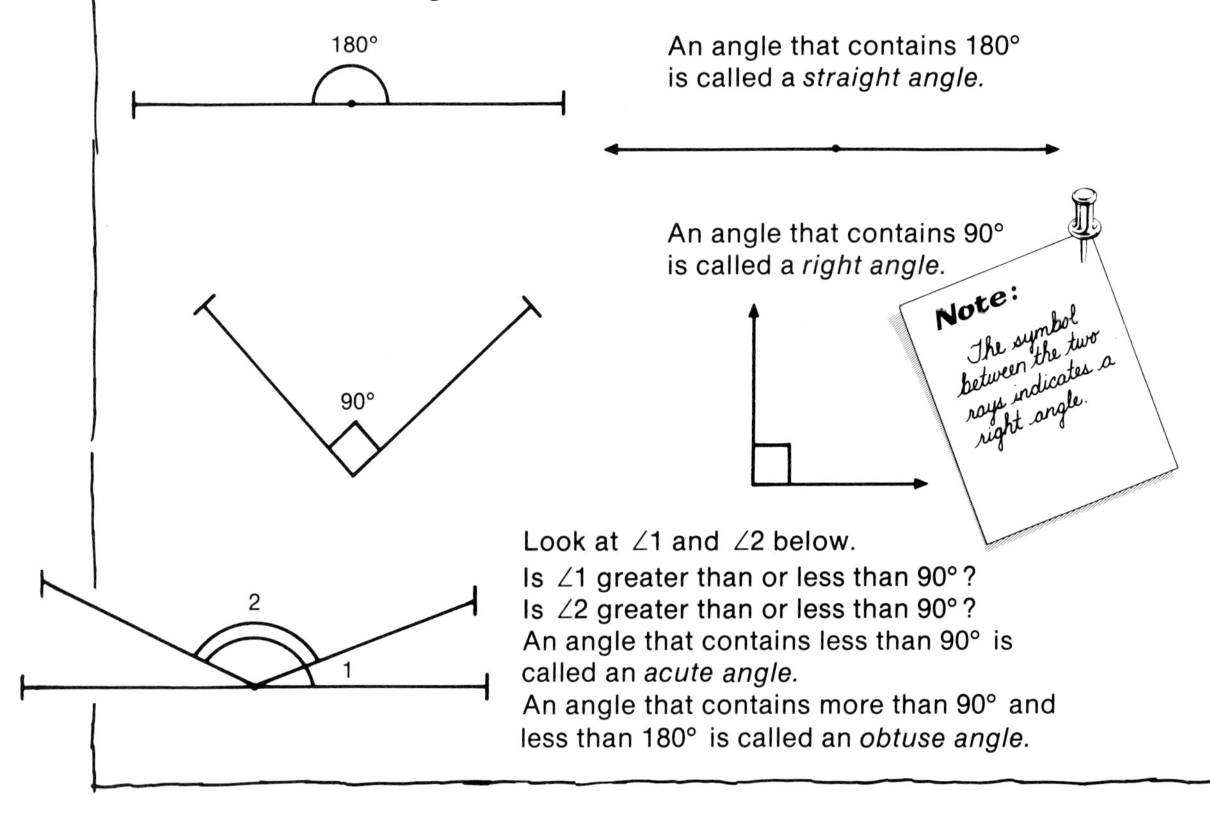

An angle that contains 180° is called a *straight angle.*

An angle that contains 90° is called a *right angle.*

Look at ∠1 and ∠2 below.
Is ∠1 greater than or less than 90°?
Is ∠2 greater than or less than 90°?
An angle that contains less than 90° is called an *acute angle.*
An angle that contains more than 90° and less than 180° is called an *obtuse angle.*

Keys to Understanding

An angle that measures 180° is a *straight angle.*
An angle that measures 90° is a *right angle.*
An angle that measures less than 90° is an *acute angle.*
An angle that measures greater than 90° and less than 180° is an *obtuse angle.*

Practice

Tell whether these angles are straight, right, acute, or obtuse.

1. $m\angle = 60°$

2. $m\angle = 90°$

3. $m\angle = 132°$

4. $m\angle = 1°$

5. $m\angle = 180°$

6. $m\angle = 94°$

7. $m\angle = 179°$

8. $m\angle = 45°$

Give the measure of each of these angles and tell what kind it is.

9.

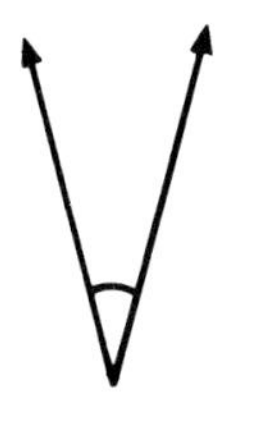

10.

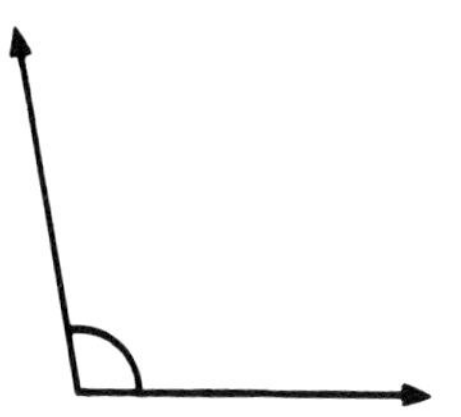

11.

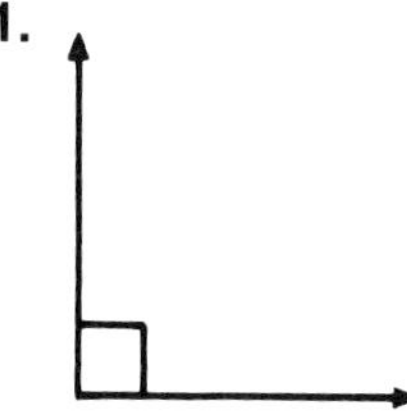

12.

13.

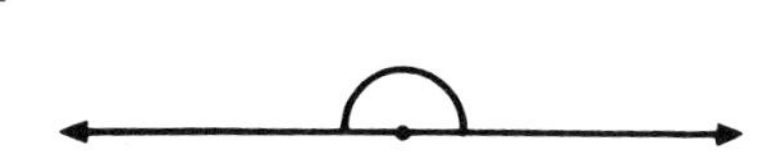

Draw these angles.

14. An acute angle that measures 98° less than a straight angle

15. An obtuse angle that measures 36° larger than a right angle

Related Angles

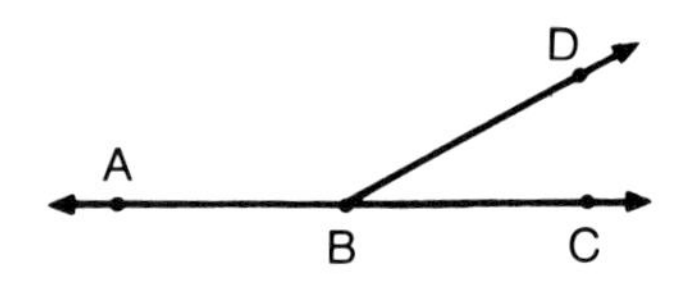

What do $\angle ABD$ and $\angle DBC$ have in common?
Do you notice the same thing about $\angle XYW$ and $\angle WYZ$?
$\angle ABD$ and $\angle DBC$ are *adjacent angles.*
$\angle XYW$ and $\angle WYZ$ are *adjacent angles.*

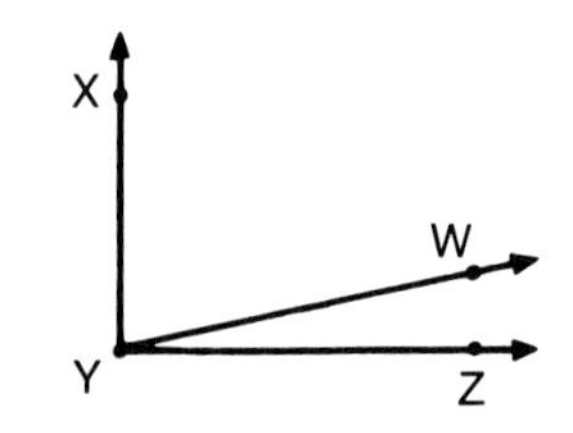

What kind of angle is $\angle ABC$?
What is the measure of $\angle ABC$?
Which two angles equal the measure of $\angle ABC$?
$\angle ABD$ and $\angle DBC$ are *supplementary angles.*
What kind of angle is $\angle XYZ$?
What is the measure of $\angle XYZ$?
Which two angles equal the measure of $\angle XYZ$?
$\angle XYW$ and $\angle WYZ$ are *complementary angles.*

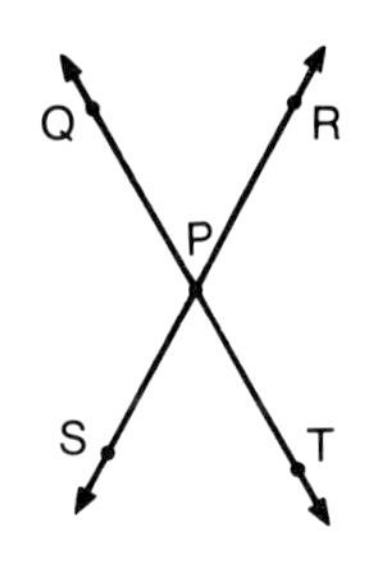

How many angles less than 180° are formed when two lines intersect?
Which two pairs of angles are opposite each other?

Measure the four angles. What do you notice?
$\angle QPR$ and $\angle SPT$ are *vertical angles* and have equal measures.
$\angle QPS$ and $\angle RPT$ are *vertical angles* and have equal measures.

Keys to Understanding

If two angles have a common vertex and a common ray between them, they are called *adjacent angles.*
If the sum of the measures of two angles is 180°, they are called *supplementary angles.*
If the sum of the measures of two angles is 90°, they are called *complementary angles.*
If two lines intersect, they form four angles. The pairs of angles opposite each other are called *vertical angles.*
Vertical angles have *equal measures.*

What do you think?

(Refer to the figures on the previous page.)

Are ∠ABD and ∠DBC adjacent supplementary angles?
Are ∠XYW and ∠WYZ adjacent complementary angles?
Do two angles have to be adjacent to be supplementary?
Do two angles have to be adjacent to be complementary?
When $\overleftrightarrow{QT}$ and $\overleftrightarrow{RS}$ intersect, are any supplementary angles formed?

Practice

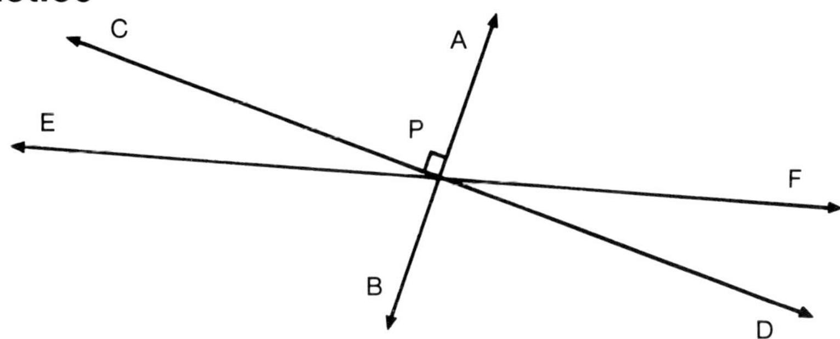

1. Name two acute angles adjacent to ∠BPD in the figure.
2. Name two pairs of supplementary angles in the figure.
3. Name two pairs of adjacent supplementary angles in the figure.
4. Name two pairs of complementary angles in the figure.
5. Name two pairs of adjacent complementary angles in the figure.
6. Name two pairs of vertical angles in the figure.

Fill in the charts.

	Angle		Supplementary Angle
	88°	—	92°
7.	63°	—	
8.	125°	—	
9.	148°	—	

	Angle		Complementary Angle
	42°	—	48°
10.	21°	—	
11.	59°	—	
12.	4°	—	

Related Lines

What can you say about the intersection of these straight train tracks?

Keys to Understanding

Perpendicular lines are lines that form right angles when they intersect (symbol $\perp$).
$\overleftrightarrow{AB} \perp \overleftrightarrow{CD}$ means "$\overleftrightarrow{AB}$ is perpendicular to $\overleftrightarrow{CD}$."

Parallel lines are lines that are in the same plane and never intersect (symbol $\parallel$).
$\overleftrightarrow{RS} \parallel \overleftrightarrow{PT}$ means "$\overleftrightarrow{RS}$ is parallel to $\overleftrightarrow{PT}$."

A *transversal* is a line that intersects two or more lines.
$\overleftrightarrow{XY}$ is a transversal.

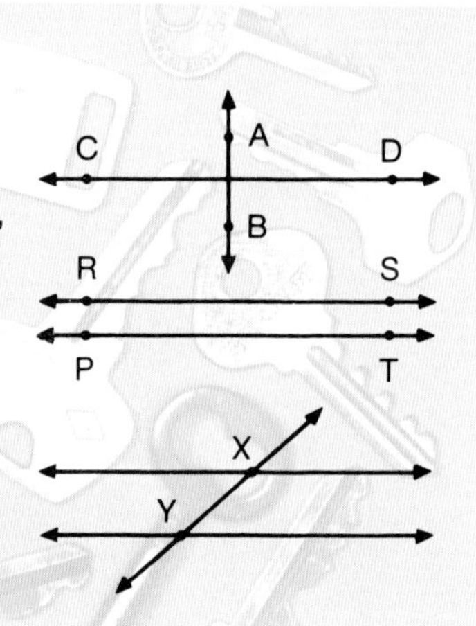

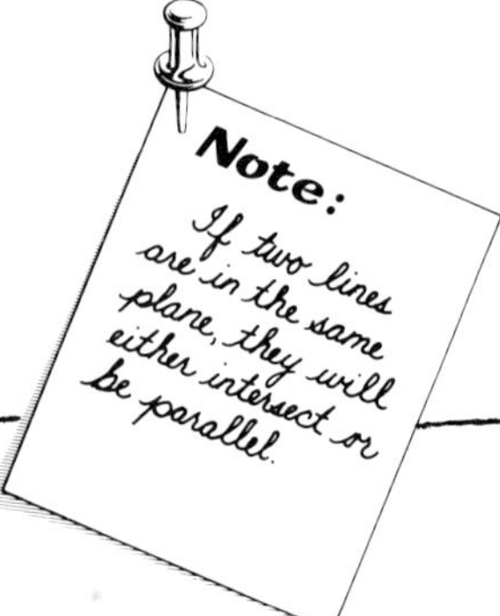

When two parallel lines are intersected by a transversal, eight special angles are formed.

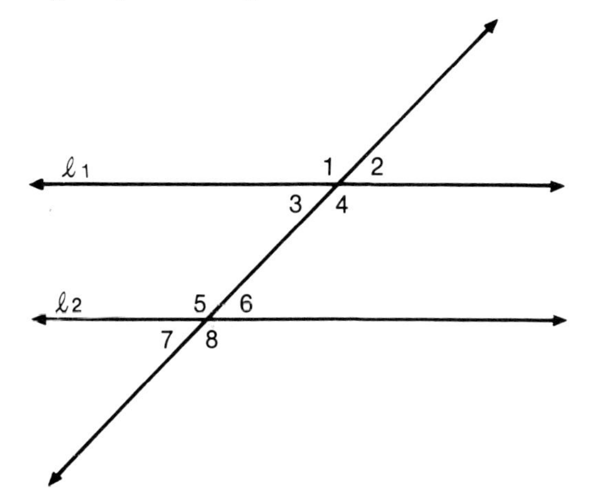

Corresponding angles

$\angle 1$ and $\angle 5$
$\angle 2$ and $\angle 6$
$\angle 3$ and $\angle 7$
$\angle 4$ and $\angle 8$

Alternate interior angles

$\angle 3$ and $\angle 6$
$\angle 4$ and $\angle 5$

Alternate exterior angles

$\angle 1$ and $\angle 8$
$\angle 2$ and $\angle 7$

Measure angles 1 through 8. What do you notice about them?

Keys to Understanding

When parallel lines are intersected by a transversal—

1. corresponding angles have the same measure;
2. alternate interior angles have the same measure;
3. alternate exterior angles have the same measure.

Practice

1. What size angles are formed by two perpendicular lines?
2. Do parallel lines form any angles?
3. Draw a transversal that is perpendicular to parallel lines.

What is the measure of each of these angles? Tell how you got your answers.

4. $\angle 8$
5. $\angle 1$
6. $\angle 6$
7. $\angle 3$
8. $\angle 7$
9. $\angle 4$

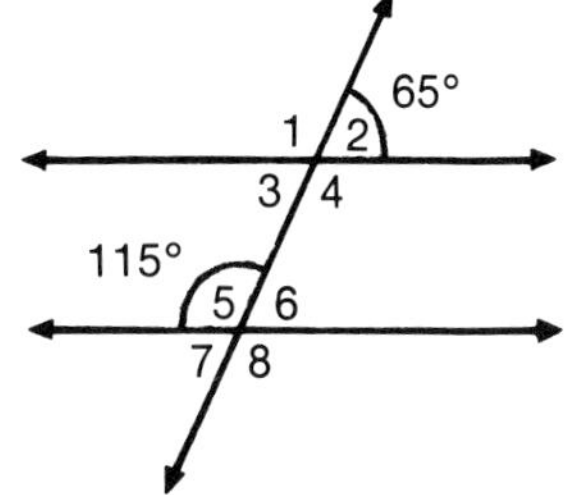

10. Name three objects in your classroom that represent perpendicular lines.

Simple Constructions

Mathematicians have been making constructions (geometric drawings) since the days of Euclid (300 B.C). He did his constructions using only a straightedge and a compass.

Note the directions for different types of constructions.

Follow these steps to construct *a line segment* the same length as $\overline{AB}$:

1. Set the compass by putting the compass point on one endpoint of the line segment and the pencil point on the other endpoint.
2. Keep the opening the same and mark the distance on a sheet of paper. Make a dot at the pencil point and at the compass point. Label the points C and D.
3. Now connect points C and D by drawing a line with a straightedge.

   You now have two line segments the same length.

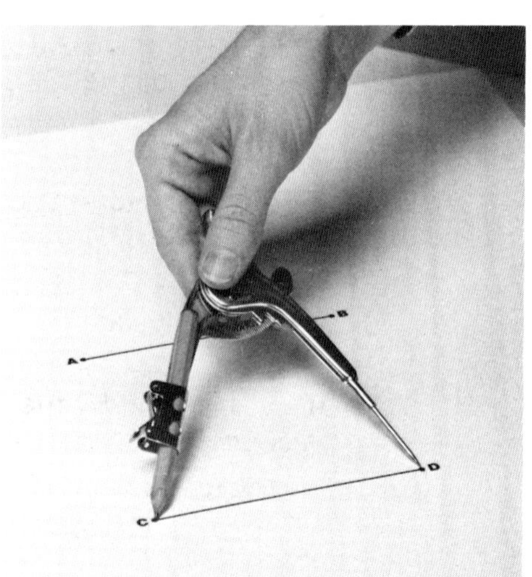

Work carefully and follow instructions.

1. Using your ruler, draw a line segment 3 inches long.
2. Now, use your compass and straightedge to copy the line segment.
3. After you have finished, measure the new line segment you constructed to make sure that it is 3 inches long. Did you do your work correctly?

Follow these steps to construct *a perpendicular bisector* of a line segment AB:

1. Set the compass so that the radius is greater than one-half the distance of the line segment. With the point of the compass on endpoint A, draw an arc as shown.
2. Using the same radius and with the compass point now on endpoint B, draw an arc so that it intersects the arc drawn in step 1. Make sure to extend your arcs so that they intersect.
3. Label the points of intersection C and D.
4. Now connect points C and D. $\overline{CD}$ is the perpendicular bisector of $\overline{AB}$.

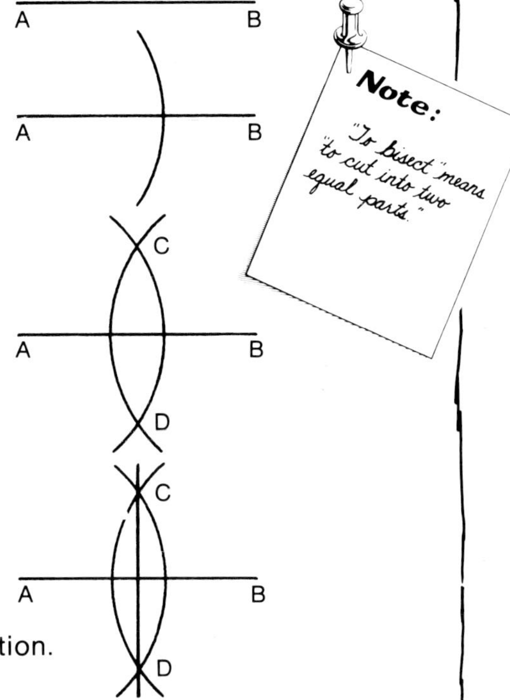

Measure the angles formed by the intersection. What do you discover?

What is a perpendicular bisector?

Practice

Do the following constructions. Follow directions carefully.

1. Using a ruler, construct a line segment. Label the segment AB.
2. Now construct another line segment with the same length as $\overline{AB}$. Label this segment CD.
3. Draw a perpendicular bisector of $\overline{CD}$. Label it XY.
4. Now draw a line segment with the same length as $\overline{XY}$. Label this segment RS.

Copying Angles

Can we copy any type of angle?

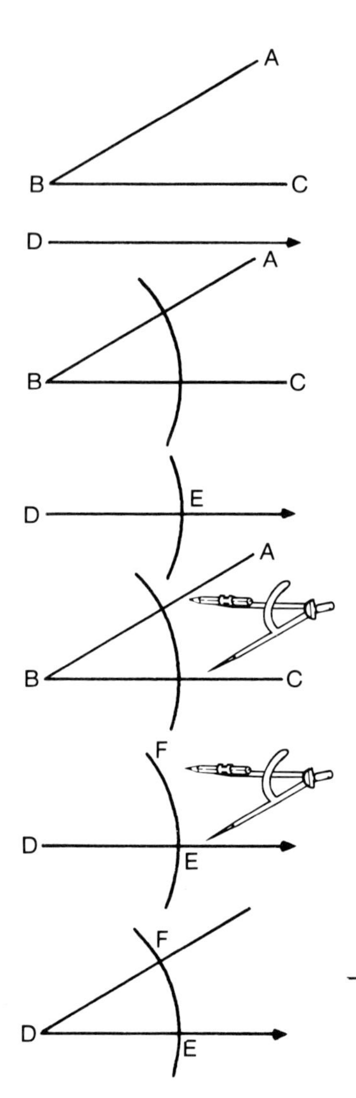

Follow these steps to construct *an angle with the same measure* as ∠ABC:

What type of angle is ∠ABC?

1. Draw a ray with endpoint D.
2. With the point of the compass on B, draw an arc intersecting both rays of the angle.
3. Using the same radius, draw an arc with the point of the compass on D. Label the point of intersection E.
4. Now measure the distance between the rays of ∠ABC, using the intersecting points as shown.
5. With the point of the compass on E, mark the distance found in step 4 on the arc. Label the point of intersection F.
6. Draw a ray from D through F. ∠FDE has the same measure as ∠ABC.

Practice

1. Draw an *acute angle* and then construct another angle with the same measure.
2. Draw an *obtuse angle* and then construct another angle with the same measure.
3. Construct a *right angle* using only a compass and a straightedge.
4. Follow the procedure below and bisect each of the three angles you made in problems 1 through 3.

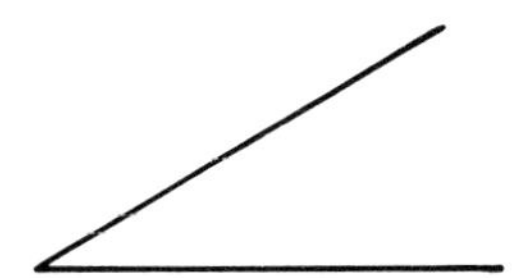

Remember, to *bisect* means "to cut into two equal parts."

Follow these steps to bisect an angle:

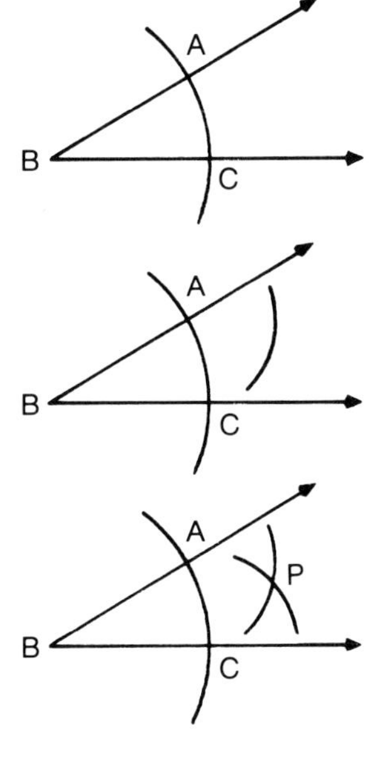

1. With the point of the compass on vertex B, draw an arc intersecting both rays of the angle. Label the points of intersection A and C.

2. Set the compass so that the radius is greater than the distance between A and C. With the point of the compass on A, draw an arc between the two rays.

3. Using the same radius and with the compass at point C, draw an arc that intersects the arc drawn in step 2. Label the point of intersection P.

4. Now draw a ray BP.
   $\overrightarrow{BP}$ is the bisector of $\angle ABC$. Why?

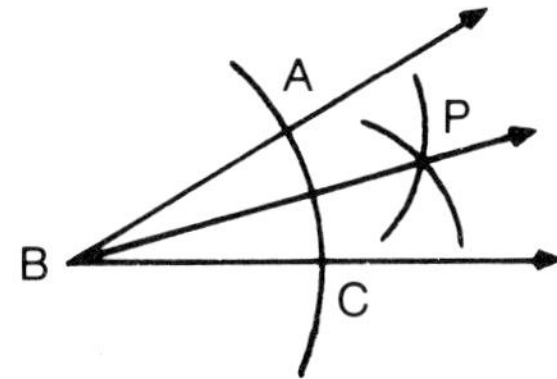

Polygons

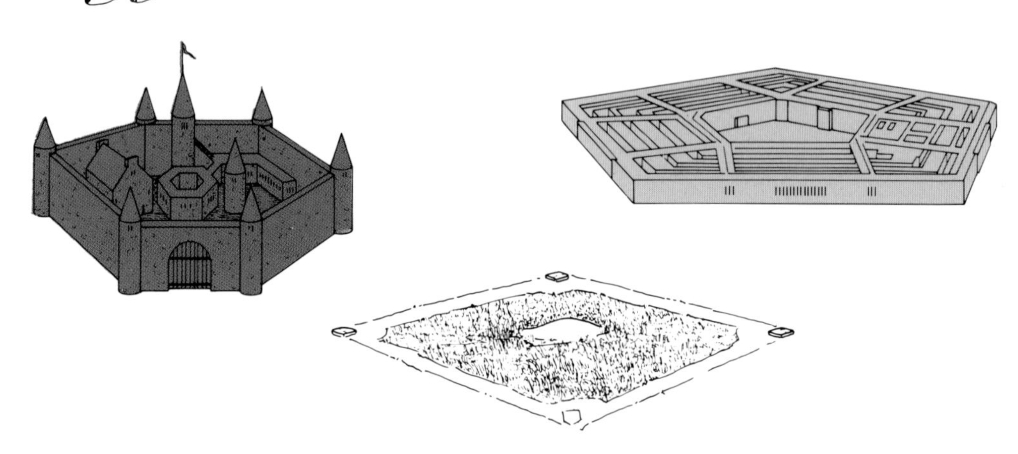

What do all the above pictures have in common?

Each of these figures is a *polygon.*

Keys to Understanding

A *polygon* is a many-sided closed figure made up of line segments.
In a *regular polygon* all the sides are the same length and all the angles have the same measure.

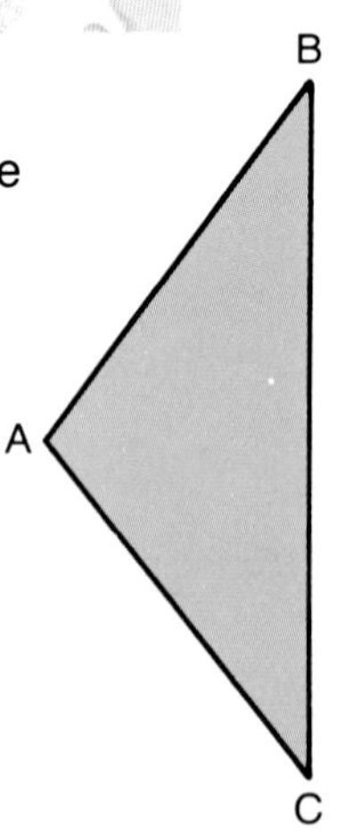

When two segments of a polygon meet, they form an angle of the polygon.

($\angle$CAB, $\angle$ACB, $\angle$ABC)

The vertex of each of these angles is also called a vertex of the polygon.

(Vertices A, B, C)

The polygon is named by using the names of the vertices in order, beginning at any one vertex. Give several names for this triangle.

Types of Polygons					
Polygon	Number of sides	Number of angles	Number of vertices	Example	Regular Polygon
triangle	3	3	3		
quadrilateral	4	4	4		
pentagon	5	5	5		
hexagon	6	6	6		
octagon	8	8	8		

What is the relationship between the number of sides, angles, and vertices?

Practice

1. Give a name to each of these figures, using the vertices.

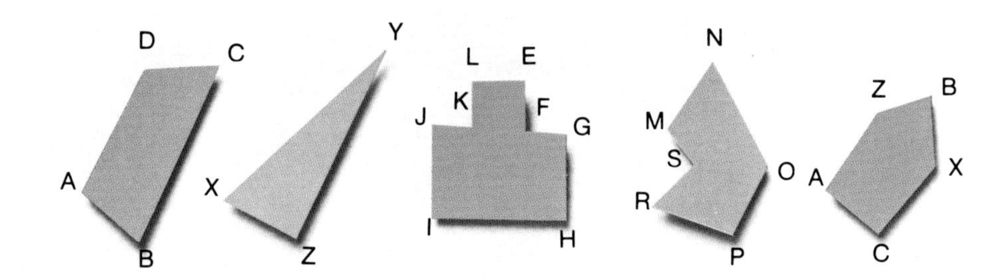

2. What type of polygon is each of these figures?
3. How many vertices does each figure have?
4. Which of the figures is a regular polygon?
5. Would two regular quadrilaterals have the same shape?
6. Would two regular quadrilaterals be the same size?
7. Draw an example of a hexagon.
8. Draw an example of an octagon.

Triangles

I DON'T KNOW WHY ONE IS "CUTER" THAN THE OTHERS.

Measure the angles of triangle ABC.
What is their sum?

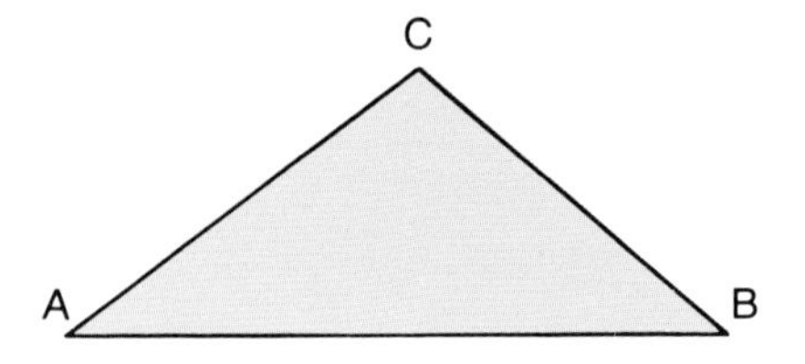

Measure the angles of triangle XYZ.
What is their sum?

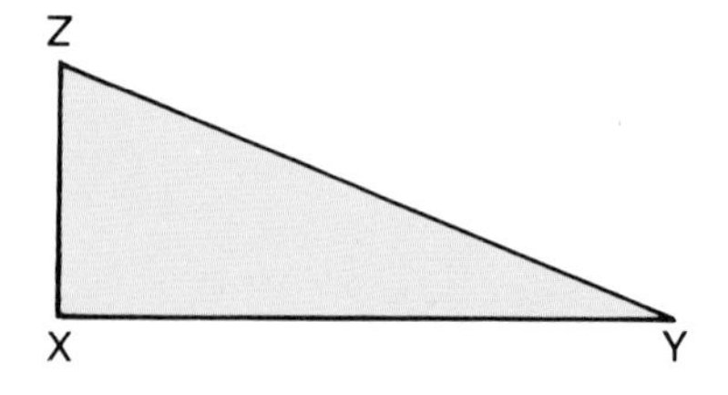

Draw any triangle you want. Measure the angles. What is their sum?
What conclusion can you draw from these examples?

Keys to Understanding

The sum of the measures of the angles of a triangle is 180°.

Types of Triangles

Classified by angles

An *acute triangle* has only acute angles.

An *obtuse triangle* has one obtuse angle.

A *right triangle* has one right angle.

Classified by sides

A *scalene triangle* has no two sides the same length.

An *isosceles triangle* has at least two sides the same length.

An *equilateral triangle* has all three sides the same length.

Practice

Classify triangles 1 through 4 by angles.
Classify triangles 5 through 8 by sides.

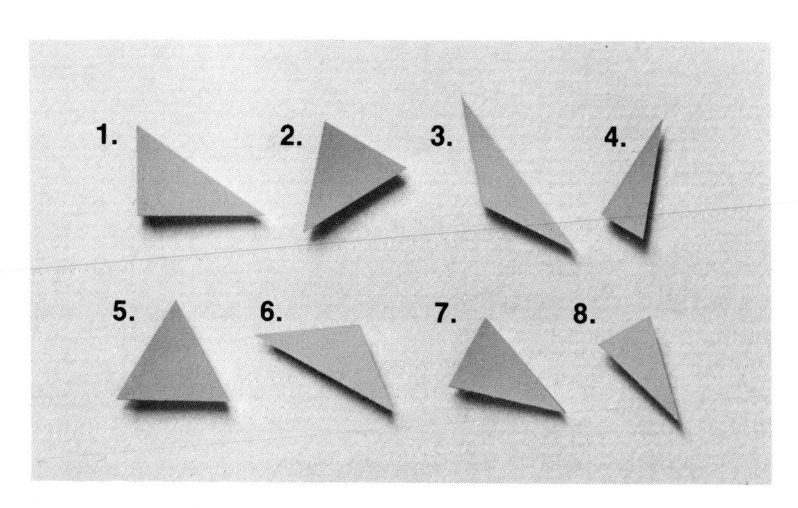

Find the measure of ∠3 of a triangle, given the measures of ∠1 and ∠2:

	m∠1	m∠2	m∠3
9.	35°	45°	?
10.	72°	72°	?
11.	25°	18°	?
12.	75°	11°	?

	m∠1	m∠2	m∠3
13.	14°	127°	?
14.	114°	10°	?
15.	53°	76°	?
16.	5°	5°	?

17. Could a triangle have two right angles? Why or why not?

18. Could a triangle have two obtuse angles? Why or why not?

19. In a right triangle, what relationship do the two acute angles have?

20. An equilateral triangle is also what other type of triangle?

Quadrilaterals

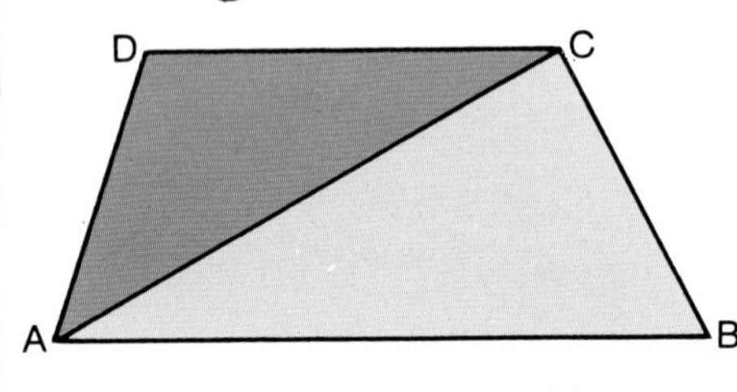

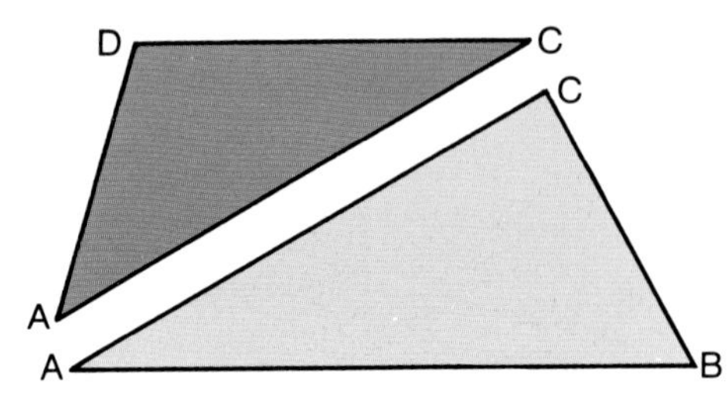

Quadrilateral ABCD = $\Delta ACD + \Delta ABC$

Draw a quadrilateral.
Try to divide it into two triangles.
Can it be done?

What do you think?

Can every quadrilateral be divided into two triangles?
Without measuring, find the sum of the measures of the angles of a quadrilateral.

Remember, the sum of the angles of a triangle is 180°.

Keys to Understanding

Quadrilateral	Description	Example
trapezoid	a quadrilateral with one pair of opposite sides parallel	
parallelogram	a quadrilateral with two pairs of opposite sides parallel	
rhombus	a parallelogram with all four sides the same length	
rectangle	a parallelogram with four right angles	
square	a rectangle with all four sides the same length	

Practice

Name the type of quadrilateral shown by each of these figures.

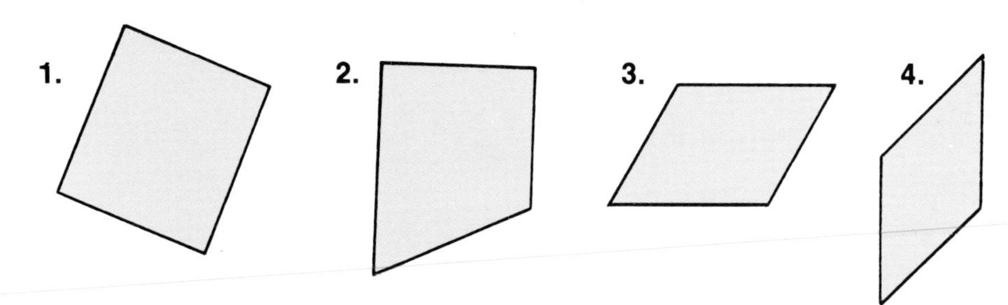

Tell whether each of the following statements is true or false.

5. Every parallelogram is also a trapezoid.
6. A square is not a parallelogram.
7. Every trapezoid is also a rectangle.
8. A rhombus is a regular polygon.
9. Every rectangle is also a trapezoid.
10. A square is a regular polygon.

Remember the facts about angles formed when parallel lines are cut by a transversal.

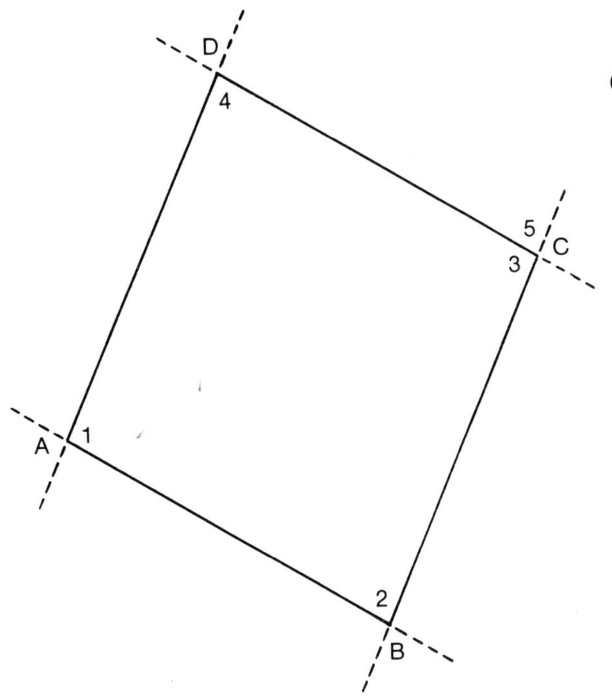

Consider parallelogram ABCD.

11. Does $\angle 2$ have the same measure as $\angle 5$? Why?
12. Does $\angle 4$ have the same measure as $\angle 5$? Why?
13. $\angle 2$ and $\angle 4$ are *opposite angles.* Do they have the same measure? How do you know?
14. $\angle 4$ and $\angle 3$ are *consecutive angles.* What is their relationship? Why?
15. State the relationship between opposite angles of a parallelogram.
16. State the relationship between consecutive angles of a parallelogram.

Math in Action

1. Most fabric comes on a bolt, or roll. How many 3-yard pieces can Mrs. Yau cut from a 22-yard bolt?
2. Mrs. Collier is hanging new draperies in her living room window. The width of the window is 60 inches, and the drapery width will be $2\frac{1}{2}$ times that. The length of the draperies will be 84 inches. How many square inches will the draperies be? How many square yards (to the nearest tenth) will they be?
3. Mrs. Bierman has a table with dimensions of 6 feet by 4 feet. She wants a tablecloth large enough to hang 12 inches on each side. What should the dimensions of the cloth be?
   How many square feet of material does she need?
4. The "yarn count" of fabric is the number of yarns in one square inch. For example, a fabric with a 100-yarn count has 50 yarns per inch running in each direction. In a piece 12 inches wide and 18 inches long, there would be 600 yarns (12 x 50) running lengthwise, and 900 yarns (18 x 50) running crosswise.
   In a piece of 200-yarn-count fabric measuring 12 inches wide by 2 feet long, how many yarns run lengthwise? crosswise?
5. In a woven design, the thickness of a stripe of color is determined by the yarn count. For example, in a 150-yarn-count fabric, each 75 yarns of a color produce 1 inch of that color.
   If a piece of 120-yarn-count fabric 45 inches wide has 1-inch stripes of blue, red, and yellow running lengthwise, how many yarns of blue run along the fabric?
   How many red? How many yellow?

Congruent and Similar Figures

Mark and Michael look alike. They are the same age, the same height, the same weight, and they even wear the same size shoes. Mark and Michael are *identical twins.*

In geometry, if two geometric figures have the same shape and size, they are *congruent.*

$\Delta ABC \cong \Delta DEF$ means "triangle ABC is congruent to triangle DEF."

Is $\overline{AB} \cong \overline{DE}$, $\angle ABC \cong \angle DEF$, and so on?

Note: ΔABC would fit exactly on top of ΔDEF.

Notice the corresponding parts of ΔABC and ΔDEF. Are corresponding parts of congruent triangles congruent?

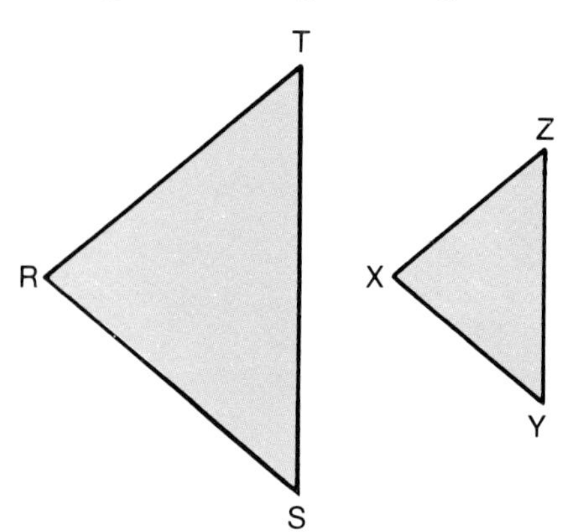

Do triangles RST and XYZ have the same shape?

Are the corresponding angles of triangles RST and XYZ congruent?

Are triangles RST and XYZ congruent?

Why or why not?

$\Delta RST \sim \Delta XYZ$ means "triangle RST is similar to triangle XYZ."

Keys to Understanding

If two geometric figures have the same size and shape, they are *congruent* figures.
The symbol ≅ means "is congruent to."
Corresponding parts of congruent figures are congruent.

If two geometric figures have the same shape but not necessarily the same size, they are *similar* figures.
The symbol ~ means "is similar to."
Corresponding angles of similar figures are congruent.

Practice

ΔFED ≅ ΔBAC

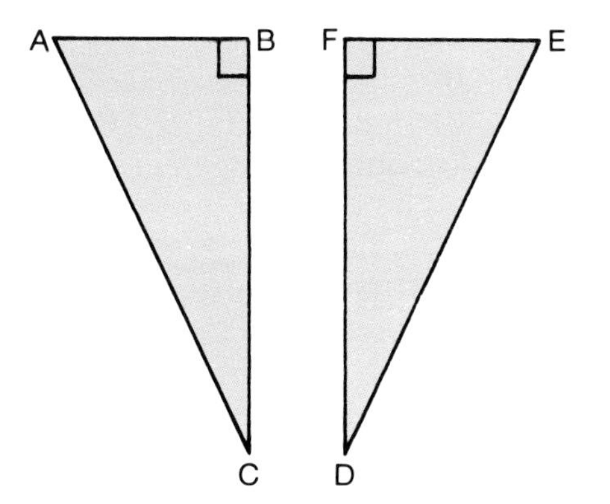

1. Which vertices must correspond?
2. Name the pairs of sides that are congruent.
3. Name the pairs of angles that are congruent.
4. Is ΔFED ~ΔBAC? Why or why not?

□RSTV~□WXYZ

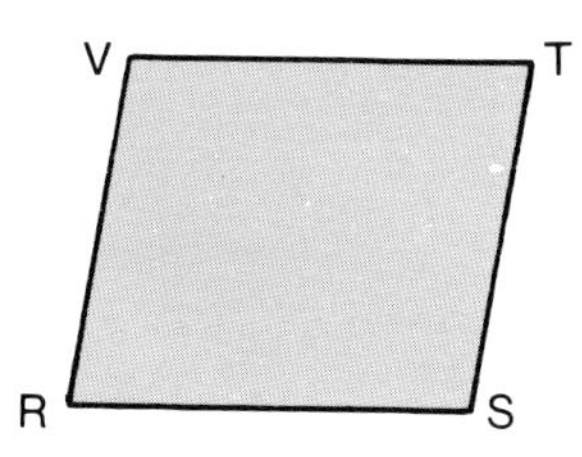

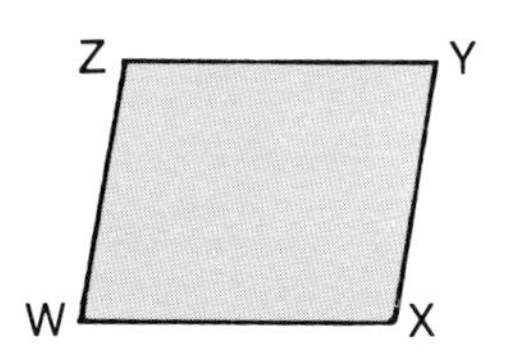

5. Name the pairs of sides that are congruent.
6. Name the pairs of angles that are congruent.
7. Is □RSTV ≅ □WXYZ? Why or why not?

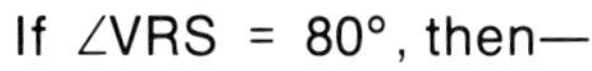

If ∠VRS = 80°, then—

8. ∠XWZ = ?
9. ∠XYZ = ?
10. ∠WXY = ?

More Constructions

A good foundation is very important in the construction of a building. God's Word says that a good foundation is also important in life (Matthew 7:24-27). As Christians we have a good foundation on which to build (Ephesians 2:20).

Is your foundation in geometry strong enough to enable you to do these constructions?

Follow these steps to construct a triangle congruent to ΔABC:

1. Copy line segment AB. Label endpoints R and S.
2. With the point of the compass on R, draw an arc with the radius of $\overline{AC}$.
3. With the point of the compass on S, draw an arc with the radius of $\overline{BC}$ so that it intersects the arc made in step 2. Label the point of intersection T.
4. Now connect the points to form segments $\overline{RT}$ and $\overline{ST}$. $\Delta RST \cong \Delta ABC$

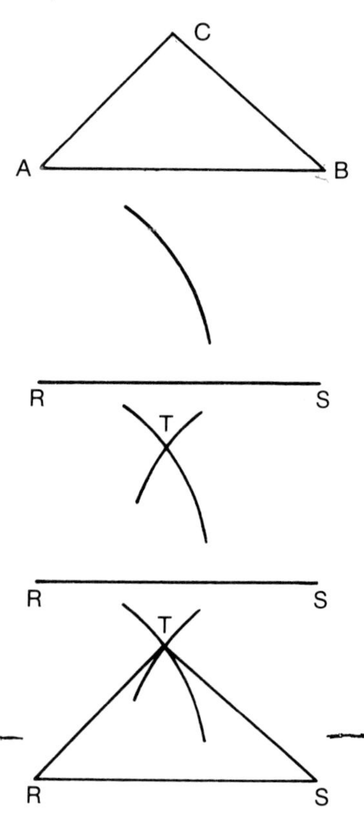

Follow these steps to construct a line perpendicular to a given line, passing through a point not on the line.

1. With the point of the compass on P, make an arc that intersects $\overline{AB}$ in two places. Label the points of intersection X and Y.
2. Now construct a perpendicular bisector of $\overline{XY}$. Label it $\overline{CD}$.
   Is $\overline{CD} \perp \overline{AB}$?
   Is P on $\overline{CD}$?

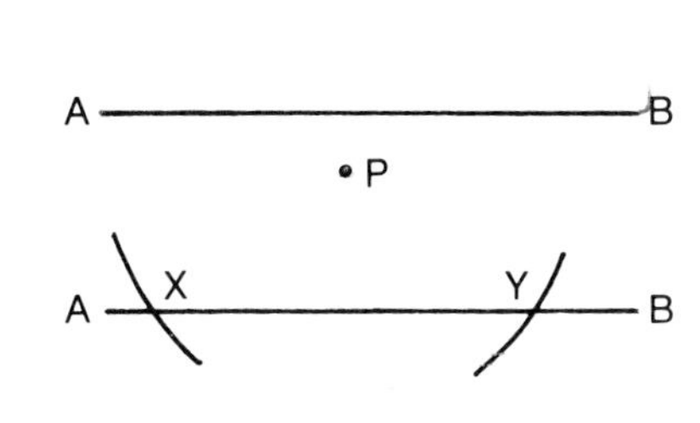

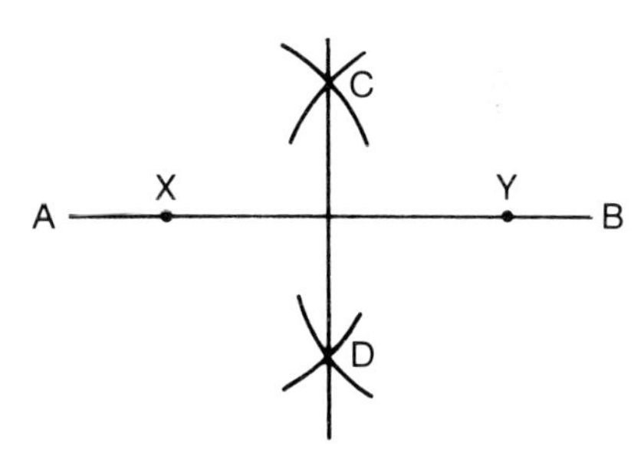

Practice

1. Construct a triangle congruent to a given triangle.
2. Construct a line perpendicular to a given line, passing through a given point not on the line.
3. Construct a square with sides congruent to a given line segment. (Make your line segment about 2 inches long.)
4. Construct an equilateral triangle with sides congruent to a given line segment. (Make your line segment about 2 inches long.)

Solid Figures

The world that God made has three dimensions: length, width, and height.

Objects that have three dimensions are called *solid figures.*

Keys to Understanding

A *polyhedron* is a solid figure with flat faces that are polygons.

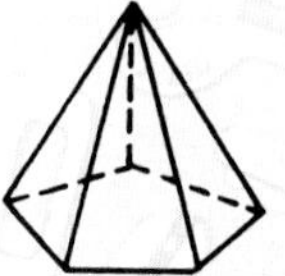

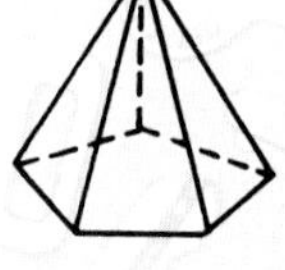

If two faces of a polyhedron are congruent and parallel, then the solid is a *prism*.

The two parallel faces are called the *bases* of the prism.

bases

Parts of the polyhedron:

face—polygon surfaces that make up the polyhedron
edge—line segment where two faces meet
vertex—point where three or more edges meet

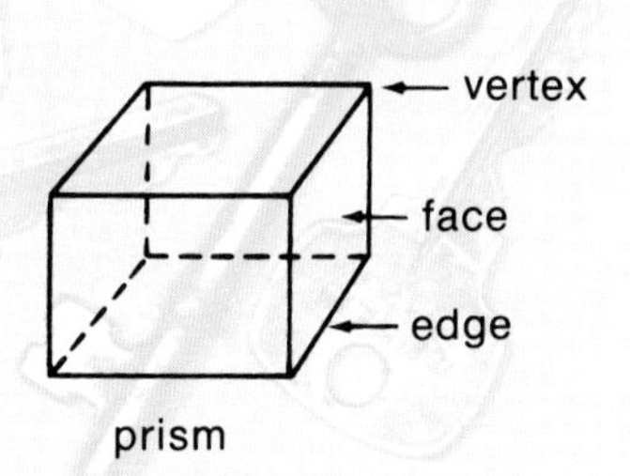

Practice

Determine which of the solids below are polyhedrons and which are prisms.

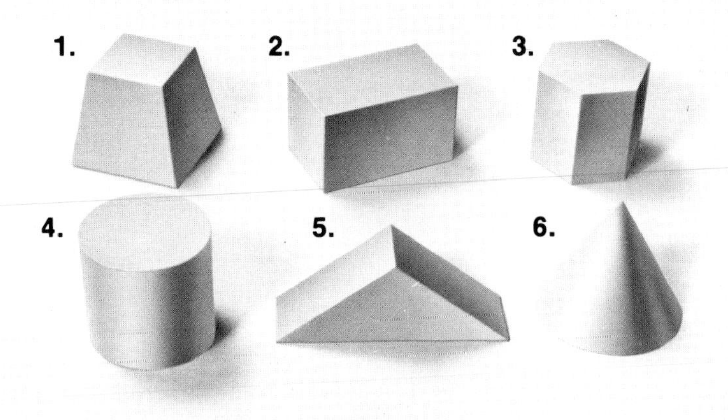

7. Draw a polyhedron of any size or shape.
8. Draw a prism of any size or shape.
9. Draw what you think a rectangular prism would look like.
10. Draw what you think a triangular prism would look like.

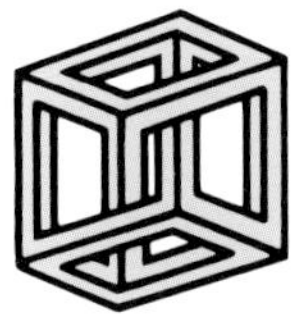

MIND BOGGLER

How many different triangles can you find in this figure?

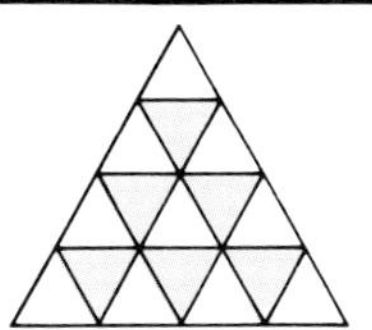

Unit Review

Match each figure with a name, using just one name with each figure.

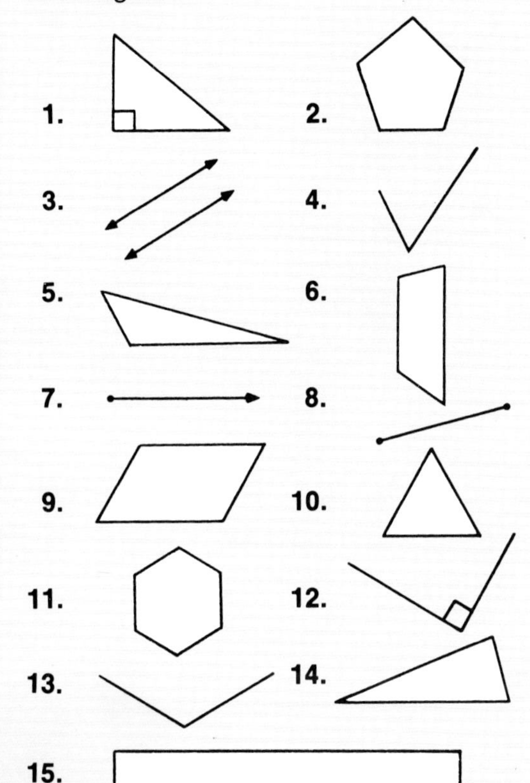

a. line segment
b. right triangle
c. parallel lines
d. hexagon
e. obtuse angle
f. point
g. right isosceles triangle
h. trapezoid
i. ray
j. obtuse scalene triangle
k. rectangle
l. equilateral triangle
m. line
n. right angle
o. rhombus
p. acute scalene triangle
q. regular pentagon
r. acute angle
s. parallelogram

MIND BOGGLER

Arrange these ten points into five line segments with four points in each segment.

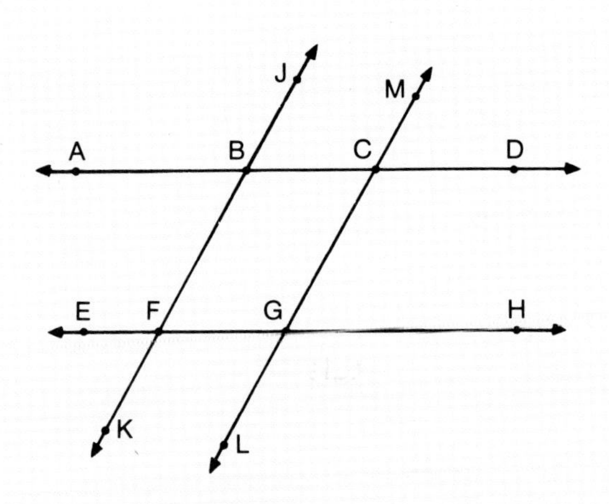

Given:
$\overleftrightarrow{AB} \parallel \overleftrightarrow{EF}$
$\overleftrightarrow{BF} \parallel \overleftrightarrow{CG}$

16. Which angles are congruent to $\angle$FBC?

17. Which angles are supplementary to $\angle$MCD?

18. Name four pairs of vertical angles.

19. Name two transversals of parallel lines AB and EF.

20. What type of quadrilateral is BCGF?

Find the third angle of a triangle, given these measures for angles 1 and 2.

21. 63°, 48°

22. 10°, 112°

23. 90°, 33°

24. 45°, 70°

25. 2°, 169°

26. 88°, 89°

Do the following constructions.

27. Draw an obtuse angle. Now bisect the angle. What kind of angles do you have after the bisection?

28. Draw a line segment about 2 inches long. Construct a perpendicular bisector of the segment.

29. Which two figures are similar?

30. Which two figures are congruent?

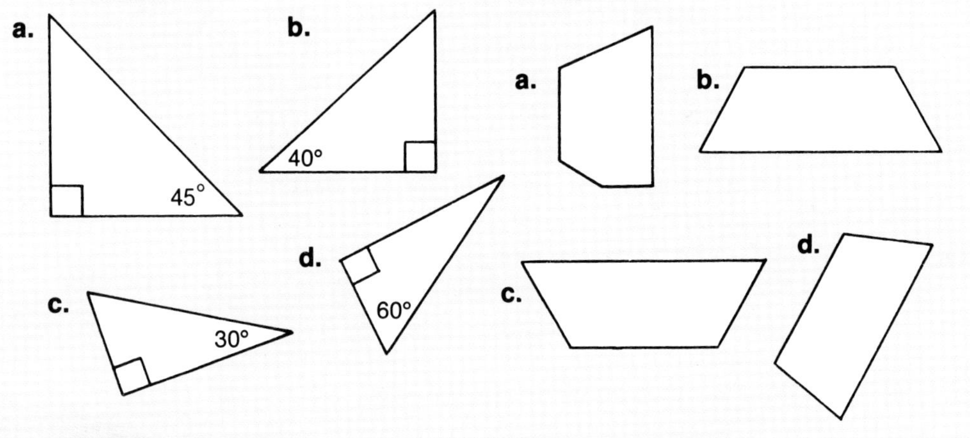

Skills Checkup

1. 48,367 + 5,007 + 84,023 + 836 + 7,886 + 96,345 + 5,892
2. 23,146 + 94,324 + 62,437 + 36,452 + 24 + 6,103 + 897
3. 94,763 + 87,712 + 59,343 + 872 + 901 + 238 + 35 + 17

4. 72,121 - 35,063
5. 78,603 - 38,069
6. 93,811 × 397
7. 53,674 × 56
8. 693 ÷ 33
9. 83,421 ÷ 27

10. $5\frac{3}{4} + 7\frac{2}{3}$
11. $8\frac{2}{3} + 4\frac{1}{2}$
12. $3\frac{1}{4} + 9\frac{1}{2}$
13. $6\frac{1}{4} + 5\frac{3}{10}$
14. $\frac{5}{6} - \frac{1}{6}$
15. $\frac{7}{8} - \frac{1}{4}$
16. $5\frac{3}{4} - 2\frac{1}{2}$
17. $12 \times \frac{3}{4}$
18. $2 \times \frac{5}{6}$
19. $\frac{2}{3} \times \frac{5}{9}$
20. $5 \times 4\frac{1}{2}$
21. $7 \div \frac{1}{6}$
22. $\frac{1}{8} \div \frac{2}{3}$
23. $\frac{3}{4} \div \frac{3}{2}$

24. Mr. Collins wants to put carpeting on the floor of his den. If the den measures 18 feet by 12 feet, how many square feet of carpeting will he need to buy?
25. How many square yards of carpeting would Mr. Collins need to buy?
26. The carpeting Mr. Collins chose cost $13.95 per square yard. How much would it cost to cover the floor of his den?
27. Jeff helped his father build a one-room cabin in the woods to use when they went hunting. The measurements of the cabin are 15 feet by 3 yards. What is the area of the floor of the cabin?
28. How many ceiling tiles, 12 inches on a side, will Jeff and his father need to cover the ceiling if it is parallel to the floor?
29. If ceiling tiles come 12 in a package, how many packages will Jeff and his father need to buy?
30. Jeff has an old rug, which measures 6 feet by 9 feet, to put on the floor of the cabin. How many square feet of the cabin floor will not be covered by a rug?

1. 93,457 + 49,019 + 74,536 + 234,902
2. 873,498 + 10,269 + 39,386 + 54,363,829
3. 987,230 - 777,777
4. 907,802 - 891,985
5. 908 × 349
6. 1,435 × 378
7. 2,322 ÷ 12
8. 282 ÷ 73

9. $\frac{2}{3} + \frac{1}{2} + \frac{3}{8}$
10. $9\frac{3}{4} + 4\frac{1}{4}$
11. $4\frac{1}{5} + 5\frac{3}{4}$
12. $5\frac{5}{6} + 3\frac{2}{9}$
13. $9\frac{2}{3} - 4\frac{5}{8}$
14. $9\frac{1}{2} - 3\frac{1}{3}$
15. $10\frac{2}{3} - 6\frac{1}{2}$
16. $6 - 1\frac{2}{3}$
17. $\frac{3}{4} \times 4$
18. $8 \times \frac{2}{3}$
19. $\frac{2}{3} \times \frac{3}{4}$
20. $6 \times 3\frac{1}{3}$
21. $\frac{5}{7} \div 1\frac{1}{3}$
22. $5 \div \frac{1}{2}$
23. $1\frac{2}{3} \div \frac{5}{3}$
24. $5 \div \frac{1}{5}$

25. How many feet of fence would it take for Chris to enclose a rectangular flower garden measuring $16\frac{5}{8}$ feet by $25\frac{1}{2}$ feet?
26. In order to prepare for their first debate of the season, the debate club practiced three afternoons. They spent $2\frac{3}{4}$ hours, $1\frac{5}{6}$ hours, and $1\frac{2}{3}$ hours practicing. How much time did they practice altogether?
27. Eastside Christian School had a talent show with $\frac{1}{2}$ hour of singing, $\frac{1}{12}$ hour of magic, $\frac{1}{4}$ hour of dramatic reading, and $\frac{1}{3}$ hour of comedy. How long did the talent show last?
28. Don spends time each afternoon making deliveries for a florist shop. On Monday he worked $1\frac{3}{4}$ hours; Tuesday, $2\frac{5}{6}$ hours; Wednesday, $1\frac{7}{12}$ hours; Thursday, $1\frac{1}{2}$ hours; and Friday, $1\frac{1}{3}$ hours. How many hours did Don work this week?
29. If Don gets paid $3.50 an hour for his labor, how much did he earn this week?
30. How much more money does Don need before he can buy a new bicycle that costs $125.95?

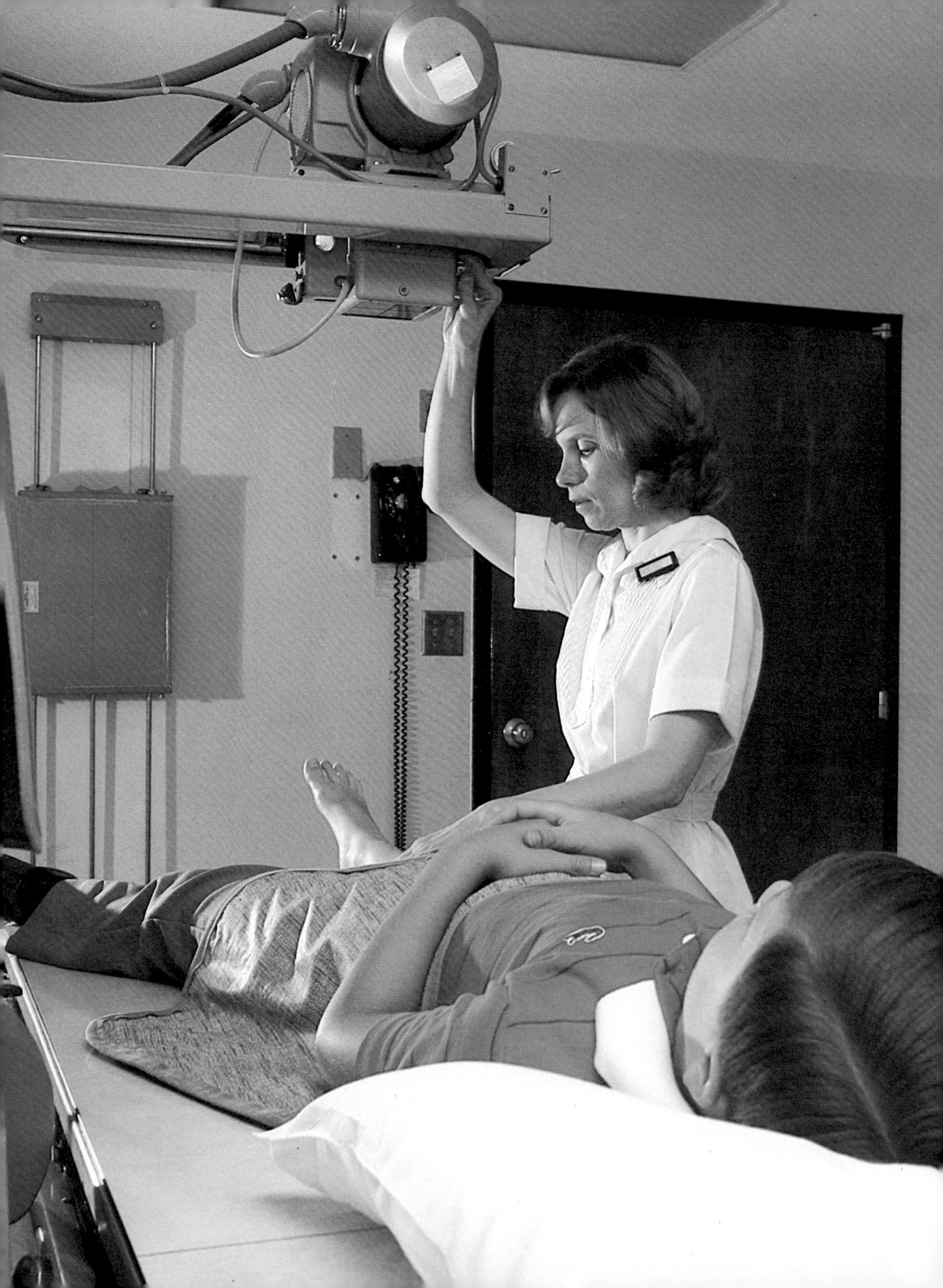

UNIT 5

X-ray Technician

"Spike it! Spike it!" The crowd was almost as involved in the game as the players were. The score was tied. Charissa jumped, spiked the ball, and put her team into the lead. The crowd roared, then suddenly became quiet. Charissa lay on the floor, holding her leg in pain. The hush of the crowd embarrassed her. She felt countless pairs of eyes staring at her. Looking up, she was comforted by the assuring smile of her coach.

"It looks broken to me. I'll help you to the car. We need to get you to the hospital for x-rays."

"Here we are, Charissa. I'll get someone to help you." A smiling nurse brought a wheelchair to the car and wheeled Charissa to the radiology wing. Mrs. Bourdeau, the x-ray technician, helped her onto the table and explained what she was going to do.

"This machine is similar to a big camera. You will need to hold very still until I take the x-ray. I'll let you know when you may move."

"Let's try it from one more angle." Mrs. Bourdeau carefully moved Charissa's leg into position. "That should do it."

The x-ray technician put the film into the developer and introduced Dr. Clarke to Charissa.

"Hmm. Looks to me like a clean break. We'll have to put her in traction for a while to get the bone lined back up." Dr. Clarke was gentle as he pronounced his diagnosis.

Once Charissa was in her room, the doctor and the cast technician set up the traction apparatus. They put a Steinman pin into her leg, attached a tibia bow, and pulled three pounds of traction. The doctor spoke with compassion as he explained what he was doing.

Josh Ingersoll, the cast technician, appeared in Charissa's room the next day. He chatted with her awhile before telling her his real reason for being there: he and the doctor were going to put a cast on her leg. The nurse prepared Charissa's leg, and Josh wrapped it with Webril to provide a padding under the cast. He cut the cast gauze and formed a cast stretching from her ankle to her thigh. As soon as the cast dried, Charissa, accompanied by a pair of crutches, was able to go home.

Charissa's brief time in the hospital was not much fun. After she left, however, and the bone began to heal, she realized how much she owed to the experts who had taken care of the injury. Like the medical personnel who treated Charissa, God has compassion on us when we face spiritual "injury." He, too, knows how to heal that injury. Sometimes He has to deal with us in a way that hurts for a time, but He always does what is best for our spiritual health. "Blessed be . . . the God of all comfort, Who comforteth us in all our tribulation, that we may be able to comfort them which are in any trouble, by the comfort wherewith we ourselves are comforted of God" (II Corinthians 1:3-4).

$1 \cdot 24 = 24$ $\quad$ $1 \cdot 36 = 36$

$2 \cdot 12 = 24$ $\quad$ $2 \cdot 18 = 36$

$3 \cdot 8 = 24$ $\quad$ $3 \cdot 12 = 36$

$4 \cdot 6 = 24$ $\quad$ $4 \cdot 9 = 36$

Each of the underlined numbers is a *factor* of 24.
The factors of 36 listed are 1, 2, 3, 4, 6, 9, 12, 18, and 36.

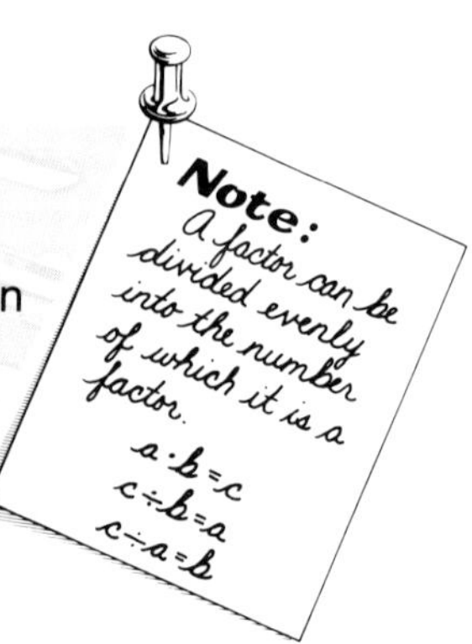

Keys to Understanding

The factors of a number are any whole numbers that when multiplied together give that number.

If $a \cdot b = c$, then a and b are factors of c.

What do you think?

Does every whole number have at least two factors?
Do any whole numbers have more than two factors?
What number is a factor of every number?
Is every whole number a factor of 0? Explain.

Remember, a missing factor can be found by dividing.

Let A = {all the factors of 24}
Let B = {all the factors of 36}
Then $A \cap B$ = {1, 2, 3, 4, 6, 12}

1, 2, 3, 4, 6, and 12 are the common factors of 24 and 36.
What is the largest element in $A \cap B$?

Remember, intersection ($\cap$) means elements common to both sets.

The largest element in the intersection of two or more sets of factors (of two or more numbers) is called the *greatest common factor* (GCF) of the numbers.

Practice

List all the factors of the following numbers.

1. 18
2. 14
3. 55
4. 48
5. 54
6. 64
7. 72
8. 27
9. 30
10. 99

List the factors of the following numbers. Do not use 1 as a factor.

11. 12
12. 16
13. 26
14. 42
15. 75
16. 81
17. 45
18. 77
19. 100
20. 144

Give the set of common factors for each pair of numbers and circle the GCF. Do not use 1 as a factor.

21. 8 and 24
22. 15 and 27
23. 18 and 32
24. 35 and 70
25. 27 and 81

Primes and Composites

Consider the following whole numbers:

2 3 5 7 11 13 17 19

What do you think?

How many factors are there for each of these numbers?
Is there a factor common to all of the numbers?
Why do you suppose 1 is not included on the list?
What will be the next five numbers on the list?
What numbers between 0 and 25 will not be on the list?

Keys to Understanding

A *prime number* is a number that has only two factors—1 and itself.

A *composite number* is a number that has more than two factors.

The computer monitor pictured is projecting the whole numbers from 1 to 28. Each of the colored bands represents the distance from one prime number to the next on the "number line." Notice that the bands are of varying widths. For years mathematicians have tried to find a pattern in the occurrence of prime numbers, but as yet they have found none. We know of no formula that will help us to know which numbers are prime. We must be able to find how many factors a number has.

Practice

List all the numbers greater than 1 and less than 50.

1. Cross out all the composite numbers.
2. Circle all the prime numbers.

Tell whether each of these numbers is prime or composite.

3. 67
4. 88
5. 138
6. 73
7. 89
8. 96
9. 111
10. 151

Remember,
check to see
if the number
is divisible
by any other number.

The Greek mathematician Eratosthenes discovered a method of identifying prime numbers.

Try his method on the whole numbers from 2 to 100.

1. Cross out all the numbers that are multiples of 2, except 2 (every second number).
2. Cross out all the numbers that are multiples of 3, except 3 (every third number).
3. Cross out all the numbers that are multiples of 5, except 5 (every fifth number).
4. Cross out all the numbers that are multiples of 7, except 7 (every seventh number).

What kind of numbers are left?

Divisibility Tests

Mr. Hargis's class is discussing whether or not 2,687,313 is divisible by any other number besides 1 and itself.
Do you think there is any way to determine what numbers will divide into another number?

Tests can be used to determine whether a whole number is divisible by 2, 3, or 5.

Divisible by	Test	Example
2	Is the number even (does it end in 0, 2, 4, 6, or 8)?	5,876 is an even number. 5,876 is divisible by 2.
3	Is the sum of the digits divisible by 3?	8 + 4 + 6 = 18 (divisible by 3) 846 is divisible by 3.
5	Does the number end with the digit 0 or 5?	12,480 ends with 0. 27,865 ends with 5. Both numbers are divisible by 5.

Practice

Tell whether each of the following numbers is divisible by 2.

1. 88 **2.** 125 **3.** 3,782 **4.** 21,485 **5.** 119,310

Tell whether each of the following numbers is divisible by 3.

6. 96 **7.** 123 **8.** 491 **9.** 1,181 **10.** 32,580

Tell whether each of the following numbers is divisible by 5.

11. 73 **12.** 127 **13.** 985 **14.** 3,470 **15.** 119,322

Using the divisibility tests, tell whether each of the following numbers is divisible by 2, by 3, and by 5.

16. 5,862 **17.** 10,580 **18.** 1,532 **19.** 20,485 **20.** 1,586,314

MIND BOGGLER

Use the divisibility tests to determine which of these numbers are divisible by 2, 3, or 5.

	2	3	5	7	11	13	17	19	23
29	31	37	41	43	47	53	59	61	67
71	73	79	83	89	97	101	103	107	109
113	127	131	137	139	149	151	157	163	167
173	179	181	191	193	197	199	211	223	227
229	233	239	241	251	257	263	269	271	277
281	283	293	307	311	313	317	331	337	347
349	353	359	367	373	379	383	389	397	401
409	419	421	431	433	439	443	449	457	461
463	467	479	487	491	499	503	509	521	523
541	547	557	563	569	571	577	587	593	599
601	607	613	617	619	631	641	643	647	653
659	661	673	677	683	691	701	709	719	727
733	739	743	751	757	761	769	773	787	797
809	811	821	823	827	829	839	853	857	859
863	877	881	883	887	907	911	919	929	937
941	947	953	967	971	977	983	991	997	1009
1013	1019	1021	1031	1033	1039	1049	1051	1061	1063
1069	1087	1091	1093	1097	1103	1109	1117	1123	1129
1151	1153	1163	1171	1181	1187	1193	1201	1213	1217

Prime Factorization

When you factor, you express a number as the product of two or more factors. When all of the factors that you use to express a number are prime, you have found the prime factorization of that number. You can express the prime factorization with either a "factor tree" or a "factor ladder."

What do you think?

Is 3 · 6 the prime factorization of 18? Why or why not?
Is 2 · 2 · 2 the prime factorization of 8? Why or why not?
Is 2 · 3 · 8 the prime factorization of 48? Why or why not?
Is 2 · 2 · 3 · 3 the prime factorization of 36? Why or why not?

Now we will construct a "factor tree" and a "factor ladder" for the number 180.

The "factor tree" is constructed by using *successive factoring*.

180

18 · 10

2 · 9 · 2 · 5

2 · 3 · 3 · 2 · 5

1. Write the number to be factored.
2. Write the number as the product of two factors. (Do not use 1.)
3. If any of the factors is not prime, express it as the product of two other factors. (Do not use 1.)
4. Repeat step 3 until all the factors are prime numbers.
5. The bottom branches of the factor tree are the prime factors of 180. $(2 \cdot 3 \cdot 3 \cdot 2 \cdot 5 = 180)$

The "factor ladder" is constructed by using *successive division.*

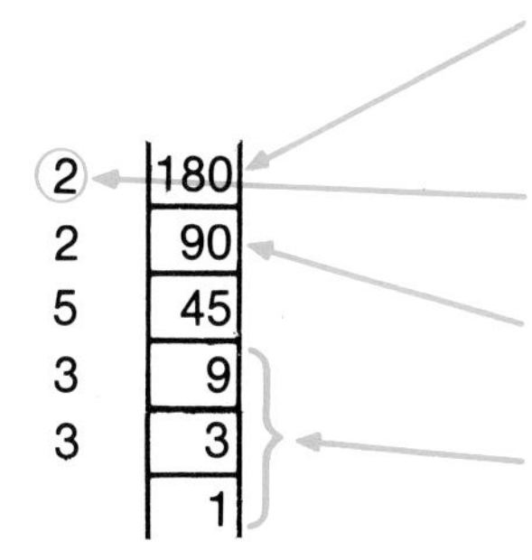

1. Put the number to be factored on the top rung of the ladder.
2. Divide the original number by a prime number so that the quotient is a whole number.
3. Put your quotient on the next rung down.
4. Repeat steps 2 and 3 until your quotient is 1.
5. The numbers on the outside of the factor ladder are the prime factors of 180. $(2 \cdot 2 \cdot 5 \cdot 3 \cdot 3 = 180)$

Remember the tests for divisibility by 2, 3, or 5.

Does the order of the factors change the answer? Why or why not?

Tree Method
(Successive Factoring)

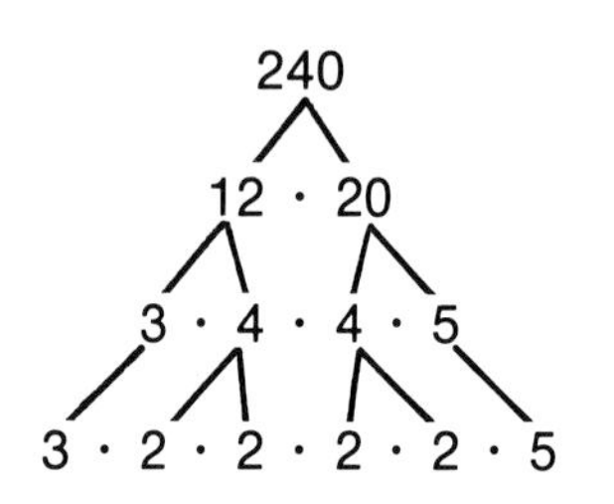

$240 = 3 \cdot 2 \cdot 2 \cdot 2 \cdot 2 \cdot 5 = 2^4 \cdot 3 \cdot 5$

Ladder Method
(Successive Division)

2	240
2	120
2	60
2	30
3	15
5	5
	1

$240 = 2 \cdot 2 \cdot 2 \cdot 2 \cdot 3 \cdot 5 = 2^4 \cdot 3 \cdot 5$

Numbers can be written in prime factorization form using exponents.

2 is prime
3 is prime
4 is $2 \cdot 2 = 2^2$
5 is prime
6 is $2 \cdot 3$
7 is prime
8 is $2 \cdot 2 \cdot 2 = 2^3$
9 is $3 \cdot 3 = 3^2$
10 is $2 \cdot 5$
11 is prime
12 is $2 \cdot 2 \cdot 3 = 2^2 \cdot 3$
13 is prime
14 is $2 \cdot 7$
15 is $3 \cdot 5$
16 is $2 \cdot 2 \cdot 2 \cdot 2 = 2^4$
17 is prime
18 is $2 \cdot 3 \cdot 3 = 2 \cdot 3^2$
19 is prime
20 is $2 \cdot 2 \cdot 5 = 2^2 \cdot 5$
21 is $3 \cdot 7$
22 is $2 \cdot 11$
23 is prime
24 is $2 \cdot 2 \cdot 2 \cdot 3 = 2^3 \cdot 3$
25 is $5 \cdot 5 = 5^2$
26 is $2 \cdot 13$
27 is $3 \cdot 3 \cdot 3 = 3^3$
28 is $2 \cdot 2 \cdot 7 = 2^2 \cdot 7$

Practice

Give the prime factorization of each of the following, using successive factoring (factor tree).

1. 18 **2.** 90 **3.** 72 **4.** 88 **5.** 128

Give the prime factorization of each of the following, using successive division (factor ladder).

6. 20 **7.** 56 **8.** 64 **9.** 99 **10.** 125

Give the prime factorization of each number, using whichever method you prefer. Be sure to express your final answer using exponents whenever possible.

11. 32 **13.** 63 **15.** 148 **17.** 327 **19.** 1,532
12. 45 **14.** 114 **16.** 846 **18.** 1,000 **20.** 3,861

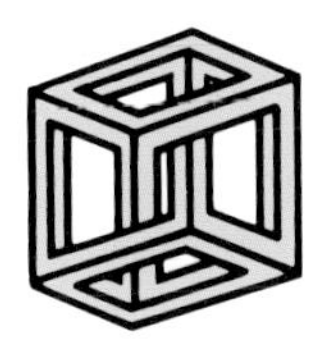

MIND BOGGLER

On a sheet of paper, copy the seven circles in the arrangement shown. Fill the circles with the consecutive prime numbers 5, 7, 11, 13, 17, 19, and 23 so that the sum of any three primes in a row or diagonal is the same prime number. What is the prime sum?

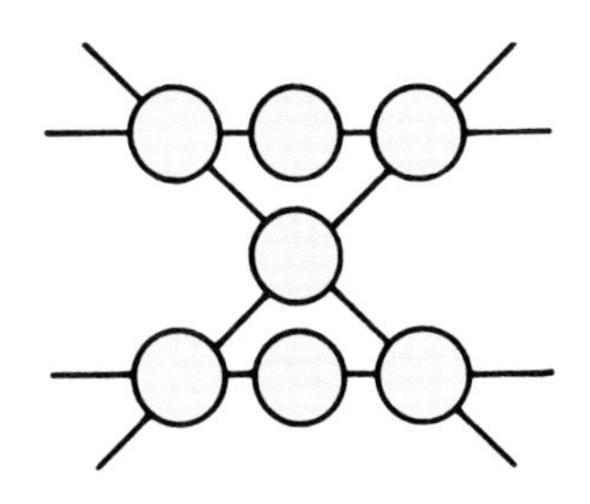

Least Common Multiples

Multiples of 8	Multiples of 12
$0 \cdot 8 = 0$	$0 \cdot 12 = 0$
$1 \cdot 8 = 8$	$1 \cdot 12 = 12$
$2 \cdot 8 = 16$	$2 \cdot 12 = 24$
$3 \cdot 8 = 24$	$3 \cdot 12 = 36$
$4 \cdot 8 = 32$	$4 \cdot 12 = 48$
$5 \cdot 8 = 40$	$5 \cdot 12 = 60$
$6 \cdot 8 = 48$	$6 \cdot 12 = 72$
$7 \cdot 8 = 56$	$7 \cdot 12 = 84$
$8 \cdot 8 = 64$	$8 \cdot 12 = 96$
$9 \cdot 8 = 72$	$9 \cdot 12 = 108$

Remember, the product of a whole number times a constant number is called a multiple of the constant number.

What are the common multiples of 8 and 12 above?
What is the smallest nonzero multiple that is common to 8 and 12?

Keys to Understanding

The smallest nonzero number that is a multiple of two (or more) numbers is called the *least common multiple* (LCM) of those numbers.

The least common multiple (LCM) of the denominators of two (or more) fractions is also the lowest common denominator (LCD) of those fractions. Remember this when adding or subtracting fractions.

$\frac{1}{2} + \frac{1}{4} + \frac{1}{5} = \frac{19}{20}$ The LCM of the denominators is 20.
The LCD for the problem is 20.

Practice

For each number, write all its multiples less than 50.

1. 4 **2.** 5 **3.** 8 **4.** 11 **5.** 13

For each number, write all its multiples less than 100.

6. 7 **7.** 15 **8.** 9 **9.** 10 **10.** 17

Find the least common multiple (LCM) of each pair of numbers below. The answers above may help.

11. 5 and 8
12. 4 and 7
13. 15 and 10
14. 11 and 4
15. 5 and 13
16. 9 and 8
17. 8 and 10
18. 4 and 17
19. 13 and 7

Find the lowest common denominator (LCD) of each of these pairs of fractions.

20. $\frac{1}{2}$ and $\frac{3}{4}$
21. $\frac{7}{8}$ and $\frac{1}{12}$
22. $\frac{2}{5}$ and $\frac{1}{2}$
23. $\frac{9}{10}$ and $\frac{3}{8}$
24. $\frac{2}{3}$ and $\frac{2}{5}$
25. $\frac{1}{2}$, $\frac{3}{5}$, and $\frac{1}{4}$

Remember, the LCM of the denominators is also the LCD.

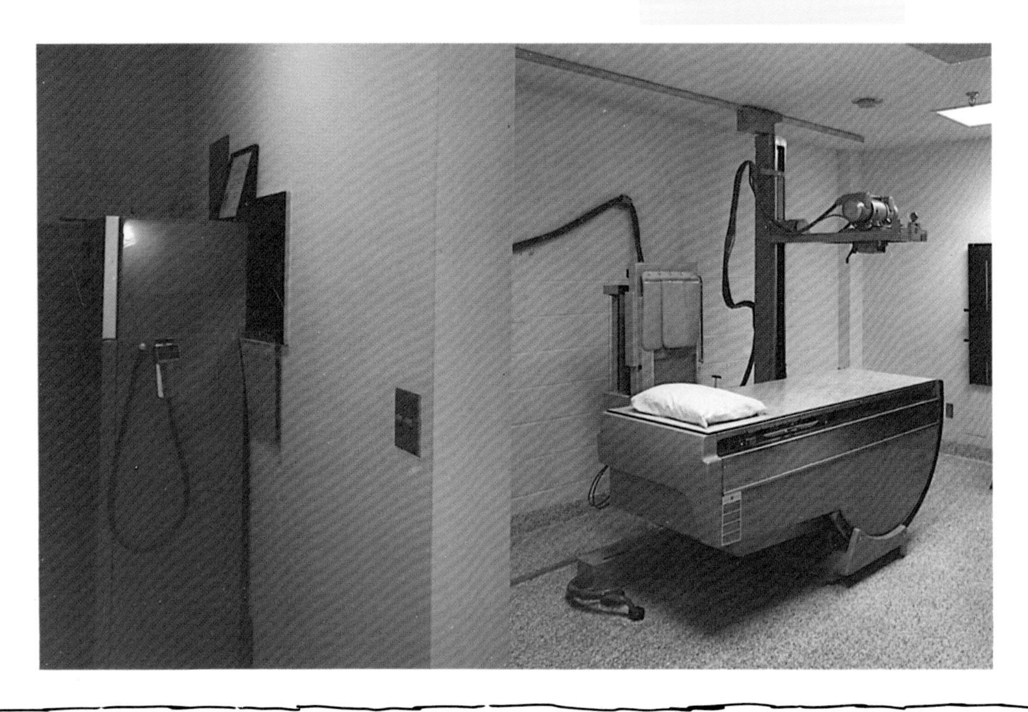

Prime Factorization

Prime factorization is the fastest and easiest way to find the greatest common factor (GCF) and the least common multiple (LCM) of numbers.

Find the greatest common factor (GCF) of 24, 60, and 168.

First find the prime factorization of each number.

$$\begin{aligned} 24 &= 2 \cdot 2 \cdot 2 \cdot 3 \\ 60 &= 2 \cdot 2 \cdot 3 \cdot 5 \\ 168 &= 2 \cdot 2 \cdot 2 \cdot 3 \cdot 7 \end{aligned}$$

The factors common to all three numbers are used.

All three numbers have two 2s and one 3.
Therefore the GCF $= 2 \cdot 2 \cdot 3 = 12$

Now find the least common multiple (LCM) of 24, 60, and 168.

Again, find the prime factorization of each number first.

$$\begin{aligned} 24 &= 2 \cdot 2 \cdot 2 \cdot 3 \\ 60 &= 2 \cdot 2 \cdot 3 \cdot 5 \\ 168 &= 2 \cdot 2 \cdot 2 \cdot 3 \cdot 7 \end{aligned}$$

Each factor is used the maximum number of times it is used in any one of the prime factorizations.

The factor 2 is used three times.
The factors 3, 5, and 7 are used one time.
Therefore the LCM $= 2 \cdot 2 \cdot 2 \cdot 3 \cdot 5 \cdot 7 = 840$

Find the GCF and LCM of 60, 210, and 495.

The prime factorization of 60 = $2 \cdot 2 \cdot 3 \cdot 5$
The prime factorization of 210 = $2 \cdot 3 \cdot 5 \cdot 7$
The prime factorization of 495 = $3 \cdot 3 \cdot 5 \cdot 11$
Therefore the GCF = $3 \cdot 5 = 15$
LCM = $2 \cdot 2 \cdot 3 \cdot 3 \cdot 5 \cdot 7 \cdot 11 = 13{,}860$

How many common factors are there in the prime factorizations of 16, 27, and 55?

$16 = 2 \cdot 2 \cdot 2 \cdot 2$
$27 = 3 \cdot 3 \cdot 3$
$55 = 5 \cdot 11$

What must their GCF be? What can be said about their LCM?

"OH, IT WORKS GREAT— EXCEPT FOR A SLIGHT VIBRATION AT 160 MPH."

Practice

Using prime factorization, find the GCF of each pair of numbers.

1. 8 and 28
2. 24 and 32
3. 16 and 27
4. 36 and 48
5. 12, 21, and 30
6. 72, 80, and 135

Using prime factorization, find the LCM of each pair of numbers.

7. 9 and 15
8. 12 and 16
9. 60 and 135
10. 20 and 42
11. 12, 15, and 21
12. 21, 25, and 26

Using prime factorization, find both the GCF and the LCM of each pair of numbers.

13. 18 and 48
14. 26, 33, and 35
15. 99, 132, and 210

Math in Action

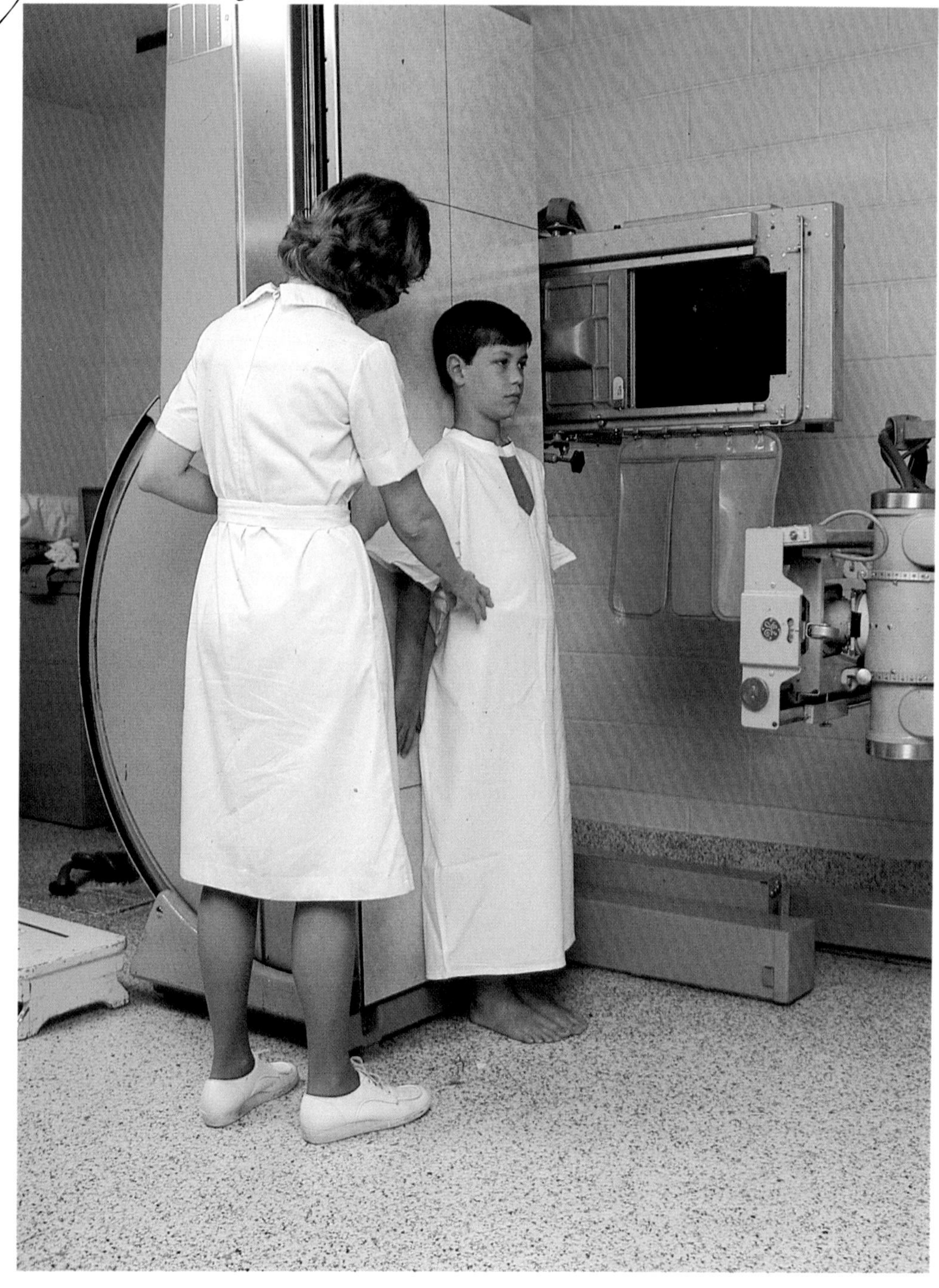

1. Craig broke his arm while playing basketball. He weighed 114 pounds before he had his arm put in a cast. Including the cast, he now weighs 117 pounds. What fraction of this weight does the cast take up?
2. The doctor must know how thick a cast is before he attempts to saw it off. A mistake in calculating could result in an injured patient. How thick is a cast made up of 8 layers of $\frac{1}{16}$-inch cast gauze?
3. Before the hospital started developing x-rays with an automatic processing machine, Mrs. Bourdeau had to develop them by hand. She submerged each x-ray in the developer for three minutes, rinsed it for thirty seconds, and then put it in the fixer for six minutes. Using this method, how long would it take her to develop 18 x-rays, one at a time? What fraction of an eight-hour work shift would this project take up?
4. Jana's arm measures $22\frac{1}{2}$ inches from shoulder to fingertip. When she broke her arm, it was put in a cast $8\frac{1}{3}$ inches long. What fraction of her arm was covered by the cast?
5. Harleyville Heights Junior High has a good soccer team, but the players are known for their injuries. This year, like last year, there are 21 boys on the team. Last year 9 of them either sprained or broke an ankle. So far this year, 3 boys have hurt themselves. None of the boys injured last year has been injured this year. What fraction of the team has been injured during the past two years?

We use fractions every day.

Fractions represent a part of a whole object or unit.

	1	2	3	4	5	6	7	8	9
Home	0	2	0	0	1				
Visitor	1	1	0	3					

$\frac{1}{2}$ played

$\frac{1}{6}$ eaten

$3\frac{1}{16}$ inches long

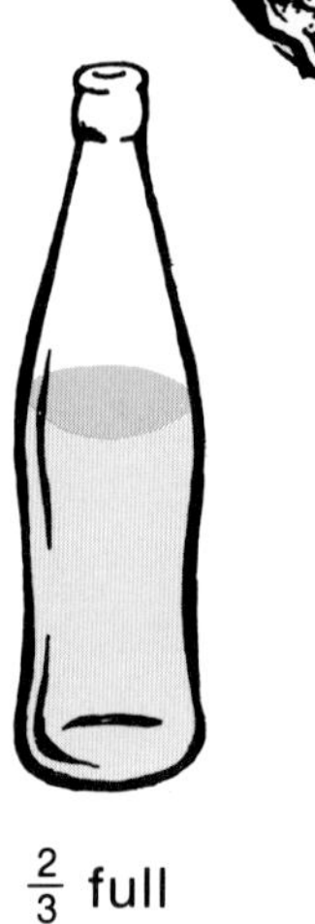

$\frac{2}{3}$ full

$\frac{3}{4}$ hour till lunchtime

Fractions may also represent a part of an entire group or set.

Of the train cars pictured,

$\frac{5}{8}$ of the cars carry passengers;
$\frac{3}{8}$ of the cars do not carry passengers;
$\frac{7}{8}$ of the cars are out of the tunnel;
$\frac{1}{8}$ of the cars is still in the tunnel

Keys to Understanding

$\frac{3}{4}$ The numerator tells the number of parts being considered (three).
The denominator tells the name (fourths) and number of the parts in the whole (four).

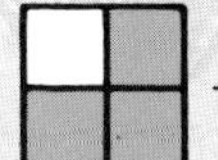
$\frac{3}{4}$ of the square is colored.

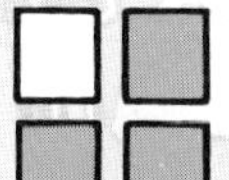
$\frac{3}{4}$ of the set is colored.

A fractional number less than 1 is called a *proper fraction.*

A fraction represents a part of a whole object or set.

Practice

Write the fraction that represents the part of each object or set that is colored.

1.

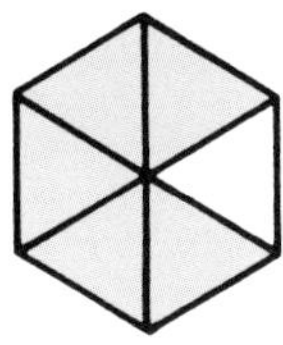

2.

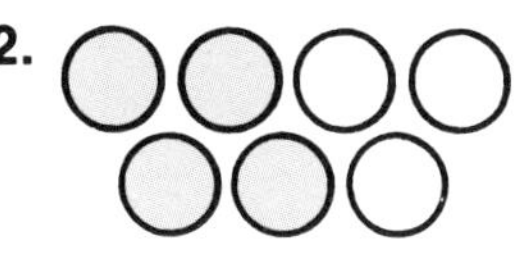

3.

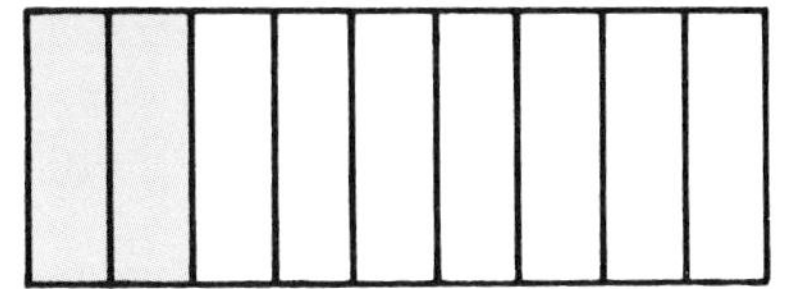

4.

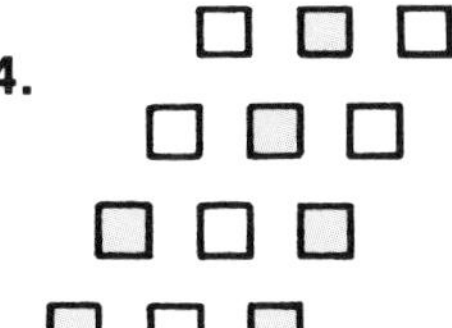

5.

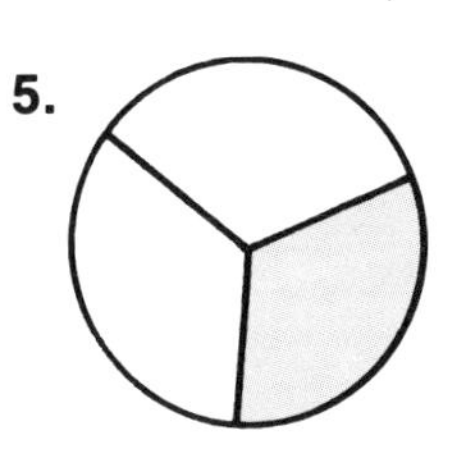

6.

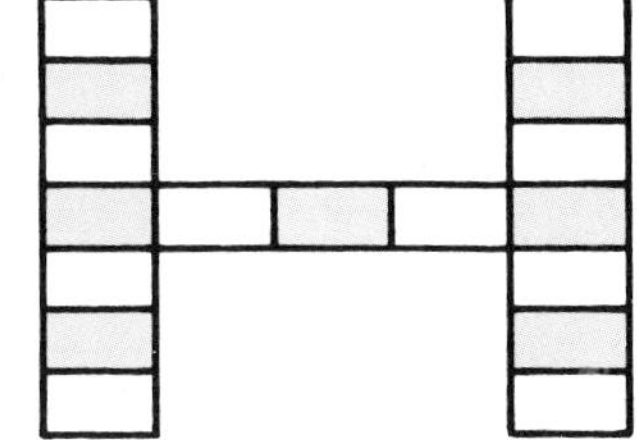

7. Draw a circle and shade $\frac{3}{4}$ of it.

8. Draw a circle and shade $\frac{5}{8}$ of it.

9. Draw a set of circles so that $\frac{5}{6}$ of them are shaded.

10. Draw a set of circles so that $\frac{7}{11}$ of them are shaded.

Fractional Answers

Fractions can be used to express answers to division problems.

How would you divide three pizzas evenly among eight boys?

How much of a pizza would each boy get?

This is a simple division problem. $3 \div 8 = ?$
First divide each pizza into eight pieces.

How many pieces should each boy get?

What fraction of a pizza should each boy get?

Each boy got $\frac{3}{8}$ of a pizza.

$$3 \div 8 = \frac{3}{8}$$

Division of numbers can be expressed using fractional notation.

$$18 \div 9 = 2$$

dividend divisor quotient

or

dividend $\frac{18}{9} = 2$ quotient
divisor

This means, "18 divided by 9 equals 2."

In a whole-number division problem, if the dividend is smaller than the divisor, the problem as expressed in *fractional form* is also the *fractional answer.*

$3 \div 8 = \frac{3}{8}$ fractional form
fractional answer

Practice

Express each of these division problems in fractional form.

1. $1 \div 6$ **4.** $8 \div 17$ **7.** $123 \div 811$

2. $5 \div 7$ **5.** $21 \div 52$ **8.** $551 \div 1{,}252$

3. $11 \div 13$ **6.** $9 \div 31$ **9.** $1{,}483 \div 10{,}629$

10. John wants to share his garden plot with five of his friends. How much of the plot will each of them get?

Fractional Form vs. Fractions

When dividing a whole number by another nonzero whole number, you can express the answer in fractional form.

$2 \div 5 = \frac{2}{5}$	$3 \div 1 = \frac{3}{1}$	$5 \div 5 = \frac{5}{5}$	$7 \div 4 = \frac{7}{4}$
2 divided by 5	3 divided by 1	5 divided by 5	7 divided by 4

Fractional Form

$\frac{2}{5}$ *is* a fraction.

$\frac{3}{1}$ *is not* a fraction, but it is the whole number 3 expressed in fractional form.

$\frac{5}{5}$ *is not* a fraction, but it is the whole number 1 expressed in fractional form.

$\frac{7}{4}$ *is not* a fraction, but it is the mixed number $1\frac{3}{4}$ expressed in fractional form.

What do you think?

Which of the following are *true* fractions?

$\frac{1}{11}$ $\frac{5}{3}$ $\frac{7}{9}$ $\frac{10}{4}$ $\frac{7}{1}$ $\frac{13}{13}$ $\frac{111}{118}$

Now do you know the difference between a *truc* fraction and a number expressed in fractional form?
What is the difference?

Practice

Express each of these division problems in fractional form and tell which ones have a fractional answer.

1. $3 \div 7 =$
2. $12 \div 4 =$
3. $6 \div 6 =$
4. $18 \div 3 =$
5. $7 \div 22 =$
6. $97 \div 97 =$
7. Express the whole number 1 in fractional form five ways.
8. Express the whole number 5 in fractional form five ways.
9. Miss Sawyer has three apples to divide evenly among four students. How much of an apple should each student get?
10. If three girls want to share equally two apples, how much of an apple should they each get?

From now on all numbers expressed in fractional form will be called fractions even though it has just been pointed out that they may represent whole or mixed numbers.

Equivalent Fractions

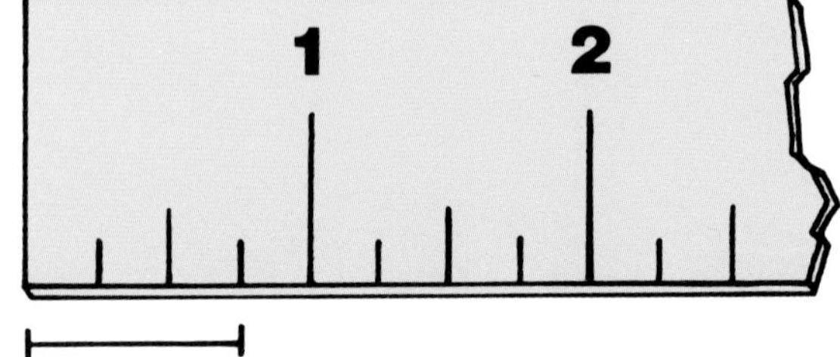

Look at line segment AB. How long is it in inches?

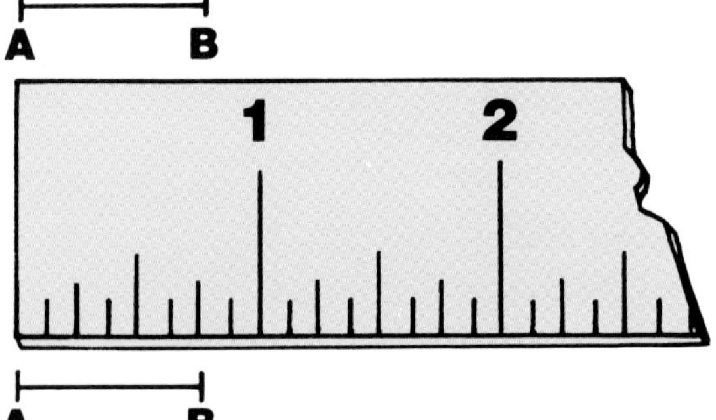

Express the length of $\overline{AB}$ using another fraction.

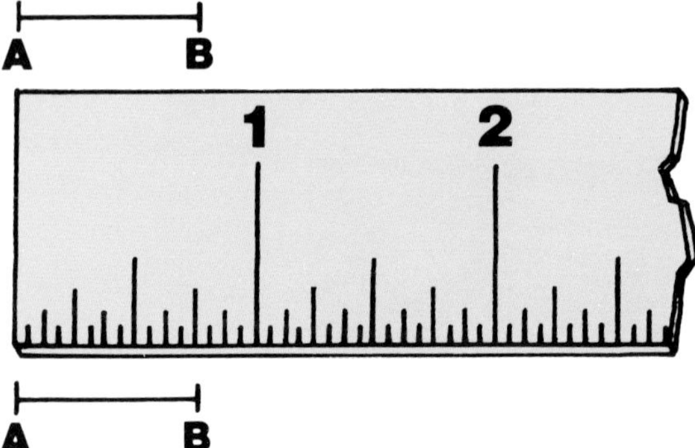

Express the length of $\overline{AB}$ using still another fraction.

What do you think?

Did the length of $\overline{AB}$ change? Did its measurement?

Write three more fractions that express the length of $\overline{AB}$.

How many different fractions could be used to express the length of $\overline{AB}$?

The fractions you found that express the same length are called *equivalent fractions.*

Keys to Understanding

Equivalent fractions are fractions that name the same number (have the same value).

Example: $\frac{1}{2} = \frac{2}{4} = \frac{3}{6} = \frac{4}{8} = \frac{5}{10} = \frac{6}{12} = \ldots$

If two fractions are equivalent, then the numerator of the first multiplied by the denominator of the second is equal to the denominator of the first multiplied by the numerator of the second. This is called *cross-product multiplication.*
If $\frac{a}{b} = \frac{c}{d}$, then $a \cdot d = b \cdot c$

Are $\frac{2}{3}$ and $\frac{12}{18}$ equivalent fractions?

$2 \cdot 18 \overset{?}{=} 3 \cdot 12$

$36 = 36$

Yes. $\frac{2}{3} = \frac{12}{18}$

Are $\frac{4}{5}$ and $\frac{9}{16}$ equivalent fractions?

$4 \cdot 16 \overset{?}{=} 9 \cdot 5$

$64 \neq 45$

No. $\frac{4}{5} \neq \frac{9}{16}$

Practice

Determine by cross-product multiplication whether each pair of fractions is equivalent or not.

1. $\frac{2}{3}$ and $\frac{4}{6}$
2. $\frac{4}{8}$ and $\frac{12}{20}$
3. $\frac{5}{7}$ and $\frac{45}{63}$
4. $\frac{7}{6}$ and $\frac{12}{10}$
5. $\frac{7}{8}$ and $\frac{37}{40}$
6. $\frac{12}{7}$ and $\frac{42}{21}$
7. $\frac{3}{10}$ and $\frac{24}{80}$
8. $\frac{11}{8}$ and $\frac{66}{42}$
9. $\frac{15}{24}$ and $\frac{3}{5}$
10. $\frac{36}{17}$ and $\frac{9}{4}$
11. $\frac{21}{54}$ and $\frac{7}{18}$
12. $\frac{52}{16}$ and $\frac{88}{24}$

Equivalent Fractions

Equivalent fractions can be found simply by multiplying or dividing the numerator and the denominator by the same nonzero whole number.

$\frac{1}{2} = \frac{1 \cdot 2}{2 \cdot 2} = \frac{2}{4}$ $\frac{3}{6} = \frac{3 \div 3}{6 \div 3} = \frac{1}{2}$ $\frac{2}{3} = \frac{2 \cdot 5}{3 \cdot 5} = \frac{10}{15}$

What do you think?

Why does this method of finding equivalent fractions work?

What number does the fraction $\frac{2}{2}$ represent? $\frac{3}{3}$? $\frac{4}{4}$?

What are you actually doing when you multiply or divide the numerator and the denominator by the same nonzero number?

What property tells us that doing so does not change the value of the fraction?

Keys to Understanding

Multiplying or dividing both the numerator and the denominator of a fraction by the same nonzero whole number does not change the value of the fraction. If k = any nonzero whole number,

then $\frac{a}{b} = \frac{a \cdot k}{b \cdot k}$ and $\frac{a}{b} = \frac{a \div k}{b \div k}$

Example: $\frac{2}{3} = \frac{2 \cdot 4}{3 \cdot 4} = \frac{8}{12}$ and $\frac{8}{12} = \frac{8 \div 4}{12 \div 4} = \frac{2}{3}$

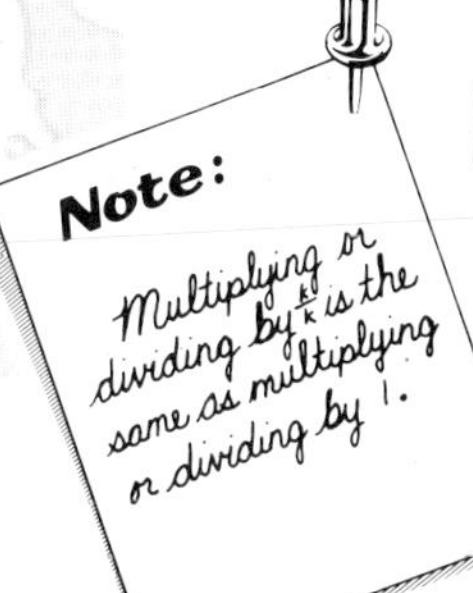

Practice

Multiply to find three equivalent fractions (expressed in higher terms) for each fraction.

1. $\frac{1}{8}$ **2.** $\frac{2}{3}$ **3.** $\frac{5}{7}$ **4.** $\frac{9}{10}$ **5.** $\frac{11}{2}$

Divide to find an equivalent fraction (expressed in lower terms) for each fraction.

6. $\frac{8}{12}$ **7.** $\frac{12}{30}$ **8.** $\frac{72}{40}$ **9.** $\frac{36}{54}$ **10.** $\frac{100}{150}$

Find two equivalent fractions for each of the following.

11. $\frac{5}{6}$ **13.** $\frac{5}{15}$ **15.** $\frac{3}{8}$ **17.** $\frac{86}{90}$ **19.** $\frac{21}{84}$

12. $\frac{1}{7}$ **14.** $\frac{6}{12}$ **16.** $\frac{10}{11}$ **18.** $\frac{42}{75}$ **20.** $\frac{111}{120}$

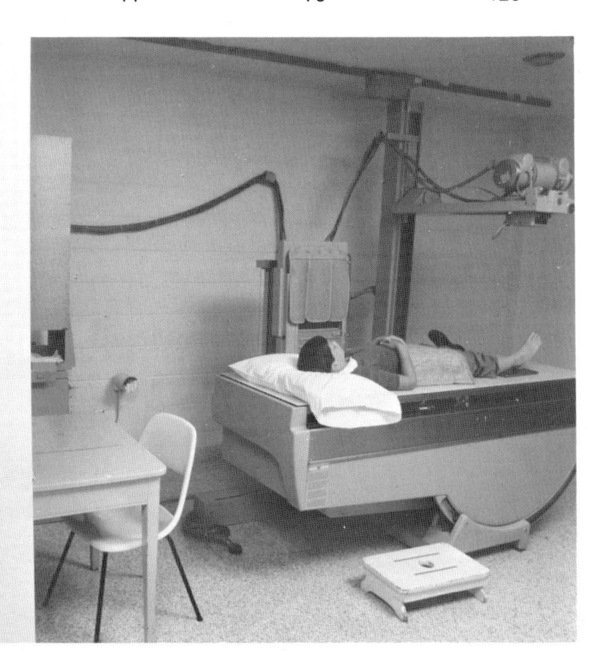

Renaming Fractions

After a lady is married, she is the same person, but she has a different name. We might say that she has simply been renamed.

We *rename fractions* using *equivalent fractions.* What part of the fraction is the name?

Rename $\frac{2}{3}$ using the name *twelfths.*

$$\frac{2}{3} = \frac{?}{12}$$

Think! $3 \cdot \square = 12$

Remember the method for finding equivalent fractions.

What factor should be in the square?
If the denominator is multiplied by 4, then the numerator must also be multiplied by 4. ($\frac{4}{4}$ is equal to 1.)

$$\frac{2 \cdot 4}{3 \cdot 4} = \frac{8}{12}$$

$\frac{2}{3}$ renamed in twelfths is $\frac{8}{12}$. Are $\frac{2}{3}$ and $\frac{8}{12}$ equivalent fractions?

Think this problem through.

$$\frac{45}{54} = \frac{?}{6}$$

$$(54 \div \square = 6)$$

$$\frac{45 \div 9}{54 \div 9} = \frac{5}{6}$$

Do these problems mentally.

$$\frac{3}{4} = \frac{?}{48}$$

$$\frac{12}{72} = \frac{?}{6}$$

Be able to explain how you got your answers.

Practice

Find the missing numerator in each of these renaming problems.

1. $\frac{1}{6} = \frac{?}{24}$
2. $\frac{3}{8} = \frac{?}{32}$
3. $\frac{2}{3} = \frac{?}{21}$
4. $\frac{2}{5} = \frac{?}{20}$
5. $\frac{2}{11} = \frac{?}{44}$
6. $\frac{9}{24} = \frac{?}{8}$
7. $\frac{25}{100} = \frac{?}{20}$
8. $\frac{12}{21} = \frac{?}{7}$
9. $\frac{16}{52} = \frac{?}{13}$
10. $\frac{12}{27} = \frac{?}{9}$
11. $\frac{8}{11} = \frac{?}{44}$
12. $\frac{6}{12} = \frac{?}{2}$
13. $\frac{7}{31} = \frac{?}{124}$
14. $\frac{24}{30} = \frac{?}{5}$
15. $\frac{15}{85} = \frac{?}{17}$

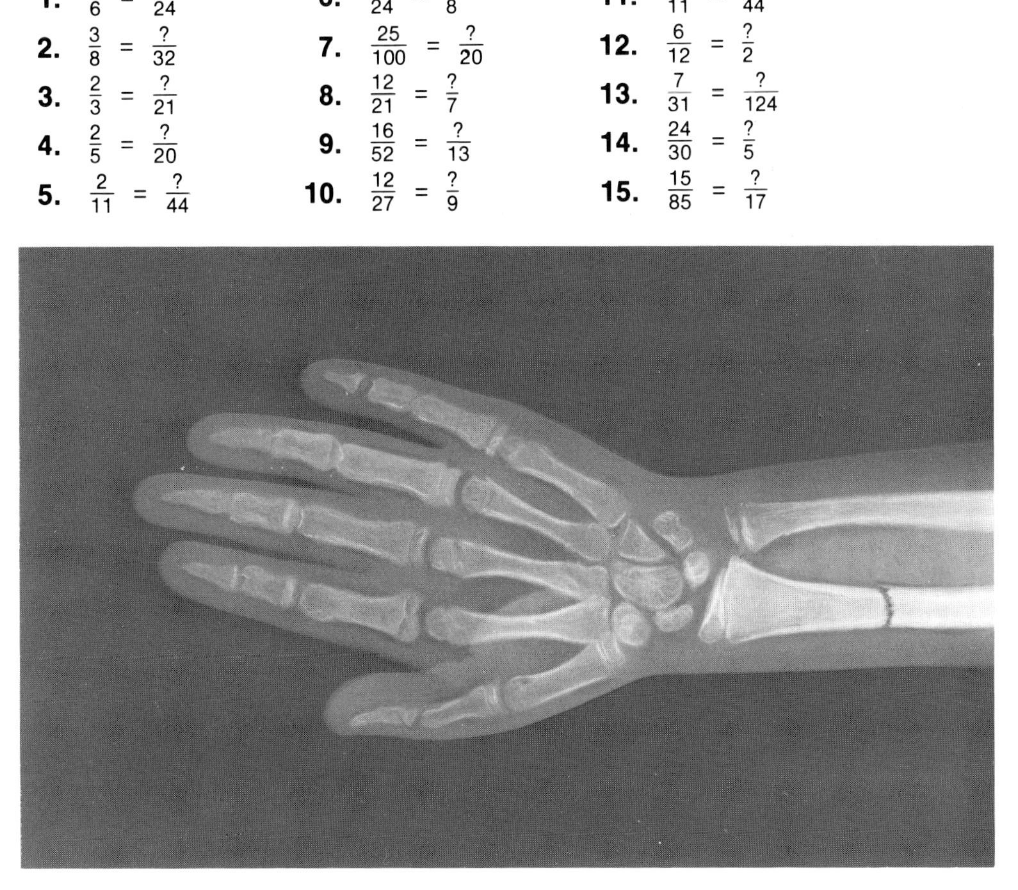

Lowest Terms

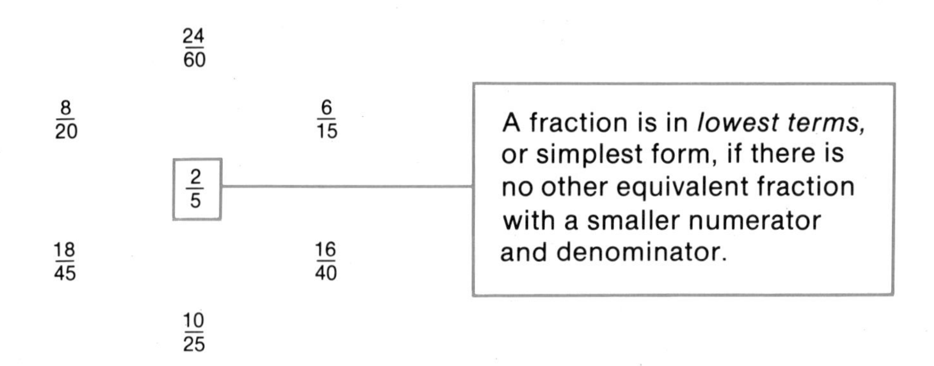

The greatest common factor (GCF) of the numerator and denominator of a fraction in lowest terms is 1.

Which of these equivalent fractions is in lowest terms?

$\frac{10}{15} = \frac{2}{3} = \frac{4}{6} = \frac{20}{30} = \frac{6}{9}$

$\frac{40}{50} = \frac{12}{15} = \frac{16}{20} = \frac{4}{5} = \frac{8}{10}$

$\frac{45}{50} = \frac{9}{10} = \frac{63}{70} = \frac{36}{40} = \frac{18}{20}$

To rename fractions, simply divide both the numerator and the denominator by their greatest common factor (GCF).

$\frac{20}{28} = \frac{20 \div 4}{28 \div 4} = \frac{5}{7}$

$\frac{36}{90} = \frac{36 \div 18}{90 \div 18} = \frac{2}{5}$

Remember how to find greatest common factor (GCF).

Using prime factorization may be a faster and easier way to rename fractions in lowest terms.

1. Find the prime factorization of the numerator and denominator.
2. Remove the factors common to the numerator and denominator by dividing.
3. Multiply the factors that remain to obtain the answer.

$\frac{20}{28} = \frac{\cancel{2} \cdot \cancel{2} \cdot 5}{\cancel{2} \cdot \cancel{2} \cdot 7} = \frac{5}{7}$ What does $\frac{2}{2}$ equal?

$\frac{36}{90} = \frac{\cancel{2} \cdot 2 \cdot \cancel{3} \cdot \cancel{3}}{\cancel{2} \cdot \cancel{3} \cdot \cancel{3} \cdot 5} = \frac{2}{5}$ What does $\frac{3}{3}$ equal?

$\frac{45}{50} = \frac{3 \cdot 3 \cdot \cancel{5}}{2 \cdot 5 \cdot \cancel{5}} = \frac{3 \cdot 3}{2 \cdot 5} = \frac{9}{10}$ What does $\frac{5}{5}$ equal?

What if there are no common prime factors in the numerator and denominator of a fraction?

Practice

Express these fractions in their lowest terms.

1. $\frac{6}{12}$ **2.** $\frac{7}{56}$ **3.** $\frac{5}{30}$ **4.** $\frac{9}{24}$ **5.** $\frac{10}{18}$

6. $\frac{15}{100}$ **7.** $\frac{9}{45}$ **8.** $\frac{6}{17}$ **9.** $\frac{19}{38}$ **10.** $\frac{32}{50}$

11. $\frac{36}{54}$ **12.** $\frac{39}{51}$ **13.** $\frac{15}{35}$ **14.** $\frac{90}{180}$ **15.** $\frac{10}{49}$

16. $\frac{128}{144}$ **17.** $\frac{125}{225}$ **18.** $\frac{63}{105}$ **19.** $\frac{91}{169}$ **20.** $\frac{15}{176}$

Match the fractions with the sets of equivalent fractions.

21. $\frac{8}{56}$ **a.** $\{\frac{2}{3}, \frac{4}{6}, \frac{6}{9}, \ldots\}$

22. $\frac{21}{35}$ **b.** $\{\frac{1}{7}, \frac{2}{14}, \frac{3}{21}, \ldots\}$

23. $\frac{54}{81}$ **c.** $\{\frac{3}{5}, \frac{6}{10}, \frac{9}{15}, \ldots\}$

24. $\frac{25}{125}$ **d.** $\{\frac{1}{2}, \frac{2}{4}, \frac{3}{6}, \ldots\}$

25. $\frac{35}{70}$ **e.** $\{\frac{1}{5}, \frac{2}{10}, \frac{3}{15}, \ldots\}$

Unit Review

Tell whether each of the following numbers is a *prime* or *composite* number. If it is a composite number, give its prime factorization.

1. 57 **3.** 121 **5.** 91 **7.** 133 **9.** 343

2. 31 **4.** 111 **6.** 17 **8.** 101 **10.** 435

Give the prime factorization of each of these numbers, using exponents.

11. 81 **12.** 126 **13.** 1,000 **14.** 291 **15.** 847

Using prime factorization, find the GCF and the LCM of each of these numbers.

16. 27 and 26 **18.** 15, 18, and 21 **20.** 54 and 81

17. 18 and 24 **19.** 18, 30, and 42 **21.** 41 and 105

Give two equivalent fractions for each fraction listed.

22. $\frac{2}{3}$ **23.** $\frac{4}{7}$ **24.** $\frac{11}{5}$ **25.** $\frac{28}{48}$ **26.** $\frac{45}{105}$

Using prime factorization, rename these fractions in lowest terms.

27. $\frac{10}{12}$ **29.** $\frac{12}{36}$ **31.** $\frac{35}{50}$ **33.** $\frac{77}{98}$ **35.** $\frac{105}{175}$

28. $\frac{14}{21}$ **30.** $\frac{6}{30}$ **32.** $\frac{45}{75}$ **34.** $\frac{12}{120}$ **36.** $\frac{39}{51}$

Find the missing numerator in each of these renaming problems.

37. $\frac{1}{4} = \frac{?}{12}$ **39.** $\frac{2}{9} = \frac{?}{81}$ **41.** $\frac{19}{50} = \frac{?}{200}$

38. $\frac{4}{9} = \frac{?}{27}$ **40.** $\frac{4}{25} = \frac{?}{100}$ **42.** $\frac{7}{31} = \frac{?}{124}$

Fill in the blanks with the appropriate term from the list below.

43. 18 is the _____ of 6 and 9.

44. A fraction represents part of a whole _____ or object.

45. Fractions that name the same number are _____ fractions.

46. If $a \cdot b = c$, then a and b are both _____ of c.

47. A number with more than two factors is a _____ number.

48. 3 is the _____ of 9 and 24.

49. If there is a fraction $\frac{a}{b}$ where $a < b$, this fraction is called a _____ fraction.

50. A number with only two factors, 1 and itself, is a _____ number.

a. composite
b. equivalent
c. factors
d. GCF
e. improper
f. LCD
g. LCM
h. prime
i. proper
j. set

MIND BOGGLER

$a \cdot b \cdot c = 1{,}001$

Find *a*, *b*, and *c* so that each letter names a different prime number.

Skills Checkup

1. 779,312 + 53,456 + 1,287 + 95,029
2. 413,946 + 8,789 + 34,925 + 74,591 + 23,584
3. 543,678 - 25,671
4. 123,768 - 99,999
5. 346 × 712
6. 988 × 675
7. 8,704 ÷ 255
8. 4,128 ÷ 11
9. $\frac{5}{6} + \frac{4}{5}$
10. $\frac{5}{8} + \frac{5}{12}$
11. $\frac{1}{2} + \frac{3}{4} + \frac{2}{3}$
12. $\frac{3}{8} + \frac{1}{6} + \frac{2}{3}$
13. $17\frac{1}{2} - 14\frac{5}{8}$
14. $12\frac{3}{4} - 4\frac{2}{3}$
15. $8\frac{3}{4} - 5$
16. $9 - 3\frac{3}{5}$
17. $2\frac{1}{2} \times 1\frac{1}{2}$
18. $2\frac{2}{3} \times 2\frac{3}{4}$
19. $20 \times \frac{3}{5}$
20. $5\frac{2}{3} \times 6\frac{3}{4}$
21. $6 \div \frac{1}{3}$
22. $\frac{2}{3} \div \frac{2}{5}$
23. $17 \div \frac{1}{8}$
24. $\frac{3}{8} \div 1\frac{1}{4}$
25. What is the perimeter of a triangular rose garden with sides measuring $7\frac{3}{4}$ feet, $5\frac{1}{6}$ feet, and $8\frac{2}{3}$ feet?
26. If fencing is bought by the yard, how many yards of fence would be necessary to completely enclose the rose garden?
27. Joel went on a hike with his Boy Scout troop. In his backpack he carried a sleeping bag weighing $9\frac{7}{8}$ pounds, $3\frac{1}{2}$ pounds of food, a $\frac{3}{4}$ pound cola, and a first-aid kit weighing $1\frac{3}{8}$ pounds. How much weight was he carrying in his pack?
28. Jared is going to plant a garden in his backyard. He needs to determine the area of his yard to figure out how much of it he wants to use for gardening. The dimensions of his yard are 60 feet by 90 feet. What is the total area of his yard?
29. If Jared plants a garden 15 feet wide and 27 feet long, what is the total amount of space used by his garden?
30. How much of Jared's yard would still be left as a yard after the garden was planted?

1. 5,656 + 807 + 7,698
2. 685 + 49 + 767 + 61
3. 2,982 + 4,156 + 806
4. 5,109,875 - 37,456
5. 716,348 - 523,896
6. 338 - 156
7. 81 × 72 × 34
8. 6,315 × 957
9. 9,024 × 86
10. 3,175 ÷ 67
11. 654 ÷ 76
12. 3,204 ÷ 18

13. $\frac{1}{6} + \frac{2}{3}$
14. $\frac{7}{8} + 3\frac{1}{8}$
15. $1\frac{7}{8} + 4\frac{1}{6}$
16. $2\frac{2}{3} - 1\frac{3}{7}$
17. $5\frac{1}{3} - 1\frac{3}{8}$
18. $2\frac{6}{11} - 1\frac{9}{11}$
19. $\frac{1}{3} \times 11$
20. $\frac{3}{10} \times 2\frac{1}{2}$
21. $6 \times 1\frac{1}{8}$
22. $12 \div \frac{1}{4}$
23. $\frac{3}{8} \div 6$
24. $\frac{2}{5} \div \frac{1}{5}$

25. Jamie bought three packages of chicken to fix for a barbecue for the church youth group. The three packages weighed 3.35 pounds, 4.6 pounds, and 3.05 pounds. How much chicken did he purchase altogether?
26. If there were only 11 people at the barbecue, how much chicken was there per person? if there were 22 people? if there were 33 people?
27. Omaha received 2.8 inches, 3.45 inches, and 3.8 inches of rain in three different months last spring. What was the total rainfall in those three months?
28. Heather Marie used $2\frac{1}{2}$ cups of flour for pie crusts, $2\frac{3}{4}$ cups in bread, and $\frac{1}{3}$ cup in cooking chicken. What was the total amount of flour used?
29. If Heather Marie had 8 cups of flour before she began cooking, how much was left when she finished?
30. The school photography club is selling candy to get money to purchase new darkroom equipment. Kathy made $3\frac{3}{4}$ pounds of fudge; Lauren made $4\frac{7}{8}$ pounds of divinity; and Heidi made $2\frac{1}{2}$ pounds of peanut brittle. How many pounds of candy did they have to begin their sale?

Recipes

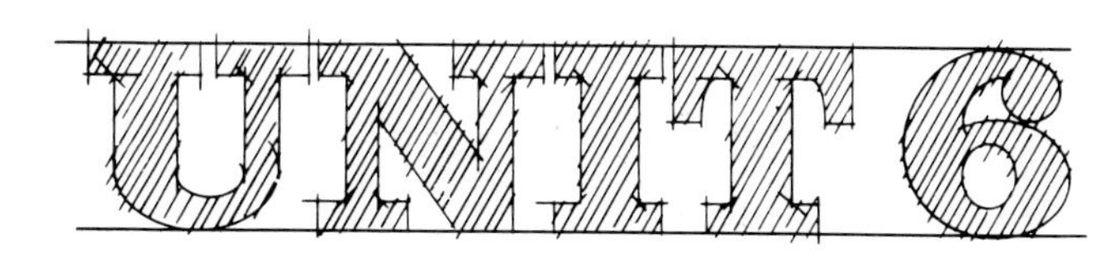

Homemaker

No one wants to work at a boring job. Everyone would like to have a job that offers challenge, excitement, and variety. Some occupations are noted for their variety. Medical workers, for example, face emergency situations every day. They must diagnose the disease or determine the injury, and then treat it correctly. When a life is at stake, their work is crucial and exciting. Another exciting job is that of the stockbroker. On the floor of the stock exchange, the broker must make decisions quickly and decisively—yet these decisions may involve thousands or even millions of dollars.

Another job offers just as much variety as either of these two, yet it is often thought of a boring or unchallenging. This "occupation" is that of the homemaker. Homemaking is an area that can be as exciting and varied as the homemaker's abilities and initiative make it. Anyone can cook a hot dog; but it takes someone with good organization, creativity, and skill to pull off a dinner party for six. Yet any homemaker who is motivated enough to try new menus and spend time experimenting with them can develop this skill.

Most homemakers can't afford to waste time and money, so careful planning, purchasing, and preparation are important. The homemaker must be adept at judging what size roast she needs to purchase to feed her family or guests. To underestimate could be embarrassing! A wise homemaker will do a little computing with unit prices to find out whether a fresh or frozen vegetable is the better bargain. And, of course, the actual preparation of a meal involves judging time, measuring quantities, and following directions precisely.

If being chief cook and dietitian were the only responsibilities of a homemaker, her life *might* become dull and routine. But the homemaker is, most likely, also the financial coordinator, interior decorator, apparel purchaser, furniture mover, and seamstress of the house. You might find her planning a budget, measuring windows for new drapes, scanning newspaper ads for smart clothing buys, rearranging furniture to get the best arrangement for the amount of space available, or altering a pattern to fit a specific person. She may also be appointed secretary of education, with the enormous challenge of helping Junior understand fractions. Duties in the church, school, and community must also get their appropriate slot in her daily schedule.

Homemaking—a dull or uninspiring calling? Hardly! Nevertheless, some women fail to see the potential in such a career. Like any other vocation, homemaking can become boring and unchallenging if the homemaker loses her love for her work and the zeal to keep it interesting. Without careful attention and cultivation, your relationship to the Lord Jesus Christ can also become wearisome. Sometimes you can solve this problem by only varying the routine; other times you must "renew a right spirit" toward that which God desires and expects (Psalm 51:10b). The body of every Christian is the temple of the Holy Spirit—His "home" (I Corinthians 6:19). What kind of "homemaker" are you?

Adding and Subtracting Fractions

Ryan had a birthday party at the skating rink and invited several of his friends. After they skated they had a birthday cake, two cartons of ice cream, and two gallons of punch. The girls drank $\frac{5}{8}$ of a gallon of punch and the boys drank $\frac{7}{8}$ of a gallon of punch.

Remember to express your answer in lowest terms.

How many gallons of punch were left?

$$\frac{3}{8} + \frac{1}{8} = \frac{4}{8} = \frac{1}{2}$$

We added the numerators and kept the denominator.
Why?

How much more punch did the boys drink than the girls?

$$\frac{7}{8} - \frac{5}{8} = \frac{2}{8} = \frac{1}{4}$$

We subtracted the numerator and kept the denominator.

Keys to Understanding

Fractions that are being added or subtracted must have the same denominator (name).

Addition

$$\frac{a}{c} + \frac{b}{c} = \frac{a + b}{c}$$

Subtraction

$$\frac{a}{c} - \frac{b}{c} = \frac{a - b}{c}$$

Ryan's mother brought both vanilla and chocolate ice cream for all the guests. They ate $\frac{1}{2}$ of a carton of vanilla and $\frac{1}{3}$ of a carton of chocolate.
How many cartons of ice cream did they eat altogether?

$$\frac{1}{2} + \frac{1}{3} = ?$$

The two fractions have different denominators. Can they be added?

To add or subtract fractions with different denominators, rename the fractions, using equivalent fractions that have the same denominator. Always use the *lowest common denominator* (LCD).

6 is the LCD.
How do we know?

$$\begin{array}{rl} \frac{1}{2} & = \frac{\square}{6} \\ + \ \frac{1}{3} & = \frac{\square}{6} \\ \hline ? & = \end{array}$$

Fill in the squares and then add.

$$\frac{3}{6} + \frac{2}{6} = \frac{5}{6}$$

How much more vanilla did they eat than chocolate?

$$\frac{1}{2} - \frac{1}{3} = ?$$

$$\frac{\square}{6} - \frac{\square}{6} = \frac{\square}{6}$$

Remember,
the lowest common denominator (LCD) is the same as the least common multiple (LCM) of the denominators.

$\frac{1}{6} + \frac{1}{4} + \frac{1}{3} = ?$

What is the lowest common denominator?
How did you find it?

$\frac{\square}{12} + \frac{\square}{12} + \frac{\square}{12} = \frac{\square}{12} = ?$

Solve by filling in the boxes.

$$\begin{array}{rcl} \frac{5}{9} & = & ? \\ - \frac{1}{6} & = & ? \\ \hline & & ? \end{array}$$

Find the lowest common denominator and then solve the problem.

Practice

Solve these problems. Be sure to express your answers in lowest terms.

1. $\frac{1}{5} + \frac{2}{5} =$
2. $\frac{3}{10} + \frac{1}{10} =$
3. $\frac{5}{8} - \frac{1}{8} =$
4. $\frac{7}{11} - \frac{4}{11} =$
5. $\frac{2}{9} + \frac{5}{9} =$
6. $\frac{2}{3} - \frac{1}{4} =$
7. $\frac{3}{10} + \frac{1}{6} =$
8. $\frac{3}{5} - \frac{1}{8} =$
9. $\frac{4}{9} - \frac{5}{16} =$
10. $\frac{3}{15} + \frac{4}{9} =$
11. $\frac{5}{8} + \frac{1}{3} =$
12. $\frac{4}{5} - \frac{3}{4} =$
13. $\frac{17}{26} - \frac{11}{65} =$
14. $\frac{5}{13} + \frac{1}{3} =$
15. $\left(\frac{3}{10} - \frac{1}{4}\right) + \frac{1}{5} =$

16. $\begin{array}{r} \frac{3}{5} \\ - \frac{2}{15} \\ \hline \end{array}$

17. $\begin{array}{r} \frac{1}{8} \\ \frac{1}{3} \\ + \frac{1}{2} \\ \hline \end{array}$

18. $\begin{array}{r} \frac{15}{16} \\ - \frac{3}{4} \\ \hline \end{array}$

19. $\begin{array}{r} \frac{2}{15} \\ \frac{3}{10} \\ + \frac{1}{3} \\ \hline \end{array}$

20. $\begin{array}{r} \frac{11}{85} \\ + \frac{4}{51} \\ \hline \end{array}$

21. Jimmy ran $\frac{2}{3}$ of a mile and then walked $\frac{1}{4}$ of a mile. How far did he travel altogether?

22. Barbara has a sack of mints that is $\frac{5}{6}$ full. Steve has a sack that is $\frac{3}{8}$ full. Who has more mints? how much of a sack more?

23. On each of the following nights Carl ate part of a gallon of ice cream: Monday, $\frac{1}{8}$; Tuesday, $\frac{1}{6}$; Wednesday, $\frac{1}{4}$. How much did he eat in three nights?

24. Find the perimeter of (distance around) a rectangle that is $\frac{1}{8}$ of an inch wide and $\frac{3}{16}$ of an inch long.

25. How much longer is $\overline{AB}$ than $\overline{CD}$?

$\frac{2}{3}$ in. A———B $\frac{3}{8}$ in. C——D

Comparing Fractions

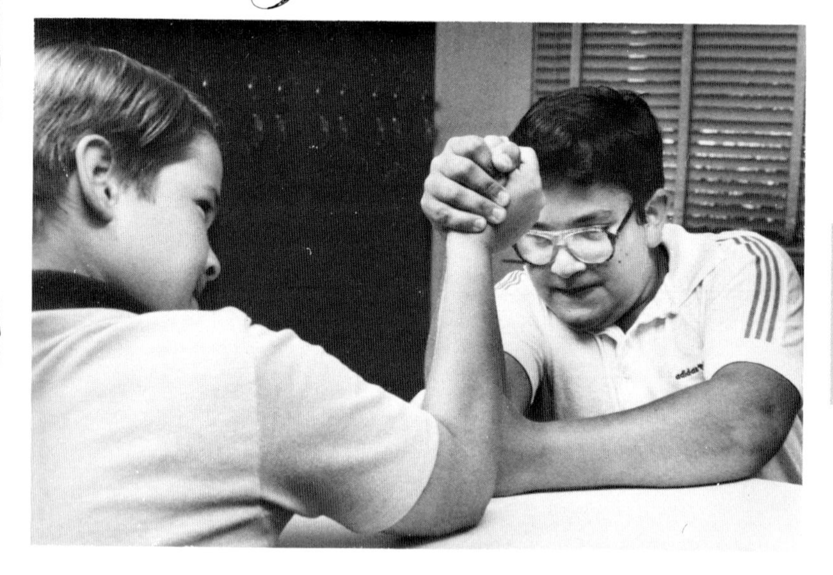

Remember the three relationships possible between numbers.

Fractions can be compared on a number line. How do we know which fraction is smaller?

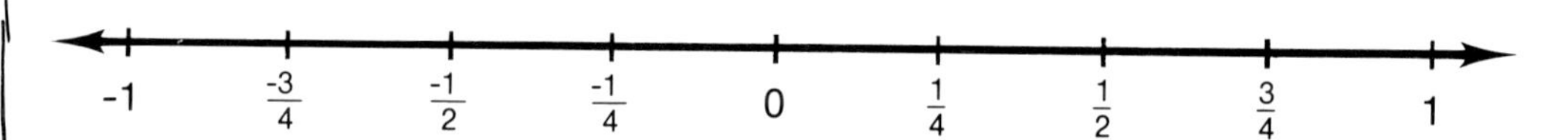

Fractions with common denominators can be compared easily.

Compare $\frac{7}{11}$ and $\frac{2}{11}$.

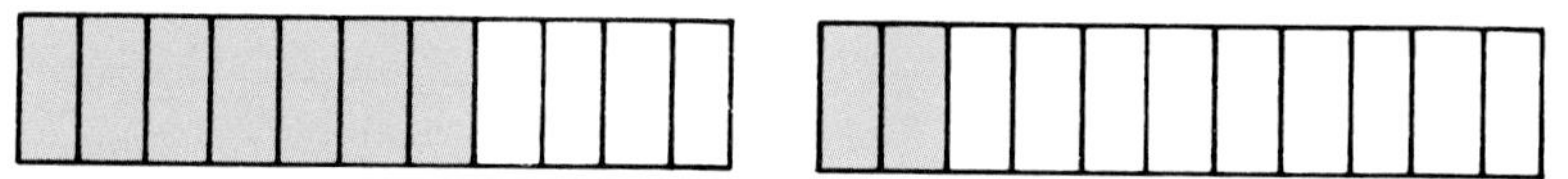

Since $7 > 2$, then $\frac{7}{11} > \frac{2}{11}$.

Fractions with common numerators can be compared easily.

Compare $\frac{3}{4}$ and $\frac{3}{7}$.

$\frac{3}{4} > \frac{3}{7}$

Why is it easy to compare fractions with the same numerators?

Fractions with different denominators can be compared.

Compare $\frac{3}{5}$ and $\frac{2}{3}$.

Express the fractions so that they have common denominators.

$\frac{3}{5} = \frac{9}{15}$

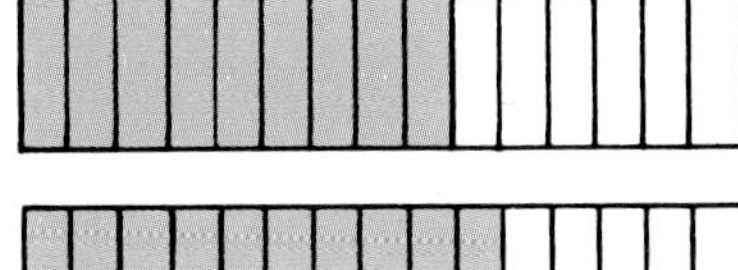

$\frac{2}{3} = \frac{10}{15}$

Since $\frac{9}{15} < \frac{10}{15}$, then $\frac{3}{5} < \frac{2}{3}$.

Practice

Draw one number line for each pair of numbers. Locate them on the number line and then compare them, using the appropriate sign ($<$, $>$, $=$).

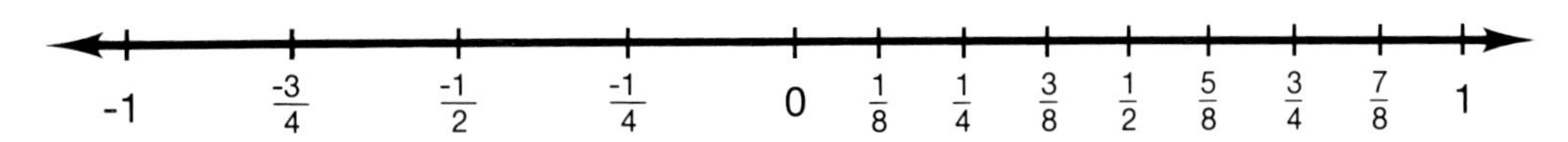

1. $\frac{1}{4}$ and $\frac{3}{8}$
2. $\frac{3}{4}$ and $\frac{1}{2}$
3. $\frac{1}{2}$ and $\frac{1}{3}$
4. 1 and $\frac{10}{11}$
5. $\frac{1}{8}$ and $\frac{2}{13}$
6. $\frac{2}{3}$ and $\frac{5}{8}$
7. $\frac{4}{7}$ and $\frac{5}{6}$
8. $\frac{1}{2}$ and $\frac{4}{5}$
9. $\frac{3}{5}$ and $\frac{4}{9}$

Express these fractions, using common denominators; then compare them, using the appropriate sign ($<$, $>$, $=$).

10. $\frac{3}{8}$ and $\frac{5}{8}$
11. $\frac{4}{9}$ and $\frac{3}{7}$
12. $\frac{1}{2}$ and $\frac{3}{10}$
13. $\frac{5}{6}$ and $\frac{7}{8}$
14. $\frac{6}{8}$ and $\frac{3}{4}$
15. $\frac{3}{9}$ and $\frac{1}{4}$
16. $\frac{8}{11}$ and $\frac{2}{3}$
17. $\frac{5}{10}$ and $\frac{13}{26}$
18. $\frac{8}{10}$ and $\frac{6}{7}$
19. $\frac{7}{11}$ and $\frac{5}{9}$
20. $\frac{9}{20}$ and $\frac{2}{5}$

Cross Multiplication

Cross multiplication is the easiest way to compare fractions.

To compare $\frac{a}{b}$ and $\frac{c}{d}$, cross multiply and compare products.

If $a \cdot d = b \cdot c$, then $\frac{a}{b} = \frac{c}{d}$.

If $a \cdot d > b \cdot c$, *then* $\frac{a}{b} > \frac{c}{d}$.

If $a \cdot d < b \cdot c$, then $\frac{a}{b} < \frac{c}{d}$.

The order in which the multiplication is done *is important*!

Examples: Compare $\frac{2}{3}$ and $\frac{3}{4}$.

Since $8 < 9$, then $\frac{2}{3} < \frac{3}{4}$.

Compare $\frac{56}{100}$ and $\frac{28}{50}$.

Since $2{,}800 = 2{,}800$, then $\frac{56}{100} = \frac{28}{50}$.

Compare $\frac{3}{5}$ and $\frac{4}{9}$.

Since $27 > 20$, then $\frac{3}{5} > \frac{4}{9}$.

Compare the examples above, using common denominators. What do you actually do when you cross multiply?

Practice

Compare these fractions, using the appropriate sign (<, >, =).

1. $\frac{1}{3}$ and $\frac{2}{3}$
2. $\frac{1}{2}$ and $\frac{4}{5}$
3. $\frac{3}{5}$ and $\frac{10}{15}$
4. $\frac{3}{8}$ and $\frac{3}{5}$
5. $\frac{2}{3}$ and $\frac{5}{8}$
6. $\frac{7}{8}$ and $\frac{6}{7}$
7. $\frac{4}{9}$ and $\frac{3}{5}$
8. $\frac{4}{13}$ and $\frac{16}{52}$
9. $\frac{2}{3}$ and $\frac{5}{7}$
10. $\frac{6}{10}$ and $\frac{5}{9}$
11. $\frac{3}{9}$ and $\frac{3}{8}$
12. $\frac{1}{10}$ and $\frac{3}{31}$
13. $\frac{2}{11}$ and $\frac{10}{51}$
14. $\frac{20}{21}$ and $\frac{80}{84}$
15. $\frac{99}{100}$ and $\frac{99}{101}$

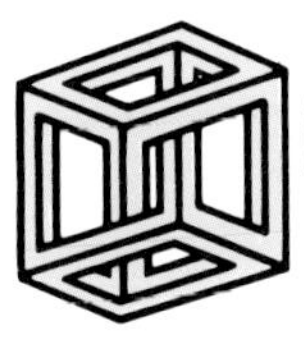

MIND BOGGLER

How many triangles can you find? Name them.

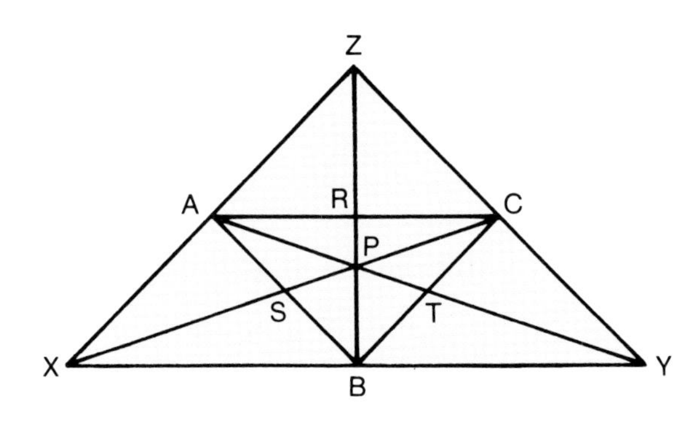

Mixed Numbers

Greg has $3\frac{1}{4}$ candy bars. How many $\frac{1}{4}$ pieces of a candy bar does he have?

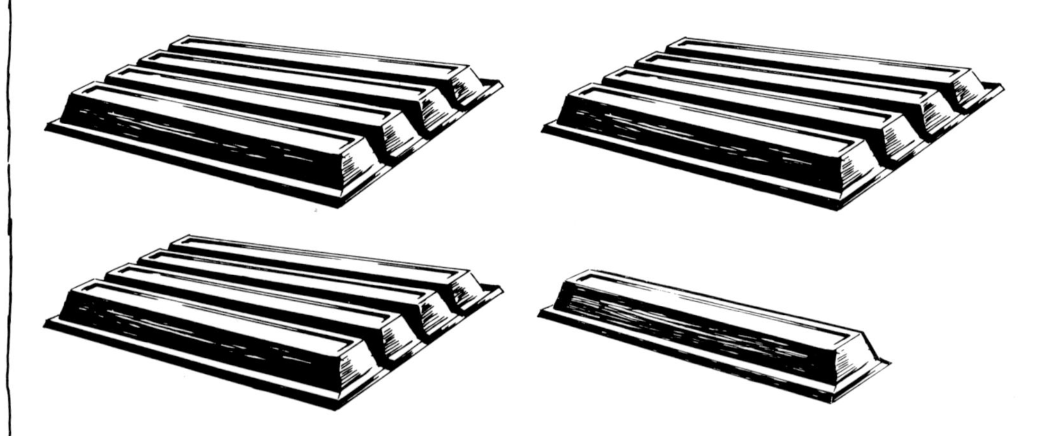

The problem is to *rename* the mixed number in fractional form.

Renaming a mixed number is actually an addition problem: 3 whole candy bars $+ \frac{1}{4}$ candy bar $(3 + \frac{1}{4})$. When you solve the addition problem, you have renamed the mixed number.

$$3 + \frac{1}{4} = ?$$

$$\frac{3}{1} + \frac{1}{4} = ?$$

$$\frac{12}{4} + \frac{1}{4} = \frac{\square}{4}$$

Fill in the box to discover your answer.

> Remember, whole numbers can be expressed in fractional form.
>
> $2 = \frac{8}{4} \quad 3 = \frac{6}{2} \quad 4 = \frac{4}{1}$

This fractional answer is called an *improper fraction.*

Keys to Understanding

A *mixed number* consists of a whole number plus a fraction.

$2\frac{3}{8} = 2 + \frac{3}{8}$ (2 → whole number; $\frac{3}{8}$ → fraction)

An *improper fraction* has a numerator greater than or equal to its denominator.

$\frac{a}{b}$ is improper if and only if *a* is greater than or equal to *b*. $(a \geq b)$

Practice

Rename these mixed numbers as improper fractions by adding the whole number and the fraction. Show your work.

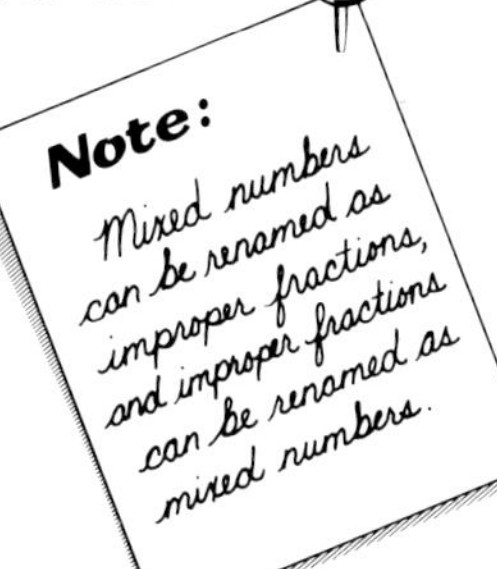

Example:

$$2\frac{3}{4} = 2 + \frac{3}{4}$$
$$= \frac{2}{1} + \frac{3}{4}$$
$$= \frac{8}{4} + \frac{3}{4} = \frac{11}{4}$$

1. $2\frac{1}{2}$ **3.** $2\frac{3}{10}$ **5.** $6\frac{1}{3}$ **7.** $5\frac{3}{4}$ **9.** $8\frac{1}{4}$

2. $1\frac{7}{8}$ **4.** $3\frac{2}{5}$ **6.** $1\frac{17}{20}$ **8.** $4\frac{3}{8}$ **10.** $3\frac{5}{6}$

Math in Action

1. Mrs. Khorev is having a dinner party for 8 people. If she needs $\frac{1}{2}$ pound of rib roast for each serving, how many pounds should she buy?
   If rib roast costs $3.49 per pound, how much will Mrs. Khorev have to spend?
2. Finding the unit price—the price per ounce, quart, etc.—of a product enables you to decide which size, brand, or packaging is the best buy. Find the unit price of these items:

Item	Size	Price	Find
peanut butter	40 oz./1,134 g	$3.69	price per oz., g
	18 oz./ 510 g	1.69	price per oz., g
rice	20 lb./9,070 g	5.99	price per lb., g
	5 lb./2,268 g	1.59	price per lb., g
bath soap	4 bars @ $3\frac{1}{2}$ oz.	0.87	price per oz.
	3 bars @ $4\frac{1}{2}$ oz.	0.85	price per oz.

3. The Berkstresser family spends $\frac{1}{4}$ of its net income on food. If Mrs. Berkstresser has $1,500 net income each month to work with, how much would she spend on food?
   About how much would she spend per week?
4. Mrs. Linderman wants to upholster several furniture items. Find out how much material she needs for each group of items.
   a. 1 tuxedo-style loveseat ($11\frac{2}{3}$ yd.)
   2 ottomans ($1\frac{3}{4}$ yd. ea.)
   1 wooden-arm chair ($1\frac{1}{2}$ yd.)
   b. 2 Duncan Phyfe sofas ($9\frac{3}{4}$ yd. ea.)
   1 lounge chair ($5\frac{7}{8}$ yd.)
5. Mrs. Kaminski wants to carpet her house. The dimensions for each part of the house are given below.

Kitchen/Dinette	11′ x 16′
Living Room	12′ x 17′
Family Room	11′ x 13′
Master Bedroom	14′ x 12′
Small Bedrooms (2)	10′ x 12′
Full Baths (2)	6′ x 10′
Hall	$4\frac{1}{2}$′x 12′

   Figure out how much carpet she needs for each area except the bathrooms and kitchen. How much carpet does she need altogether?

Shortcuts

There is a shortcut for renaming mixed numbers.

Follow these steps to rename $5\frac{3}{4}$:

1. Multiply $5 \cdot 4$. $\quad 5 \cdot 4 = 20$
2. Add 3 to the answer you got in step 1. $\quad 20 + 3 = 23$
3. Use the number you got in step 2 as the numerator and keep the same denominator. $\quad = \frac{23}{4}$

This shortcut should be done mentally. $\quad 5\frac{3}{4} = \frac{23}{4}$ (× then +)

Can you explain why this shortcut works?

There is a shortcut for renaming improper fractions.

To rename an improper fraction as a mixed number, just divide the numerator by the denominator.

$\frac{22}{7} = 22 \div 7 = 3\frac{1}{7} \qquad \frac{14}{3} = 14 \div 3 = 4\frac{2}{3}$

This shortcut should be done mentally whenever possible.

Can you explain why this shortcut works?

Practice

Rename these mixed numbers as improper fractions.

1.	$3\frac{1}{2}$	**6.**	$2\frac{2}{5}$	**11.**	$10\frac{2}{3}$	**16.**	$10\frac{7}{11}$
2.	$4\frac{3}{8}$	**7.**	$3\frac{5}{9}$	**12.**	$7\frac{1}{7}$	**17.**	$11\frac{3}{7}$
3.	$6\frac{1}{3}$	**8.**	$6\frac{1}{10}$	**13.**	$16\frac{1}{2}$	**18.**	$6\frac{8}{9}$
4.	$5\frac{4}{5}$	**9.**	$8\frac{2}{3}$	**14.**	$30\frac{1}{4}$	**19.**	$20\frac{1}{8}$
5.	$1\frac{7}{8}$	**10.**	$5\frac{5}{6}$	**15.**	$15\frac{4}{9}$	**20.**	$33\frac{4}{5}$

Rename these improper fractions as mixed numbers.

21.	$\frac{7}{2}$	**26.**	$\frac{47}{6}$	**31.**	$\frac{17}{8}$	**36.**	$\frac{51}{13}$
22.	$\frac{12}{7}$	**27.**	$\frac{13}{5}$	**32.**	$\frac{55}{30}$	**37.**	$\frac{91}{6}$
23.	$\frac{7}{5}$	**28.**	$\frac{29}{10}$	**33.**	$\frac{87}{8}$	**38.**	$\frac{61}{9}$
24.	$\frac{13}{6}$	**29.**	$\frac{58}{5}$	**34.**	$\frac{69}{7}$	**39.**	$\frac{124}{20}$
25.	$\frac{25}{4}$	**30.**	$\frac{32}{9}$	**35.**	$\frac{53}{12}$	**40.**	$\frac{75}{24}$

True or False

4. An improper fraction is a function of two integers a and b written $\frac{a}{b}$ where the absolute value of the numerator is greater than the absolute value of the denominator.

Mixed Numbers

Mr. Martinez has $3\frac{9}{10}$ gallons of gas in one can and $4\frac{4}{5}$ gallons of gas in another can. How much gasoline does he have altogether?

$$3\tfrac{9}{10} + 4\tfrac{4}{5} = ?$$

$$\begin{array}{rcl} 3\frac{9}{10} & = & 3\frac{9}{10} \\ + \; 4\frac{4}{5} & = & 4\frac{8}{10} \\ \hline & & 7\frac{17}{10} = 8\frac{7}{10} \end{array}$$

Renaming

$$\begin{aligned} 7\tfrac{17}{10} &= 7 + \tfrac{17}{10} \\ &= 7 + 1\tfrac{7}{10} \\ &= 8 + \tfrac{7}{10} \\ &= 8\tfrac{7}{10} \end{aligned}$$

On Saturday Mr. Martinez started mowing yards. He brought with him $7\frac{3}{4}$ gallons of gas. He mowed all day and used $3\frac{1}{3}$ gallons. How much gasoline did he have at the end of the day?

$$7\tfrac{3}{4} - 3\tfrac{1}{3} = ?$$

$$\begin{array}{rcl} 7\frac{3}{4} & = & 7\frac{9}{12} \\ - \; 3\frac{1}{3} & = & 3\frac{4}{12} \\ \hline & & 4\frac{5}{12} \end{array}$$

The next week Mr. Martinez started mowing with $8\frac{1}{3}$ gallons of gas. He used $4\frac{5}{6}$ gallons. How much gas did he have left?

$$8\tfrac{1}{3} - 4\tfrac{5}{6} = ?$$

$$\begin{array}{rcccl} 8\frac{1}{3} & = & 8\frac{2}{6} & = & 7\frac{8}{6} \\ - \; 4\frac{5}{6} & = & 4\frac{5}{6} & = & 4\frac{5}{6} \\ \hline & & & & 3\frac{3}{6} = 3\frac{1}{2} \end{array}$$

Always rename in lowest terms.

Renaming

$$\begin{aligned} 8\tfrac{2}{6} &= 8 + \tfrac{2}{6} \\ &= 7 + 1\tfrac{2}{6} \\ &= 7 + \tfrac{8}{6} \\ &= 7\tfrac{8}{6} \end{aligned}$$

Practice

Follow the operation signs and solve these problems. Be sure to express your answers in lowest terms.

1. $2\frac{1}{3} + 4\frac{1}{3} =$

2. $4\frac{1}{2} + 5\frac{1}{5} =$

3. $7\frac{1}{3} - 4\frac{1}{4} =$

4. $7\frac{5}{12} - 2\frac{2}{3} =$

5. $1\frac{7}{10} + 6\frac{3}{4} =$

6. $12\frac{1}{2} - 9\frac{7}{10} =$

7. $5\frac{1}{3} - 3\frac{4}{5} =$

8. $16\frac{1}{6} + 31\frac{3}{4} =$

9. $16\frac{1}{4} - 12\frac{3}{8} =$

10. $14\frac{7}{8} - 9\frac{5}{6}$

11. $10\frac{1}{2} - 6\frac{3}{5}$

12. $14\frac{1}{2} + 7\frac{2}{3}$

13. $19\frac{2}{5} + 12\frac{3}{7}$

14. $16\frac{1}{2} - 8\frac{2}{5}$

15. $22\frac{1}{8} - 15\frac{3}{4}$

16. $2\frac{1}{2} + 3\frac{2}{5} + 4\frac{1}{4} + 5\frac{3}{10} =$

17. $8\frac{1}{4} - 3\frac{5}{6} =$

18. On four workdays a salesman traveled $185\frac{3}{5}$ miles, $68\frac{9}{10}$ miles, $225\frac{1}{2}$ miles, and $109\frac{1}{5}$ miles. What was the total number of miles he covered during these four days?

19. John weighs $167\frac{5}{8}$ pounds. His younger sister weighs $99\frac{3}{4}$ pounds. How much heavier is John?

20. A bolt of material contained 10 yards. Three pieces of cloth were cut from the bolt in the following lengths: $3\frac{1}{4}$ yards, $2\frac{1}{2}$ yards, and $1\frac{5}{6}$ yards. How much material remained on the bolt?

Multiplying Fractions

Jennifer has a candy bar that is in four equal pieces. She has agreed to give Dawn $\frac{1}{2}$ of one of the pieces. How much of the candy bar will Dawn receive?

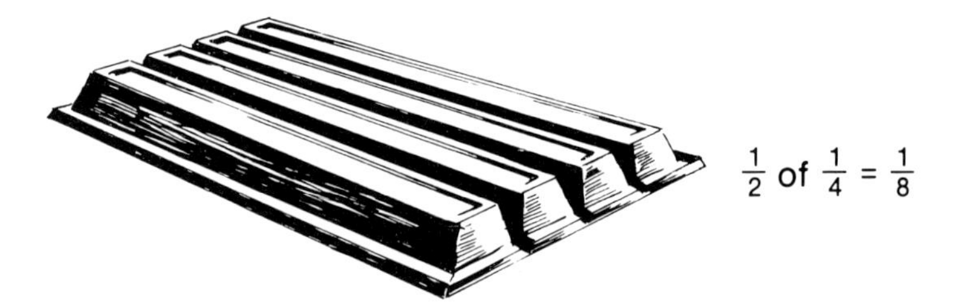

$\frac{1}{2}$ of $\frac{1}{4} = \frac{1}{8}$

If you multiply the numerator of one fraction by the numerator of the other $(1 \cdot 1)$ and do the same with the denominators $(2 \cdot 4)$, you get the answer. Therefore, instead of writing "of," we write $\frac{1}{2} \cdot \frac{1}{4} = \frac{1}{8}$. We call this *multiplication of fractions.*

Find $\frac{2}{3}$ of $\frac{4}{5}$.
Write $\frac{2}{3} \cdot \frac{4}{5}$.
Solve: $\frac{2}{3} \cdot \frac{4}{5} = \frac{2 \cdot 4}{3 \cdot 5} = \frac{8}{15}$

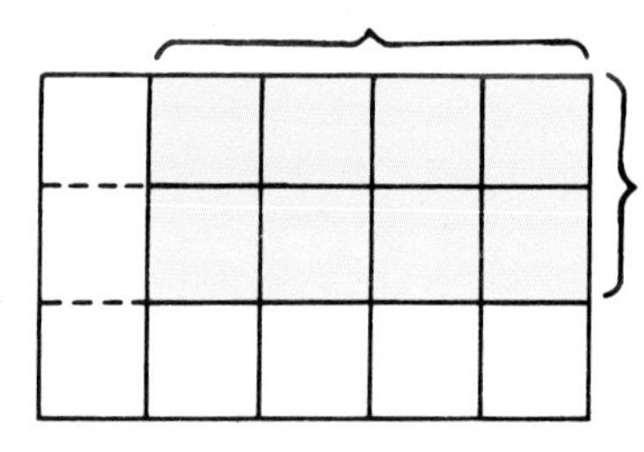

Keys to Understanding

To multiply fractions, multiply their numerators to obtain the numerator of the answer, and multiply their denominators to obtain the denominator of the answer.

$$\frac{a}{b} \cdot \frac{c}{d} = \frac{a \cdot c}{b \cdot d}$$

When you multiply, you are actually dividing the whole into more parts. This process is called multiplication because the operation used to obtain the answer is multiplication.

Practice

Multiply these fractions. Be sure to express your answers in lowest terms.

1. $\frac{3}{4} \cdot \frac{1}{2} =$

2. $\frac{3}{5} \cdot \frac{3}{4} =$

3. $\frac{1}{3} \cdot \frac{3}{8} =$

4. $\frac{5}{6} \cdot \frac{5}{6} =$

5. $\frac{5}{6} \cdot \frac{3}{4} =$

6. $\frac{7}{12} \cdot \frac{5}{8} =$

7. $\frac{5}{12} \cdot \frac{3}{12} =$

8. $\frac{7}{15} \cdot \frac{3}{10} =$

9. $\frac{6}{7} \cdot \frac{5}{12} =$

10. $\frac{3}{8} \cdot \frac{7}{15} =$

11. $\frac{9}{11} \cdot \frac{17}{20} =$

12. $\frac{11}{15} \cdot \frac{13}{15} =$

Write the multiplication equation that represents each set of figures.

Example:

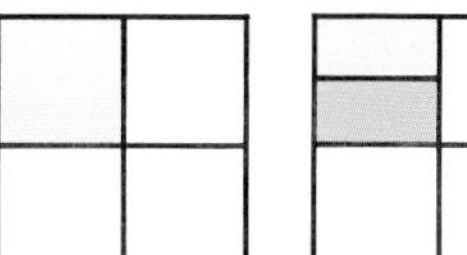

$\frac{1}{2}$ of $\frac{1}{4} = \frac{1}{2} \cdot \frac{1}{4} = \frac{1}{8}$

13.

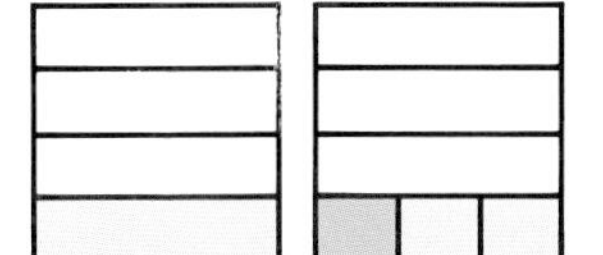

14.

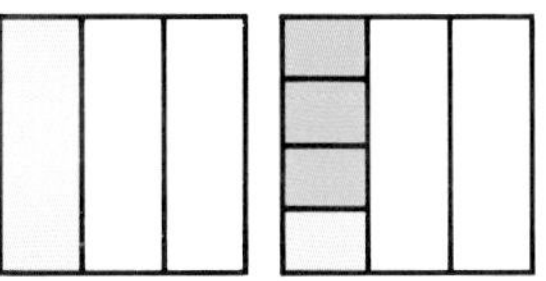

15.

Multiplying Mixed Numbers

The girls are having a slumber party. They have decided to make muffins for breakfast. The recipe calls for $1\frac{2}{3}$ cups of flour to make 1 dozen muffins. However, the girls want to make $2\frac{1}{2}$ dozen muffins. How much flour do they need?

Multiplying Mixed Numbers

$2\frac{1}{2} \cdot 1\frac{2}{3} = \frac{5}{2} \cdot \frac{5}{3}$	Rename the mixed numbers as improper fractions.
$= \frac{5 \cdot 5}{2 \cdot 3}$	Follow the procedure for multiplying fractions.
$= \frac{25}{6}$	
$= 4\frac{1}{6}$	Rename as a mixed number in lowest terms.

The girls need $4\frac{1}{6}$ cups of flour.

What do you think?

How would you multiply a whole number and a fraction?

Can you illustrate this problem?

$\frac{5}{6} \cdot 5 = ?$

Is there another way to find the answer?

Remember how to express a whole number in fractional form.

Practice

Solve these problems. Be sure to express your answers in lowest terms.

1. $\frac{1}{2}$ of 4 =
2. $\frac{1}{4}$ of $\frac{3}{5}$ =
3. $\frac{2}{3}$ of $1\frac{1}{4}$ =
4. $\frac{5}{8}$ of $\frac{2}{7}$ =
5. $\frac{3}{11}$ of 10 =
6. $\frac{1}{21}$ of $\frac{2}{3}$ =
7. $\frac{3}{7}$ of $2\frac{1}{2}$ =
8. $\frac{2}{9}$ of 8 =
9. $\frac{7}{8}$ of 112 =
10. $\frac{1}{6} \cdot \frac{1}{3} =$
11. $\frac{5}{9} \cdot \frac{1}{5} =$
12. $5 \cdot \frac{1}{2} =$
13. $3\frac{1}{3} \cdot 1\frac{1}{4} =$
14. $\frac{3}{8} \cdot \frac{7}{9} =$
15. $7\frac{1}{7} \cdot 10 =$
16. $\frac{3}{7} \cdot 4\frac{2}{3} =$
17. $\frac{10}{11} \cdot \frac{3}{5} =$
18. $7 \cdot \frac{5}{6} =$
19. $\frac{1}{3} \cdot \frac{3}{4} \cdot \frac{1}{3} =$
20. $1\frac{1}{8} \cdot \frac{1}{2} \cdot 1\frac{1}{4} =$
21. $5\frac{5}{6} \cdot 6\frac{1}{2} \cdot 2\frac{2}{3} =$

22. Roy ate $\frac{2}{3}$ of a half-gallon of ice cream. How much of a gallon of ice cream did he eat?
23. Terry is $\frac{5}{6}$ the age of Ron. Ron is 30 years old. How old is Terry?
24. One-tenth of the student body at Community Christian School sings in the school choir. One-eighth of the school choir also sings in the church choir. What fraction of the student body sings in the church choir?
25. A bus traveled for $4\frac{2}{3}$ hours at an average speed of 50 miles per hour. How far did the bus travel?

Canceling Fractions

There is a shortcut to use when multiplying fractions with common factors.

$$\frac{3}{5} \cdot \frac{5}{12} = \frac{3 \cdot 5}{5 \cdot 12} = \frac{3 \cdot 5}{12 \cdot 5} = \frac{3 \cdot 5}{3 \cdot 4 \cdot 5} = \frac{1 \cdot 1}{1 \cdot 4 \cdot 1} = \frac{1}{4}$$

shortcut $\frac{\overset{1}{\cancel{3}}}{\underset{1}{\cancel{5}}} \cdot \frac{\overset{1}{\cancel{5}}}{\underset{4}{\cancel{12}}} = \frac{1}{1} \cdot \frac{1}{4} = \frac{1}{4}$

In multiplication of fractions, the common factors of the numerator and denominator can be canceled out by dividing the numerator and the denominator by the same factor. This process does not change the problem.

$\frac{\overset{1}{\cancel{3}}}{\underset{2}{\cancel{14}}} \cdot \frac{\overset{1}{\cancel{7}}}{\underset{3}{\cancel{9}}} = \frac{1}{6}$ $\frac{\overset{2}{\cancel{4}}}{\underset{3}{\cancel{15}}} \cdot \frac{\overset{1}{\cancel{5}}}{\underset{3}{\cancel{6}}} = \frac{2}{9}$

Why is canceling possible?

When working with mixed numbers, first rename the mixed numbers as improper fractions.

$$1\frac{5}{9} \cdot 1\frac{1}{2} = \frac{\overset{7}{\cancel{14}}}{\underset{3}{\cancel{9}}} \cdot \frac{\overset{1}{\cancel{3}}}{\underset{1}{\cancel{2}}} = \frac{7}{3} = 2\frac{1}{3}$$

$$2\frac{2}{5} \cdot 8\frac{1}{3} = \frac{\overset{4}{\cancel{12}}}{\underset{1}{\cancel{5}}} \cdot \frac{\overset{5}{\cancel{25}}}{\underset{1}{\cancel{3}}} = \frac{20}{1} = 20$$

Practice

Multiply, using the shortcut whenever possible. Be sure to express your answers in lowest terms.

1. $\frac{3}{4} \cdot \frac{2}{3} =$

2. $\frac{5}{8} \cdot \frac{2}{15} =$

3. $\frac{7}{9} \cdot 1\frac{1}{8} =$

4. $\frac{3}{8} \cdot \frac{4}{21} =$

5. $\frac{6}{18} \cdot \frac{9}{12} =$

6. $\frac{5}{7} \cdot 2\frac{1}{10} =$

7. $\frac{3}{4} \cdot 12 =$

8. $\frac{4}{9} \cdot \frac{15}{10} =$

9. $\frac{14}{21} \cdot \frac{3}{7} =$

10. $1\frac{2}{3} \cdot 27 =$

11. $1\frac{11}{21} \cdot 7 =$

12. $\frac{2}{21} \cdot 10\frac{1}{2} =$

13. $\frac{3}{18} \cdot \frac{5}{9} \cdot \frac{3}{10} =$

14. $2\frac{1}{4} \cdot \frac{2}{3} \cdot \frac{1}{5} =$

15. $\frac{13}{38} \cdot \frac{19}{52} =$

Reciprocals

By what number would you multiply $\frac{2}{3}$ so that your product is 1?

$$\frac{2}{3} \cdot \frac{\square}{\square} = 1$$

$\frac{3}{2}$ is the reciprocal of $\frac{2}{3}$.

$$\frac{2}{3} \cdot \frac{3}{2} = \frac{6}{6} = 1$$

By what number would you multiply $\frac{5}{7}$ so that your product is 1?

$$\frac{5}{7} \cdot \frac{\square}{\square} = 1$$

$\frac{7}{5}$ is the reciprocal of $\frac{5}{7}$.

$$\frac{\overset{1}{\cancel{5}}}{\underset{1}{\cancel{7}}} \cdot \frac{\overset{1}{\cancel{7}}}{\underset{1}{\cancel{5}}} = 1$$

What do you think?

Can every fractional number be multiplied by another number (reciprocal) so that the product is 1?
Can every whole number be multiplied by another number (reciprocal) so that the product is 1?
Can every mixed number be multiplied by another number (reciprocal) so that the product is 1?

Keys to Understanding

Two numbers whose product is 1 are called *reciprocals* of each other.

$$\frac{a}{b} \cdot \frac{b}{a} = 1$$

$\frac{b}{a}$ is the reciprocal of $\frac{a}{b}$; $\frac{a}{b}$ is the reciprocal of $\frac{b}{a}$.

Does this illustration suggest an easy way to remember what the reciprocal of a number is? How would you state a rule for finding reciprocals?

Practice

Write the reciprocals of these numbers.

1. $\frac{3}{11}$
2. 7
3. $\frac{5}{3}$
4. $\frac{8}{15}$
5. $2\frac{1}{3}$
6. $\frac{1}{9}$
7. 1
8. $3\frac{2}{5}$
9. $\frac{11}{20}$
10. $6\frac{1}{2}$

Multiply. Be sure to express your answers in lowest terms.

11. $\frac{2}{3} \cdot \frac{3}{2} =$
12. $\left(\frac{2}{5} \cdot \frac{5}{2}\right) \cdot \frac{3}{7} =$
13. $1\frac{1}{2} \cdot \left(\frac{2}{3} \cdot \frac{3}{2}\right) =$
14. $\frac{2 \cdot 4 \cdot 3}{8 \cdot 2 \cdot 9} =$
15. $\left(\frac{15}{2} \cdot \frac{16}{3}\right) \cdot 3\frac{1}{2} =$

Remember, rename mixed numbers as improper fractions before proceeding.

Dividing Fractions

Jim has $\frac{3}{4}$ of a candy bar and wants to share it with his friends. How much of a candy bar will each of the four boys get if they divide it equally?

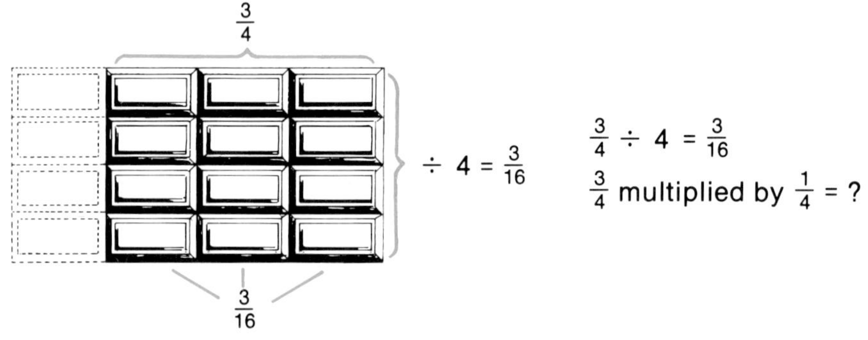

$\frac{3}{4} \div 4 = \frac{3}{16}$

$\frac{3}{4}$ multiplied by $\frac{1}{4}$ = ?

What relationship has $\frac{1}{4}$ to 4?

Steve has a board $\frac{3}{4}$ of a meter long. He wants to divide the board into pieces $\frac{3}{8}$ of a meter long. How many pieces will he have?

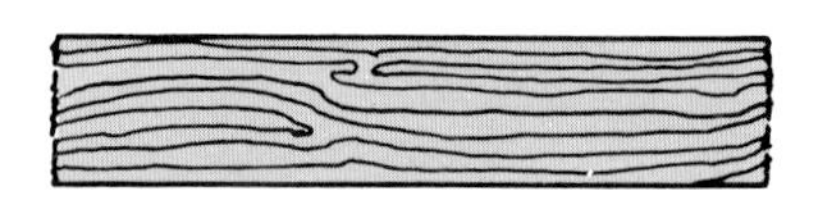

Steve can divide the board into two pieces $\frac{3}{8}$ of a meter long.

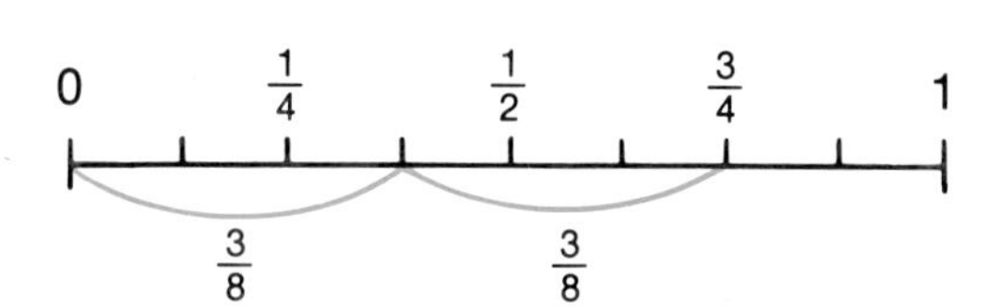

$\frac{3}{4} \div \frac{3}{8} = 2$

$\frac{3}{4}$ multiplied by $\frac{8}{3}$ = ?

What relationship has $\frac{8}{3}$ to $\frac{3}{8}$?

Keys to Understanding

Dividing by a fraction is the same as multiplying by its reciprocal.

$\frac{a}{b} \div \frac{c}{d} = \frac{a}{b} \cdot \frac{d}{c}$

In order to divide with fractions, multiply by the reciprocal of the divisor.

Dividing Mixed Numbers

$10\frac{4}{5} \div 2\frac{7}{10} = \frac{54}{5} \div \frac{27}{10}$ Rename the mixed numbers as improper fractions.

$= \frac{54}{5} \cdot \frac{10}{27}$ Multiply by the reciprocal of the divisor.

$= \frac{\overset{2}{\cancel{54}}}{\underset{1}{\cancel{5}}} \cdot \frac{\overset{2}{\cancel{10}}}{\underset{1}{\cancel{27}}} = 4$ Solve by using the shortcut.

Practice

Divide. Be sure to express your answers in lowest terms.

1. $\frac{3}{4} \div \frac{1}{3} =$
2. $\frac{1}{8} \div \frac{1}{8} =$
3. $2\frac{1}{2} \div \frac{2}{3} =$
4. $\frac{5}{8} \div 2\frac{1}{3} =$
5. $6 \div \frac{1}{4} =$
6. $\frac{4}{5} \div \frac{2}{3} =$
7. $3\frac{1}{2} \div \frac{3}{8} =$
8. $\frac{3}{4} \div 1\frac{1}{2} =$
9. $\frac{7}{8} \div 3 =$
10. $1\frac{1}{2} \div 1\frac{1}{8} =$
11. $3\frac{1}{2} \div \frac{3}{4} =$
12. $1\frac{3}{4} \div 1\frac{7}{8} =$
13. $2\frac{1}{2} \div 1\frac{1}{4} =$
14. $2\frac{5}{6} \div 1\frac{2}{5} =$
15. $40 \div 3\frac{1}{3} =$

Fractional Form Division

$$\frac{2}{3} \div \frac{1}{2} = \frac{\frac{2}{3}}{\frac{1}{2}}$$

Division of fractions can also be expressed in fractional form.

$$4\frac{1}{2} \div 1\frac{3}{8} = \frac{4\frac{1}{2}}{1\frac{3}{8}}$$

$$6 \div 3\frac{1}{5} = \frac{\frac{6}{1}}{3\frac{1}{5}}$$

By solving a fractional division problem that is expressed in fractional form, we can also show why dividing by a fraction is the same as multiplying by its reciprocal.

$$\frac{4}{5} \div \frac{3}{4} = \frac{\frac{4}{5}}{\frac{3}{4}}$$

$$\frac{\frac{4}{5} \cdot \frac{4}{3}}{\frac{3}{4} \cdot \frac{4}{3}}$$

Why did we pick the number $\frac{4}{3}$ to multiply by?

Remember, we can multiply numerator and denominator by the same number without changing the fraction.

The problem could also be written this way.

$$\frac{\frac{4}{5} \cdot \frac{4}{3}}{1} = \frac{\frac{16}{15}}{1} = \frac{16}{15} = 1\frac{1}{15}$$

Remember, any number divided by 1 equals that number.

Practice

Divide these fractions. Be sure to express your answers in lowest terms.

1. $\frac{4}{5} \div \frac{1}{3} =$
2. $\frac{3}{7} \div \frac{2}{5} =$
3. $\frac{7}{8} \div \frac{3}{4} =$
4. $\frac{3}{7} \div \frac{1}{11} =$
5. $\frac{7}{12} \div \frac{2}{5} =$
6. $\frac{3}{8} \div \frac{2}{7} =$
7. $5 \div \frac{3}{5} =$
8. $\frac{2}{9} \div 8 =$
9. $\frac{6}{7} \div \frac{5}{14} =$
10. $2\frac{2}{3} \div 1\frac{1}{2} =$
11. $7\frac{1}{3} \div 3\frac{1}{2} =$
12. $\frac{8}{9} \div 2 =$
13. $4\frac{2}{7} \div 1\frac{2}{3} =$
14. $3\frac{1}{4} \div \frac{5}{8} =$
15. $36 \div \frac{3}{4} =$
16. $9\frac{1}{3} \div 1\frac{3}{4} =$
17. $4\frac{2}{7} \div 2\frac{3}{4} =$
18. $6\frac{1}{12} \div 2\frac{1}{3} =$

Solve these problems.

19. Joan has $10\frac{1}{2}$ yards of ribbon. She needs to divide the ribbon into pieces $\frac{7}{8}$ of a yard long. How many pieces will she have?
20. Dennis jogged $4\frac{1}{8}$ miles in $\frac{3}{4}$ of an hour. What was his average speed in miles per hour?

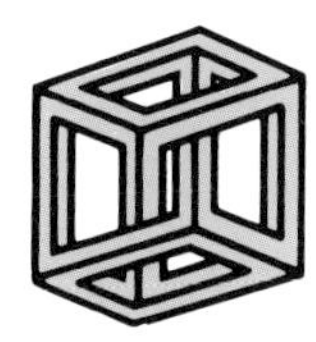

MIND BOGGLER

$$\frac{1}{a} + \frac{1}{b} + \frac{1}{c} = 1$$

a, *b*, and *c* are different whole numbers.
What are these numbers?

$a = ?$ $b = ?$ $c = ?$

Unit Review

Solve these problems. Be sure to express your answers in lowest terms.

1. $\frac{3}{4} + \frac{3}{10} =$
2. $\frac{4}{7} - \frac{2}{5} =$
3. $2\frac{1}{2} + 4\frac{1}{3} =$
4. $4\frac{4}{5} - 2\frac{1}{3} =$
5. $\frac{13}{4} + 2\frac{5}{6} =$
6. $5 - 2\frac{2}{11} =$
7. $7\frac{1}{3} - 2\frac{5}{7} =$
8. $3\frac{1}{4} + 2\frac{5}{6} + 8\frac{2}{3} =$
9. $\frac{2}{5} + 1\frac{5}{8} + 5\frac{1}{2} =$
10. $\frac{1}{5} \cdot \frac{3}{4} =$
11. $\frac{3}{4} \div \frac{1}{3} =$
12. $\frac{5}{6} \div \frac{2}{3} =$
13. $2\frac{3}{4} \cdot 1\frac{2}{3} =$
14. $2\frac{3}{8} \div 1\frac{5}{6} =$
15. $3\frac{3}{5} \cdot 4 =$
16. $1\frac{7}{8} \div 5 =$
17. $3\frac{5}{11} \cdot 2\frac{1}{8} =$
18. $11\frac{6}{7} \div 2\frac{1}{2} =$

Compare these fractions, using the appropriate sign ($<$, $>$, $=$).

19. $\frac{5}{9}$ and $\frac{3}{4}$
20. $\frac{3}{8}$ and $\frac{3}{9}$
21. $\frac{16}{20}$ and $\frac{4}{5}$
22. $\frac{6}{7}$ and $\frac{7}{8}$
23. $\frac{10}{11}$ and $\frac{20}{21}$
24. $\frac{12}{21}$ and $\frac{25}{43}$

Rename the following mixed numbers as improper fractions and the improper fractions as mixed numbers.

25. $\frac{7}{6}$
26. $1\frac{2}{3}$
27. $5\frac{6}{11}$
28. $2\frac{5}{9}$
29. $\frac{11}{4}$
30. $\frac{31}{23}$
31. $7\frac{3}{10}$
32. $\frac{19}{5}$
33. $\frac{86}{11}$

MIND BOGGLER

Time: 8:24
Determine what fraction of the total clock is shaded.

34. On Tuesday Mark spent $\frac{1}{3}$ of an hour practicing the piano and $\frac{1}{2}$ of an hour at a piano lesson. How much time did he spend altogether at the piano?

35. How many bags of peanuts can be filled from a box containing $\frac{3}{4}$ of a pound if each bag will contain $\frac{1}{8}$ of a pound?

36. The school track is $\frac{1}{4}$ of a mile around. If the runners in a race are to go $\frac{1}{2}$ of this distance, how far will they run?

37. Betty's mother had $\frac{7}{8}$ of a cup of melted butter when she began her cooking. She used $\frac{1}{3}$ of a cup in the frosting for a cake. How much remained?

38. One cubic foot of water weighs $62\frac{1}{2}$ pounds. How much will 12 cubic feet of water weigh?

39. A certain piece of equipment can produce a piece of work in $\frac{5}{6}$ of an hour. How many pieces of work can be completed by this machine in a 40-hour work week?

40. How much will 24 boxes of crackers weigh if each one weighs $\frac{3}{4}$ of a pound?

41. Jennifer had saved $36 to go shopping. She took $\frac{2}{3}$ of the money with her to the store and spent $\frac{3}{4}$ of the money she took. How much money did she spend?

42. Steven walks $\frac{7}{8}$ of a mile to go to school. After walking $\frac{2}{3}$ of the way one day, he met his friend Scott and walked the rest of the way with him. How far did they walk together?

Skills Checkup

1. $347 + 253{,}456 + 847 + 9{,}143$
2. $65{,}478 + 83{,}561 + 794{,}947$
3. $18{,}412 + 9{,}724 + 164{,}837$
4. $62{,}569 + 6{,}615{,}374 + 7{,}247{,}843$
5. $976{,}300 - 244{,}527$
6. $523{,}149 - 41{,}698$
7. $648{,}264 - 349{,}898$
8. $7{,}030{,}345 - 234{,}571$
9. $2{,}527 \times 824$
10. $429{,}258 \times 75$
11. $47{,}354 \times 604$
12. $4{,}567 \times 307$
13. $2{,}016 \div 59$
14. $8{,}525 \div 341$
15. $5{,}535 \div 41$
16. $237{,}273 \div 569$
17. $\frac{2}{7} + \frac{3}{7} + \frac{4}{7}$
18. $\frac{3}{4} + \frac{1}{4} + \frac{7}{4}$
19. $\frac{5}{6} + \frac{3}{8} + \frac{3}{4}$
20. $\frac{4}{5} + \frac{3}{25} + \frac{7}{10}$
21. $3\frac{1}{6} + \frac{5}{6}$
22. $6\frac{3}{8} + 4\frac{1}{6}$
23. $3\frac{4}{5} + 2\frac{1}{2}$
24. $3\frac{1}{4} + 2\frac{5}{6} + 1\frac{1}{3}$
25. $\frac{5}{8} - \frac{3}{8}$
26. $2\frac{3}{4} - 1\frac{2}{3}$
27. $7\frac{1}{2} - 3\frac{4}{5}$
28. $8\frac{5}{8} - 2\frac{3}{10}$
29. $\frac{2}{3} \times \frac{4}{5}$
30. $\frac{3}{4} \times \frac{3}{8}$
31. $1\frac{1}{2} \times \frac{8}{15}$
32. $2 \times \frac{3}{8}$
33. $1\frac{1}{2} \times 3$
34. $2\frac{3}{4} \times \frac{2}{3}$
35. $7\frac{3}{5} \times 10$
36. $1\frac{5}{6} \times 2\frac{3}{8}$
37. $\frac{3}{4} \div \frac{1}{3}$
38. $\frac{5}{6} \div 12$
39. $\frac{7}{8} \div 3$
40. $\frac{5}{6} \div 5$
41. $5\frac{1}{3} \div \frac{1}{3}$
42. $3\frac{3}{4} \div 1\frac{7}{8}$
43. $1\frac{1}{2} \div 1\frac{1}{8}$
44. $3\frac{1}{2} \div 2$
45. The Bunker family had $10,500 in a savings account. One week they made deposits of $335 and $57.75 and withdrew $2,070. How much money is now in the Bunkers' savings account?
46. Joe and Maria each have a part-time job. If Joe worked $3\frac{1}{2}$ hours on Friday and $6\frac{1}{4}$ hours on Saturday, and Maria worked $2\frac{1}{4}$ hours on Friday and $5\frac{1}{2}$ hours on Saturday, who worked more hours? how many more?
47. Katrina is going to sew costumes for the school play. It takes $3\frac{1}{2}$ yards of material to make one costume. The program director found 40 yards of material on sale. How many costumes will Katrina be able to make from this much material? How much material will be left?
48. There were 280 students at the pep rally. Three-fourths of them were eighth-graders. How many eighth-graders were at the pep rally?

1. 707,897 + 213,793 + 445,881,798 + 652,683 + 33,090 + 34,567

2. 37,487 + 503 + 77,604 + 49 + 500,786 + 23,009,017 + 17 + 432

3. 375,420 - 277,584

4. 857,234 - 555,745

5. 440,623 - 116,697

6. 803 × 113

7. 425 × 175

8. 1,632 × 23

9. 3,472 × 21

10. 23,451 ÷ 227

11. 25,637 ÷ 84

12. 32,437 ÷ 139

13. $\frac{5}{8} + \frac{1}{4}$

14. $\frac{7}{6} + \frac{2}{3}$

15. $\frac{3}{8} + \frac{11}{12}$

16. $\frac{1}{6} + \frac{2}{9} + \frac{5}{12}$

17. $\frac{2}{3} + \frac{3}{5} + \frac{7}{9}$

18. $2\frac{2}{3} + 1\frac{4}{9}$

19. $\frac{13}{14} - \frac{5}{6}$

20. $\frac{4}{5} - \frac{3}{10}$

21. $1\frac{7}{18} - \frac{23}{24}$

22. $1\frac{1}{4} - \frac{7}{12}$

23. $7\frac{5}{8} - 3\frac{5}{24}$

24. $\frac{1}{2} \times \frac{4}{5}$

25. $3\frac{1}{2} \times 4\frac{2}{3}$

26. $5\frac{1}{3} \times 3$

27. $\frac{1}{5} \times \frac{3}{4}$

28. $\frac{5}{12} \times \frac{3}{10}$

29. $7 \times \frac{2}{3}$

30. $\frac{3}{4} \times 8$

31. $1\frac{1}{2} \times \frac{5}{6}$

32. $\frac{3}{7} \div \frac{3}{8}$

33. $\frac{7}{9} \div \frac{14}{15}$

34. $\frac{24}{17} \div \frac{36}{51}$

35. $1\frac{5}{6} \div 2$

36. $1\frac{1}{3} \div 3\frac{1}{5}$

37. $4\frac{2}{5} \div 1\frac{1}{10}$

38. $5\frac{1}{4} \div 2\frac{1}{3}$

39. If Ward needs to use a $2\frac{1}{2}$ gallon can to fill a 20-gallon tank, how many times must he fill the can to fill the tank? how many times for a 50-gallon tank?

40. Staley's Bakery uses $9\frac{1}{2}$ ounces of flour to bake a loaf of bread. They bake an average of 2,500 loaves every day of the year. How many ounces of flour do they use in one day? how many pounds in one day?

41. The school cafeteria holds 300 people, and the gymnasium will seat 540. If both places are used for lunch, and $\frac{2}{3}$ of the cafeteria and $\frac{5}{6}$ of the gymnasium are filled, how many people are having lunch?

42. Mr. Franklin owns $\frac{1}{4}$ of the stock of Lane's Flower Company. His wife owns $\frac{5}{6}$ as much as he does. How much stock does Mrs. Franklin own? How much stock is owned by people besides the Franklins?

SNELLING OF GREENVILLE
232-5181

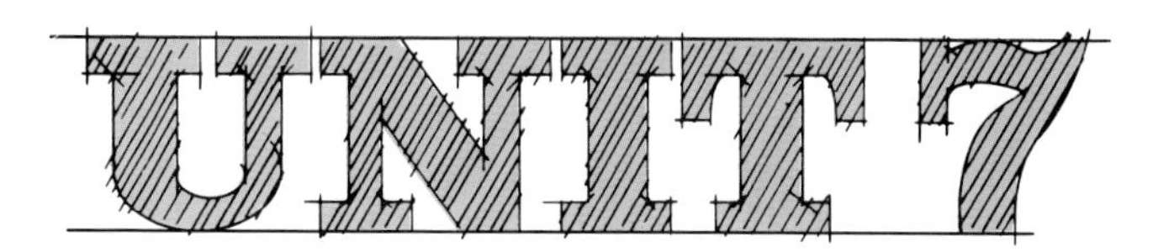

Secretary

"I'll get right on it, Mr. Keller." *Let's see—if he flies the Houston-Atlanta-Chicago route, leaving Houston at 9:05 A.M., he'll be in Chicago by 3:10 P.M. I hate to see him stuck with a three-hour layover in Atlanta, but the only other option is to take a night flight, which is a real killer the day before the convention starts. Of course it* will *save about $100 on flight costs and give him more flexibility in entertaining our clients in Chicago.*

"Mr. Keller's office, Miss Sawyer speaking. One moment, Mr. Barr, and I'll look that up for you. You said your system is the 4200TX model and you'd like to switch over to the 5200TX system? Including installation costs, that would run you about $7,200. As you know, it would increase your productivity and more than pay for itself within about six months. Anything else I can do for you? Okay. Just give us a call back when you decide. Thank you for calling."

Now to that chart Mr. Keller wanted typed. I have a total of 56 letters across my longest line, and I need 6 spaces between each of the 4 columns. That means I'll indent 14 spaces from the left. I should begin on line 12 of the page, since this chart takes up 42 lines. Okay, I guess I'm ready to go, once I count across and get my tabs set and headings centered. I'd better mark these down for reference later. Oh, the phone again.

"Mr. Keller's office, Miss Sawyer speaking. Sure, I'll send those time sheets up right away." *Oops, forgot to calculate the daily and weekly totals. They'll love me in payroll if I leave those off!*

Now back to the chart. I think this one would qualify to go on the computer so that I could just key in the variable information and send it through each time. That new terminal definitely makes life easier, as many letters and forms as I type each day.

Have you ever considered the variety of abilities it takes to be an efficient secretary? Depending on the field you enter, a secretarial position could involve anything from typing letters and answering the phone to arranging a flight itinerary for your boss and setting up his expense account for the trip.

A secretary's job is to carefully organize and keep track of the numerous details involved in her particular responsibilities. Carelessness in her work can be, at best, inconvenient and, more likely, unprofitable to her employer. God is concerned with details, but never carelessly. He tells us that even the hairs of our head are numbered. His loving direction of each tiny aspect of our lives gives us comfort and hope. "He knoweth the way that I take" (Job 23:10).

Decimal Fractions

Fractional Place-Value Chart							
Numbers less than one expressed in—	Exponential notation	$\frac{1}{10^1}$	$\frac{1}{10^2}$	$\frac{1}{10^3}$	$\frac{1}{10^4}$	$\frac{1}{10^5}$	$\frac{1}{10^6}$
	Fractions	$\frac{1}{10}$	$\frac{1}{100}$	$\frac{1}{1{,}000}$	$\frac{1}{10{,}000}$	$\frac{1}{100{,}000}$	$\frac{1}{1{,}000{,}000}$
	Decimal fractions	0.1	0.01	0.001	0.0001	0.00001	0.000001
	Place names	tenths	hundredths	thousandths	ten-thousandths	hundred-thousandths	millionths

We can use decimal fractions to express fractional numbers less than 1.

seven-tenths $= \frac{7}{10} = 0.7$

twenty-one hundredths $= \frac{21}{100} = 0.21$

We can also use decimal fractions to express mixed numbers.

four and one-tenth $= 4\frac{1}{10} = 4.1$

five and forty-seven hundredths $= 5\frac{47}{100} = 5.47$

two hundred and three-thousandths $= 200\frac{3}{1{,}000} = 200.003$

Can you write the above five numbers in expanded form, using exponents? Try it.

Equivalent decimal fractions

$$0.7 = \frac{7}{10} \cdot \frac{10}{10} = \frac{70}{100} = 0.70$$

$$0.7 = \frac{7}{10} \cdot \frac{100}{100} = \frac{700}{1,000} = 0.700$$

$$0.7 = \frac{7}{10} \cdot \frac{1,000}{1,000} = \frac{7,000}{10,000} = 0.7000$$

$$0.7 = 0.70 = 0.700 = 0.7000$$

Remember, we can multiply numerator and denominator by the same number.

Practice

Express these fractions and mixed numbers in decimal form.

1. $\frac{9}{10}$
2. $\frac{1}{100}$
3. $4\frac{71}{100}$
4. $\frac{57}{1,000}$
5. $3\frac{289}{1,000}$
6. $27\frac{27}{100}$
7. $562\frac{433}{10,000}$
8. $1,836\frac{51}{100}$
9. $\frac{11}{1,000,000}$
10. $516\frac{2,431}{100,000}$

Express these decimal fractions as common fractions or mixed numbers.

11. 0.13
12. 1.79
13. 0.003
14. 56.71
15. 100.01
16. 0.00033
17. 7.057
18. 0.1111
19. 1,320.23
20. 0.59741

Write these numbers as decimals.

21. Twenty-seven and seven-hundredths
22. Twenty-five ten-thousandths
23. Three hundred six and five hundred thirteen thousandths
24. Four hundred seventy-three hundred-thousandths
25. One million five hundred thousand and nine-tenths

Fractions to Decimals

Fractions can be changed to decimal form, and decimals can be changed to fractional form.

As you have seen, it is easy to write a decimal as a fraction.

$0.91 = \frac{91}{100} \qquad 0.3 = \frac{3}{10} \qquad 0.147 = \frac{147}{1{,}000}$

The denominator of a decimal fraction is always a power of 10.

Note: The denominator has the same number of zeros in it as the decimal has digits (including zeros) to the right of the decimal point.

Changing a fraction to a decimal is easy to do if the denominator of the fraction is a power of 10.

$\frac{37}{100} = 0.37 \qquad \frac{9}{10} = 0.9 \qquad \frac{863}{1{,}000} = 0.863$

Changing a fraction to a decimal is easy even if the denominator is not a power of 10. It involves one additional step. Just find an equivalent fraction with a denominator that is a power of 10 and then write it as a decimal.

$\frac{4}{5} = \frac{4}{5} \cdot \frac{2}{2} = \frac{8}{10} \qquad \frac{17}{20} = \frac{17}{20} \cdot \frac{5}{5} = \frac{85}{100} \qquad \frac{5}{8} = \frac{5}{8} \cdot \frac{125}{125} = \frac{625}{1{,}000}$

$\frac{8}{10} = 0.8 \qquad \frac{85}{100} = 0.85 \qquad \frac{625}{1{,}000} = 0.625$

NO, REALLY, OFFICER, YOU CAN ASK MY MATH TEACHER.
I'M REALLY NOT VERY GOOD WITH NUMBERS.

Division can be used to change a fraction to a decimal.

$\frac{5}{8}$ can represent a division problem: $8\overline{)5}$

$$\begin{array}{r} 0.625 \\ 8\overline{)5.000} \\ \underline{4\,8} \\ 20 \\ \underline{16} \\ 40 \\ \underline{40} \\ 0 \end{array}$$

Remember how to divide by annexing zeros after the decimal point.

$8\overline{)5} = \frac{5}{8} = 0.625$

Practice

Change these decimals to fractions. Be sure to express your answers in lowest terms.

1. 0.8 **3.** 4.35 **5.** 12.5 **7.** 1.25 **9.** 111.75

2. 0.55 **4.** 0.002 **6.** 0.375 **8.** 10.125 **10.** 0.0015

Change these fractions to decimals.

11. $\frac{3}{100}$ **13.** $\frac{2}{5}$ **15.** $91\frac{1}{4}$ **17.** $1\frac{3}{8}$ **19.** $\frac{21}{5}$

12. $\frac{7}{8}$ **14.** $5\frac{7}{20}$ **16.** $\frac{1,481}{10,000}$ **18.** $\frac{3}{4}$ **20.** $\frac{15}{2}$

21. Solve this problem:

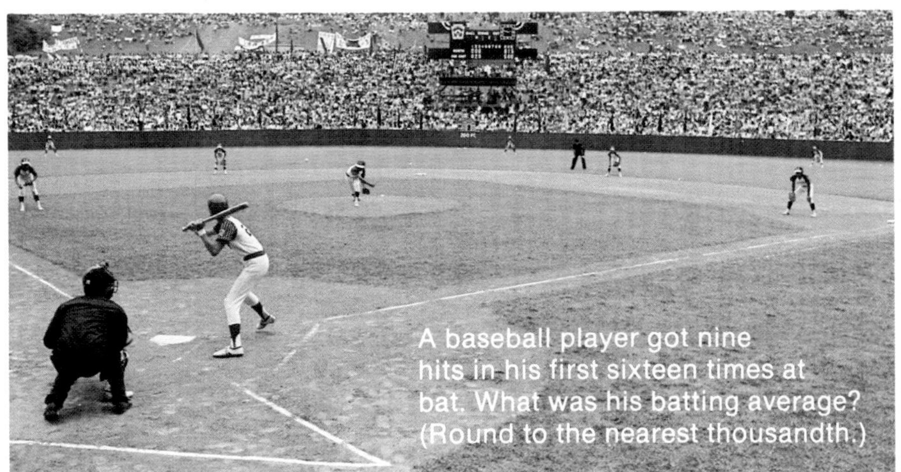

A baseball player got nine hits in his first sixteen times at bat. What was his batting average? (Round to the nearest thousandth.)

Terminating and Repeating Decimals

Mr. Fredericks is explaining to his class that since they now have a good understanding of fractions, they are going to learn how to change fractions to decimals.

$$\frac{2}{3} = 3\overline{)2.0000000}\quad = .6666666$$

```
      .6666666
2/3 = 3)2.0000000
        1 8
          20
          18
           20
           18
            20
            18
             20
             18
              20
              18
               20
               18
                20
```

$$\frac{6}{7} = 7\overline{)6.000000000}\quad = .857142857$$

```
      .857142857
6/7 = 7)6.000000000
        5 6
          40
          35
           50
           49
            10
             7
             30
             28
              20
              14
               60
               56
                40
                35
                 50
                 49
                  10
```

Division is used to change fractions to decimals. These decimals may be either *terminating decimals* or *repeating decimals*.

Note: In a repeating decimal a bar is drawn over the repeating digit or digits.
$\frac{2}{3} = 0.\overline{6}$
$\frac{6}{7} = 0.\overline{857142}$

Keys to Understanding

When using division to change a fraction to a decimal—

if the remainder is 0 after several steps, the division ends and the resulting decimal is called a *terminating decimal*;

if the remainder is never zero, the resulting decimal is called a *repeating decimal*.

Is $\frac{3}{8}$ a terminating decimal?

Yes, $\frac{3}{8}$ is a terminating decimal: 0.375.

$$
\begin{array}{r}
.375 \\
8\overline{)3.000} \\
\underline{2\,4} \\
60 \\
\underline{56} \\
40 \\
\underline{40} \\
0
\end{array}
\quad \text{remainder}
$$

Is $\frac{1}{6}$ a terminating decimal?

No, $\frac{1}{6}$ is a repeating decimal: $0.1\overline{6}$.

$$
\begin{array}{r}
.166 \\
6\overline{)1.000} \\
\underline{6} \\
40 \\
\underline{36} \\
40 \\
\underline{36} \\
40
\end{array}
\quad \text{remainder}
$$

Practice

Express each of the following fractions in decimal form. Then write *T* or *R* to indicate whether each is a terminating or repeating decimal.

1. $\frac{1}{4}$
2. $\frac{1}{11}$
3. $\frac{5}{6}$
4. $\frac{3}{10}$
5. $\frac{7}{50}$
6. $\frac{1}{2}$
7. $\frac{3}{7}$
8. $\frac{1}{8}$
9. $\frac{2}{13}$
10. $\frac{5}{8}$
11. $\frac{5}{9}$
12. $\frac{3}{11}$
13. $\frac{3}{5}$
14. $\frac{1}{3}$
15. $\frac{3}{4}$
16. $\frac{3}{8}$
17. $\frac{1}{30}$
18. $\frac{3}{25}$
19. $\frac{4}{7}$
20. $\frac{7}{40}$
21. $\frac{2}{7}$
22. $\frac{1}{9}$
23. $2\frac{1}{6}$
24. $\frac{4}{3}$
25. $\frac{5}{11}$

Math in Action

1. An elite typewriter will type 12 letters per inch across the page. If Miss Kizer has a piece of paper 8.5 inches wide, how many spaces across the page does she have available?
   If she wants to type a chart with 5 columns, each 8 spaces wide, and 6 spaces between each column, how many spaces will she use?
   How many spaces will that leave across the page?
   If she leaves an equal margin on each side of the chart, how many spaces will she indent to start the first column?
2. Miss Canaday's desk is 4.2 feet long and 2.7 feet wide. How many square feet of area does she have on which to work?
3. Miss Learn needs to purchase various office supplies at the following prices:

2 calendars	$3.00 ea.
4 boxes of pens	2.00 ea.
1 typewriter ribbon	2.25
2 bottles of correction fluid	1.00 ea.
4 stacking trays	3.00 ea.

   What is the total cost of the supplies?
4. Miss Ashburn has received several donation checks for the Christian college at which she works. She will deposit them into the school's account after she totals them. What is their total? (Any notation for amounts other than a donation should *not* go into the donation total amount.)

Donor	*Amount of donation*
Mt. Calvary Baptist Church	$250
Mr. and Mrs. Craig Potter	25
Mrs. Charles Drake ($70 for Elisa's Tuition)	150
Miss Laura Keeter	10
Miss Teresa Urey ($50 for loan payment)	60
Grace Baptist Church	120

5. A typewriter will type 6 lines per inch down the page. If Mrs. Syrja wants to center a chart that takes up 46 lines on a page 11 inches long, how many lines of margin will she leave at the top of the page before typing?

Adding and Subtracting Decimals

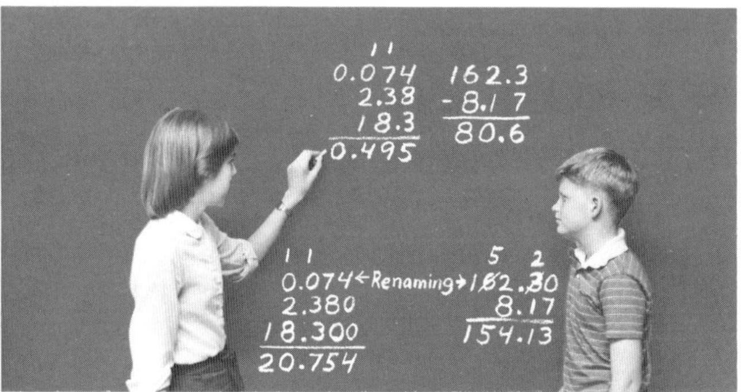

Each of these students worked an addition and a subtraction problem. One of them remembered a very important step and solved both problems correctly. The problems at the bottom are correct. Why? Notice the use of the zeros. Are they all necessary?

What do you think?

What does the decimal point do in decimal numbers?

Why is it important that the decimal points be lined up in addition and subtraction?

When zeros are added to the right of the last decimal digit, how is the decimal changed?

Decimal problems can be worked using fractional form.

	Addition		Subtraction
	$\frac{74}{1,000} + 2\frac{38}{100} + 18\frac{3}{10} =$		$162\frac{3}{10} - 8\frac{17}{100} =$
Express with LCD.	$\frac{74}{1,000} + 2\frac{380}{1,000} + 18\frac{300}{1,000} =$	Express with LCD.	$162\frac{30}{100} - 8\frac{17}{100} =$
Add and express as a decimal.	$20\frac{754}{1,000} = 20.754$	Subtract and express as a decimal.	$154\frac{13}{100} = 154.13$

Which is easier, decimal or fractional form?

Practice

Solve these addition and subtraction problems.

1. $\begin{array}{r} 0.24 \\ +\ \underline{0.32} \end{array}$ **2.** $\begin{array}{r} 0.47 \\ -\ \underline{0.35} \end{array}$ **3.** $\begin{array}{r} 2.76 \\ +\ \underline{3.85} \end{array}$

4. 7.63 - 4.6 =

5. 7.2 - 0.49 =

6. 3.2 - 2.33 =

7. 6.34 + 2.7 =

8. 7 + 2.357 =

9. 4 - 0.487 =

10. 3.982 + 4.7 =

11. 6.739 + 17.96 =

12. 70.25 - 37.89 =

13. 1.4 - 0.127 =

14. 8.054 + 3.72 =

15. 4.007 - 3.982 =

16. 65.6 + 2.385 + 0.12 + 3.1 + 7 =

17. 28.235 + 7.2 + 3.22 + 3.692 + 76.93 + 11.297 =

18. Dave is running in a 3-mile cross-country race. He has run 1.3 miles already. How much farther does he have to go?

19. Jamie has a fever 3.25 degrees above normal. What is her temperature? (Normal is 98.6 degrees.)

20. John bought a new football for $17.95. He gave the clerk a $20 bill. How much change should he get back?

Multiplying Decimals

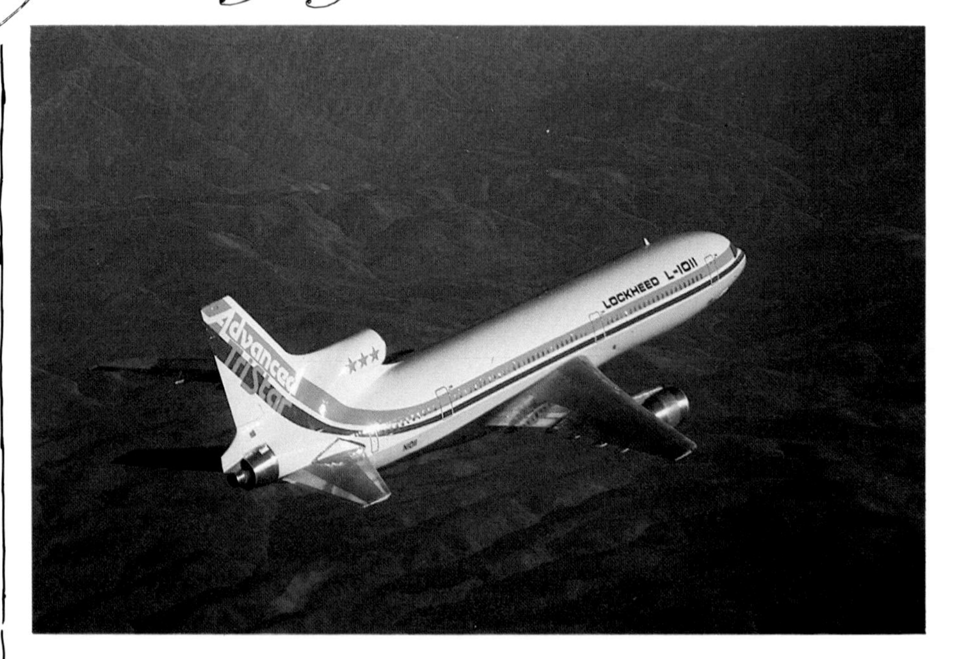

A nonstop airline flight from Chicago to Los Angeles took 3.6 hours. If the jet flew at an average speed of 485.7 miles per hour, how many miles did it travel?

Do you recognize this as a multiplication problem? This problem requires you to multiply decimal fractions.

$485.7 \cdot 3.6 = ?$

We know how to multiply two fractions.

$$485.7 \cdot 3.6 = 485\tfrac{7}{10} \cdot 3\tfrac{6}{10}$$

$$= \frac{4{,}857}{10} \cdot \frac{36}{10}$$

$$= \frac{174{,}852}{100}$$

$$= 1{,}748\,\frac{52}{100} = 1{,}748.52$$

We can also multiply the numbers as if they were whole numbers.

$$\begin{array}{r} 485.7 \\ \times\ 3.6 \\ \hline 29142 \\ 14571 \\ \hline 174852 \end{array}$$

Where should the decimal point be placed? How did you know?

When multiplying with decimals, multiply the numbers as if they were whole numbers and then place the decimal point.

```
   485.7 ←┐
 ×   3.6 ←┘ 2
  ------
   29142
  14571
  --------
1,748.52 ← 2
```

Count the total number of digits to the right of the decimal point in both factors.

The total number of digits found to the right of the decimal point in the factors (two) will be the same number of digits to the right of the decimal point in the answer (two).

Examples:

```
   28          2.8 ←┐        0.28 ←┐
 x 0.4 ← 1   x 0.4 ←┘ 2    x  0.4 ←┘ 3
 -----       -----         ------
  11.2 ← 1    1.12 ← 2     0.112 ← 3
```

```
  0.28 ←┐
x 0.04 ←┘ 4
------
0.0112 ← 4
↑
Why was this zero
placed here?
```

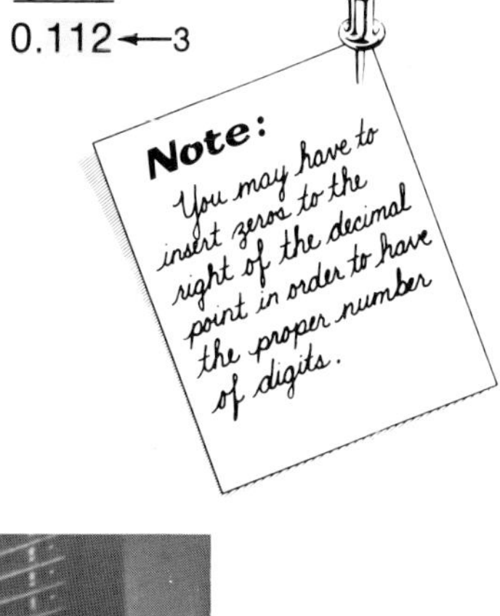

Practice

Solve these problems.

1. $\begin{array}{r} 1.7 \\ \times\ 0.3 \\ \hline \end{array}$

2. $\begin{array}{r} 98.6 \\ \times\ 0.13 \\ \hline \end{array}$

3. $\begin{array}{r} 9.86 \\ \times\ 0.02 \\ \hline \end{array}$

4. $\begin{array}{r} 3.76 \\ \times\ 4.2 \\ \hline \end{array}$

5. $\begin{array}{r} 41.3 \\ \times\ 6 \\ \hline \end{array}$

6. $\begin{array}{r} 3.5 \\ \times\ 2.8 \\ \hline \end{array}$

7. $\begin{array}{r} 0.22 \\ \times\ 0.11 \\ \hline \end{array}$

8. $\begin{array}{r} 0.0018 \\ \times\ 0.007 \\ \hline \end{array}$

9. $4.7 \cdot 0.3 =$

10. $0.33 \cdot 0.4 =$

11. $12.3 \cdot 0.12 =$

12. $0.19 \cdot 1.5 =$

13. $0.01 \cdot 0.02 =$

14. $.75 \cdot 2.1 =$

15. If a pound of hamburger costs $1.79, how much would 2.4 pounds cost?

16. The church bought 5.6 acres of land for their new school building. What was their total cost if they paid $5,000 per acre?

17. If one pound of peanuts costs $2.19, how much would $\frac{3}{4}$ of a pound cost?

18. There are 2.54 centimeters in an inch. How many centimeters are there in 6.3 inches?

19. Mark is 0.98 meters tall. Mark's dad is twice as tall as he is. How tall is Mark's dad?

20. Mr. Jones used 12.4 gallons of gas on a trip to the mountains. If he got 18.6 miles to the gallon of gas, how far did he travel?

A good way to check the placement of the decimal point is to estimate the answer by rounding the factors.

$$\begin{array}{r} 28.6 \doteq 30 \\ \times\ \underline{2.3 \doteq \times\ 2} \\ 65.78 \doteq 60 \end{array}$$

Would 657.8 have been a sensible answer? Why or why not?

Remember, $\doteq$ means "approximately equal to."

Practice

Estimate to tell whether the answers to the following problems make sense. If the decimal point is in the wrong place, correct it.

1. $27.2 \cdot 4 = 1{,}088$
2. $13.71 \cdot 1.2 = 164.52$
3. $3.05 \cdot 0.2 = 0.61$
4. $94.1 \cdot 3.6 = 33.876$
5. $2.45 \cdot 0.68 = 1.666$
6. $13.3 \cdot 0.96 = 127.68$
7. $512.5 \cdot 3.8 = 1{,}947.5$

Write an estimated answer to each problem. Then solve and give the exact answer.

8. $33.8 \cdot 12 =$
9. $19.84 \cdot 1.7 =$
10. $71.3 \cdot 2.01 =$
11. $0.02 \cdot 0.05 =$
12. $5.91 \cdot 2.2 =$
13. $1{,}002.8 \cdot 2.1 =$
14. $0.31 \cdot 0.29 =$
15. $21.64 \cdot 0.9 =$

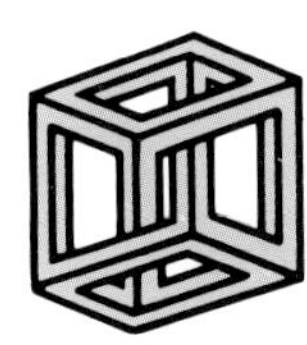

MIND BOGGLER

• • •

• • •

• • •

Connect these nine dots with four straight lines without allowing your pencil to leave the paper.

Dividing Decimals

Mrs. Saliba is buying 2.78 pounds of hamburger. She wants the meat cutter to divide the meat into two packages of equal weight. How will the meat cutter determine the amount of hamburger to put into each package? How much meat will each of the packages contain?

He could use fractions.

$$2.78 \div 2 = 2\frac{78}{100} \div 2$$
$$= \frac{278}{100} \div 2$$
$$= \frac{278}{100} \cdot \frac{1}{2}$$
$$= \frac{139}{100}$$
$$= 1\frac{39}{100} = 1.39$$

He could use decimals.

$$2\overline{)2.78}\quad 1.39$$

When dividing a decimal by a whole number, divide as if both numbers were whole numbers and then place the decimal point in the quotient directly above the decimal point in the dividend. Be sure to keep the numbers lined up.

Which way is faster?

How would you divide $3.68 equally among four people? Would you have to make change?

Remember, money is expressed using decimals.

What do you think?

What will you have to do to divide these numbers?

$4\overline{)0.2}$ $8\overline{)3}$ $4\overline{)2.39}$

Find the answers.

Practice

Solve these problems. Be sure to keep the decimal points and the numbers lined up.

1. $2\overline{)64.2}$
2. $34\overline{)10.2}$
3. $32\overline{)16}$
4. $9\overline{)47.7}$
5. $15\overline{)62.25}$
6. $63\overline{)5.04}$
7. $4\overline{)2.96}$
8. $16\overline{)2.4}$
9. $12\overline{)6.5}$
10. $6\overline{)48.72}$
11. $42\overline{)3,612}$
12. $16\overline{)8.9}$
13. $12\overline{)2.4}$
14. $14\overline{)1.1564}$
15. $116\overline{)4.002}$
16. The total rainfall in Greenville for September was 6.51 inches. What was the average rainfall per day?
17. Ken ran a total of 12.4 miles in a five-day period. He runs the same distance each morning. How far does he run each day?
18. If four boys are going to share the cost of a pizza that costs $9, how much will each boy have to pay?
19. Susan wants to divide 5.3 liters of punch equally among her eight friends. How much should each person get?
20. Change the fraction $\frac{2}{3}$ to a decimal. What do you notice?

Multiplying and Dividing by Powers of 10

2.581 ×	10	100	1,000	10,000	100,000	1,000,000
=	25.81	258.1	2,581	25,810	258,100	2,581,000

Notice what happens when we multiply a decimal number by a power of 10. Can you explain this?

What do you think?

How many places to the right would you move the decimal point—

- **a.** when multiplying by 10 (10^1)?
- **b.** when multiplying by 100 (10^2)?
- **c.** when multiplying by 1,000 (10^3)?
- **d.** when multiplying by 100,000 (10^5)?
- **e.** when multiplying by 10,000,000 (10^7)?

Can you state a rule for multiplying by powers of 10?

258.1 ÷	10	100	1,000	10,000	100,000	1,000,000
=	25.81	2.581	0.2581	0.02581	0.002581	0.0002581

Notice what happens when we divide a decimal number by a power of 10. Can you explain this?

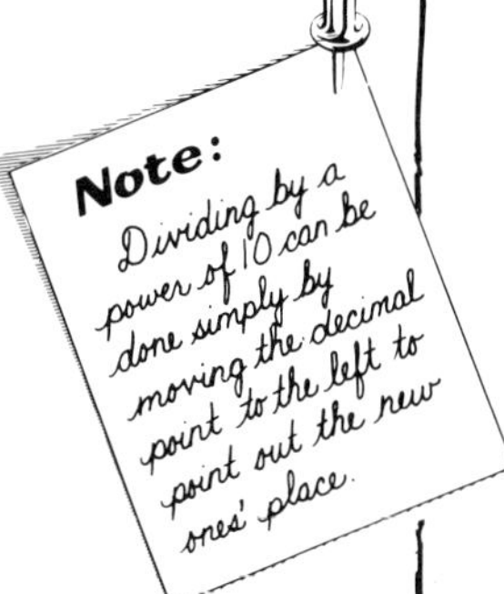

What do you think?

How many places to the left would you move the decimal point—

- **a.** when dividing by 10 (10^1)?
- **b.** when dividing by 100 (10^2)?
- **c.** when dividing by 1,000 (10^3)?
- **d.** when dividing by 100,000 (10^5)?
- **e.** when dividing by 10,000,000 (10^7)?

Can you state a rule for dividing by powers of 10?

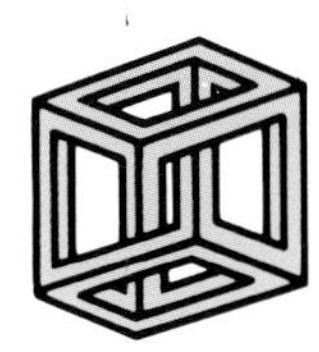

MIND BOGGLER

Notice that these sixteen matches form five squares. Move only two matches to new positions so that the sixteen matches form only four squares.

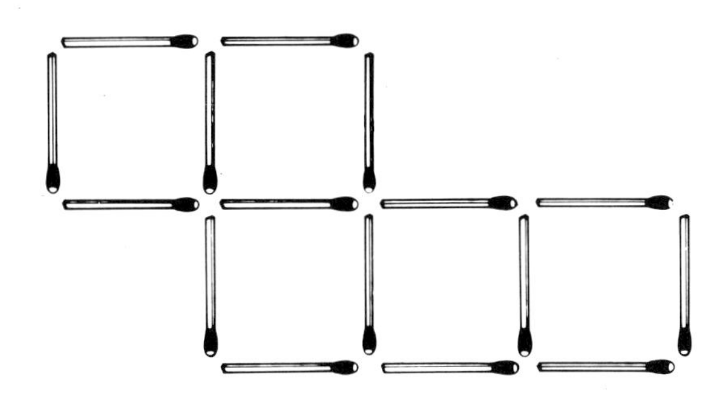

A Shortcut

To save time, use the quick and easy method to multiply and divide decimals by powers of 10.

Multiplying by powers of 10

To multiply a decimal number by a power of 10, move the decimal point to the *right* the same number of places as there are factors of 10 in the multiplier.

$2.182 \cdot 100 = ?$
Move the decimal point
two places to the right.
$2.18.2 \cdot 100 = 218.2$

Remember
the way to determine quickly
the number of factors of
10 in a number.
$100{,}000 = 10^5$ five factors

Dividing by powers of 10

To divide a decimal number by a power of 10, move the decimal point to the *left* the same number of places as there are factors of 10 in the divisor.

$635 \div 1{,}000 = ?$
Move the decimal point
three places to the left.
$635 \div 1{,}000 = 0.635$

Note:
$1000 = 10 \cdot 10 \cdot 10 = 10^3$
three factors of 10

What does the decimal point do?

When we move the decimal point, what are we actually doing to the place value of a number?

Practice

Multiply, using the quick method.

1. $0.38 \cdot 10 =$
2. $21.6 \cdot 100 =$
3. $0.0032 \cdot 1{,}000 =$
4. $3.68 \cdot 100 =$
5. $0.0009 \cdot 10^3 =$
6. $1.0038 \cdot 10^2 =$
7. $0.0591 \cdot 10^4 =$
8. $81.36 \cdot 10^1 =$
9. $16 \cdot 100 =$
10. $0.0000567 \cdot 1{,}000{,}000 =$
11. $8.94 \cdot 10 =$
12. $0.34 \cdot 100 =$
13. $6.182 \cdot 1{,}000 =$
14. $3.4 \cdot 10^3 =$
15. $1.005 \cdot 10{,}000 =$
16. $3.876 \cdot 10^1 =$
17. $0.006 \cdot 100 =$
18. $0.482 \cdot 100{,}000 =$
19. $81.6 \cdot 10^2 =$
20. $0.73 \cdot 10^4 =$

Divide, using the quick method.

21. $0.83 \div 10 =$
22. $2.1 \div 100 =$
23. $18 \div 1{,}000 =$
24. $73.3 \div 100 =$
25. $638 \div 10^4 =$
26. $12{,}362 \div 10^3 =$
27. $0.02 \div 10^3 =$
28. $3{,}561 \div 10^4 =$
29. $25.6 \div 10 =$
30. $939{,}000 \div 1{,}000{,}000 =$
31. $91 \div 10 =$
32. $12.6 \div 100 =$
33. $1{,}680 \div 1{,}000 =$
34. $18.6 \div 10^3 =$
35. $61.1 \div 10^2 =$
36. $985 \div 10^1 =$
37. $8{,}631 \div 10{,}000 =$
38. $0.1 \div 100 =$
39. $672 \div 100 =$
40. $437.1 \div 10^5 =$

NOW, DEL, CHANGE IT TO A DECIMAL.

Dividing by a Decimal

The Watson family took a 142.8-mile trip to the state park. Their car used 8.5 gallons of gas. What gas mileage did the car get on the trip?

Of course, this is a division problem.

$$142.8 \div 8.5 = ?$$

If we could make the divisor a whole number, then we could work the problem as a regular division problem.

$142.8 \div 8.5 = ?$

Express the problem in fractional form. $\frac{142.8}{8.5}$

Multiply the numerator and denominator by 10. $\frac{142.8 \cdot 10}{8.5 \cdot 10} = \frac{1,428}{85}$

Do the division.

```
       16.8
85)1,428.0   zero
    85       annexed
    578
    510
     68 0
     68 0
        0
```

Remember what happens to the decimal point when multiplying by 10.

This multiplication can be done in the original problem.

```
        1 6.8
8.5.)142.8.0  zero annexed
 ×10      ×10

        60.
0.13.)7.80.  zero annexed
 ×100  ×100
```

Keys to Understanding

Follow these steps to divide a decimal number by another decimal number:

1. Multiply the divisor by a power of 10 to make a whole number.

   $0.088\overline{)8.14088}$
   $\times$ 1,000

2. Multiply the dividend by the same power of 10 as you did to make the divisor a whole number.

   $88.\overline{)8.140.88}$
   $\times$ 1,000

3. Divide the decimal by the whole number.

   $$\begin{array}{r} 92.51 \\ 88\overline{)8{,}140.88} \end{array}$$

What do you think?

Why does the method shown above work?

Place the decimal point in the answers to the following equations to make them true.

1. $9.04 \div 0.2 = 452$
2. $0.84 \div 0.08 = 105$
3. $11.564 \div 1.4 = 826$
4. $6.0408 \div 7.2 = 839$
5. $28.71 \div 0.29 = 990$
6. $5.568 \div 8.7 = 64$

Practice

Solve these problems.

1. $0.8\overline{)756.8}$
2. $6.3\overline{)61.11}$
3. $8.3\overline{)603.41}$
4. $0.3\overline{)6.03}$
5. $9.2\overline{)8.464}$
6. $0.49\overline{)46.55}$
7. $0.09\overline{)9.27}$
8. $1.9\overline{)50.35}$
9. $2.08\overline{)169.52}$

Find the quotient to the place indicated.

Remember how to round numbers.

10. $2 \div 3$ to the nearest hundredth
11. $5 \div 11$ to the nearest ten-thousandth
12. $6.751 \div 4.3$ to the nearest tenth
13. $15.99 \div 0.41$ to the nearest ten
14. $2.473 \div 0.5$ to the nearest thousandth
15. $16.315 \div 0.023$ to the nearest tenth
16. $0.087 \div 0.0031$ to the nearest hundredth

Solve these problems.

17. Bill receives 15¢ for each paper he delivers. He collected a total of \$22.65. How many papers did he deliver?
18. A plane travels 843.6 miles in 2.4 hours. How fast is the plane traveling?
19. Jan has 0.875 yard of material. How many pieces, each measuring 0.4 yard long, can she cut from this material?
20. The area of a certain rectangle in a scale drawing is 0.625 square inches. The width of the rectangle is $\frac{1}{4}$ of an inch. What is the length?

area 0.625 in.^{2} $\frac{1}{4}$ in.

Unit Review

Express these fractions in decimal form.

1. $\frac{3}{10}$
2. $\frac{17}{1,000}$
3. $2\frac{1}{4}$
4. $\frac{19}{20}$
5. $17\frac{2}{5}$
6. $\frac{23}{2}$
7. $\frac{261}{10,000}$
8. $161\frac{1}{50}$
9. $23\frac{3}{8}$
10. $134\frac{4}{25}$

Solve these problems.

11. 2.83 + 63.1 =

12. 57.15 - 9.6 =

13. 0.15 + 0.024 =

14. 1.57 - 0.99 =

15. 16.1 + 3.76 =

16. 8 - 0.731 =

17. 17.45 + 6.8 + 0.32 + 121.514 + 1.015 =

18. $\begin{array}{r} 2.15 \\ \times\ .32 \\ \hline \end{array}$

19. $\begin{array}{r} \$3.18 \\ \times\ 7 \\ \hline \end{array}$

20. $\begin{array}{r} 0.015 \\ \times\ 1.2 \\ \hline \end{array}$

21. $\begin{array}{r} 18.73 \\ \times\ 2.2 \\ \hline \end{array}$

22. $0.34\overline{)10.2}$

23. $4.2\overline{)361.2}$

24. $4.3\overline{)6.751}$

25. $0.116\overline{)40.02}$

26. 3.1 · 4.6 =

27. 0.04 · 2.37 =

28. 3.68 ÷ 4.6 =

29. 0.377 ÷ 0.13 =

30. 8.614 · 1,000 =

31. 3.612 ÷ 0.42 =

32. 81.6 · 4.3 =

33. 0.58 ÷ 100 =

34. 0.006 · 8.2 =

35. 11.564 ÷ 0.14 =

Do these operations mentally. Write only the answers.

36. $8.315 \cdot 1{,}000 =$

37. $123.4 \div 100 =$

38. $0.0156 \cdot 10^4 =$

39. $258 \div 10^5 =$

40. $0.0001568 \cdot 10^8 =$

Solve these problems.

41. The weather bureau of Hartland reported that for the first six months of the year, rainfalls had totaled 39.61 inches. The rainfall measurements for July were 1.8 in., 0.13 in., 2 in., 0.4 in., and 1.05 in. What was the total rainfall for the first seven months of the year?

42. If Sue charges $1.25 an hour to babysit, how many hours will it take her to earn $15?

43. A plane averaged 382.5 miles per hour. How far did it travel in 3.25 hours?

44. Mr. Stevens needs to grind a piece of metal to reduce its thickness from 2.1 cm to 1.955 cm. How much metal must be ground off?

45. A store owner was able to buy 5.5 dozen boys' shirts to be sold during the big holiday sale. He paid a total of $235.75. About how much was this per dozen? (Round to the nearest cent.)

MIND BOGGLER

Miles per second	
186,282.38	186,282.40
186,282.51	186,282.45
186,282.48	186,282.42
186,282.54	186,282.56
186,282.41	186,282.47

A scientist measured the speed of light ten different times and got the numbers shown here. He expressed the numbers with this formula:

$$(1.8628246 \pm n) \cdot 10^5 \text{ mi./sec.}$$

What number do you think he used for n?

Skills Checkup

1. 32,416,891 + 1,234,697 + 29,346,888 + 3,147,682 + 17,346,054
2. 86 + 8,175 + 10,250 + 5,007,995 + 258,797 + 35,789 + 4,532
3. 300,000 - 789
4. 7,000,000 - 43,978
5. 436,784 - 219,025
6. 31,740 × 47
7. 1,537 × 225
8. 346 × 307
9. 586 × 673
10. 5,382 ÷ 263
11. 35,174 ÷ 86
12. 19,649 ÷ 46
13. 14,353 ÷ 23
14. $4\frac{3}{8} + 6\frac{2}{5}$
15. $14\frac{4}{6} + 7\frac{2}{3}$
16. $8\frac{1}{3} + 9\frac{1}{4}$
17. $6\frac{3}{5} - 2\frac{1}{2}$
18. $4\frac{5}{6} - 1\frac{3}{8}$
19. $7\frac{1}{2} - 3\frac{2}{5}$
20. $2\frac{2}{3} \times 5\frac{3}{4}$
21. $\frac{3}{4} \times 2\frac{1}{2}$
22. $3\frac{2}{5} \times 2\frac{1}{2}$
23. $\frac{3}{4} \div 1\frac{1}{2}$
24. $2\frac{1}{3} \div 5\frac{3}{4}$
25. $\frac{3}{4} \div 2$
26. 157.1 + 32.138 + 75.061 + 3.211
27. 0.987 + 0.21957 + 32.45876 + 43.3
28. 54.21 - 47.3437
29. 5.218 - 1.0265
30. 12.3 - 0.849
31. 10.3 × 37.4
32. 18.25 × 9.7
33. 100.61 × 82.05
34. 2.149 ÷ 7
35. 74.4 ÷ 31
36. 0.096 ÷ 0.024
37. Pamela is saving money to buy a Christmas gift for her mother. She can put $1.65 into her savings account each week from the money she earns baby-sitting. How many weeks will it take her to save enough to buy a $50 gift?
38. A certain computer can read 985 cards in one minute. How many cards can it read in one hour? in one 8-hour workday?
39. The Boy Scouts are going on a hike. If they go 5 miles every hour, how far will they walk if they begin at 7:45 A.M., stop for lunch from 11:30 to 12:15, and then end their hike at 3:45?

1. 3,421 + 1,817,210 + 17,147 + 217,967 + 12,071 + 1,082 + 43,548
2. 23,251 + 4,195 + 709 + 41,215 + 7,189 + 116 + 71,115 + 233,459

3. 7,000,000 - 43,977
4. 9,678,092 - 8,652
5. 78,987 - 59,639
6. 2,317 × 234
7. 31,215 × 241
8. 12,714 × 117
9. 5,130 ÷ 15
10. 8,478 ÷ 314
11. 352,512 ÷ 816

12. $1\frac{1}{2} + 2\frac{1}{3} + 3\frac{1}{4}$
13. $3\frac{1}{6} + 4\frac{1}{3} + 5\frac{1}{5}$
14. $7\frac{5}{6} + \frac{7}{8}$
15. $7\frac{4}{9} - 1\frac{2}{9}$
16. $7\frac{5}{8} - 6\frac{5}{6}$
17. $4\frac{5}{8} - 3\frac{2}{3}$
18. $2 \times \frac{5}{12}$
19. $\frac{1}{3} \times 1\frac{1}{2}$
20. $4 \times 3\frac{1}{2}$
21. $5\frac{1}{2} \div \frac{3}{5}$
22. $1\frac{1}{2} \div 1\frac{3}{4}$
23. $3\frac{1}{6} \div \frac{3}{8}$

24. 12.319 + 3.21 + 6.4175 + 0.9 + 0.191 + 25.0198 + 3.00194 + 52.6
25. 313.21 + 1,269.174 + 501.01825 + 0.0112 + 82.763 + 591.276 + 32.1487

26. 34.27 - 2.1368
27. 158.3 - 23.719
28. 5 - 1.7872
29. 101.2 × 1.348
30. 2.413 × 998.76
31. 0.612 × 100.581
32. 5.75 ÷ 0.23
33. 4.536 ÷ 0.56

34. Mr. Schwartz works as a salesman. He received a raise of $2,300 a year. He is now making $24,500 a year. What was he making per year before his raise? With his new salary, how much will he make each month?
35. If there are 21 kilograms of oxygen in every 100 kilograms of air, then how much is there in 1,300 kilograms of air?
36. Of 100 blue-collar workers, 12.5 are unemployed. How many would be unemployed in a group of 15,400 blue-collar workers?
37. Five years ago there were 656,389 people living in Sandstone. Today 497,856 people live there. Has the population increased or decreased? How much? At the present, there is an average of four people per house in Sandstone. How many houses are there?

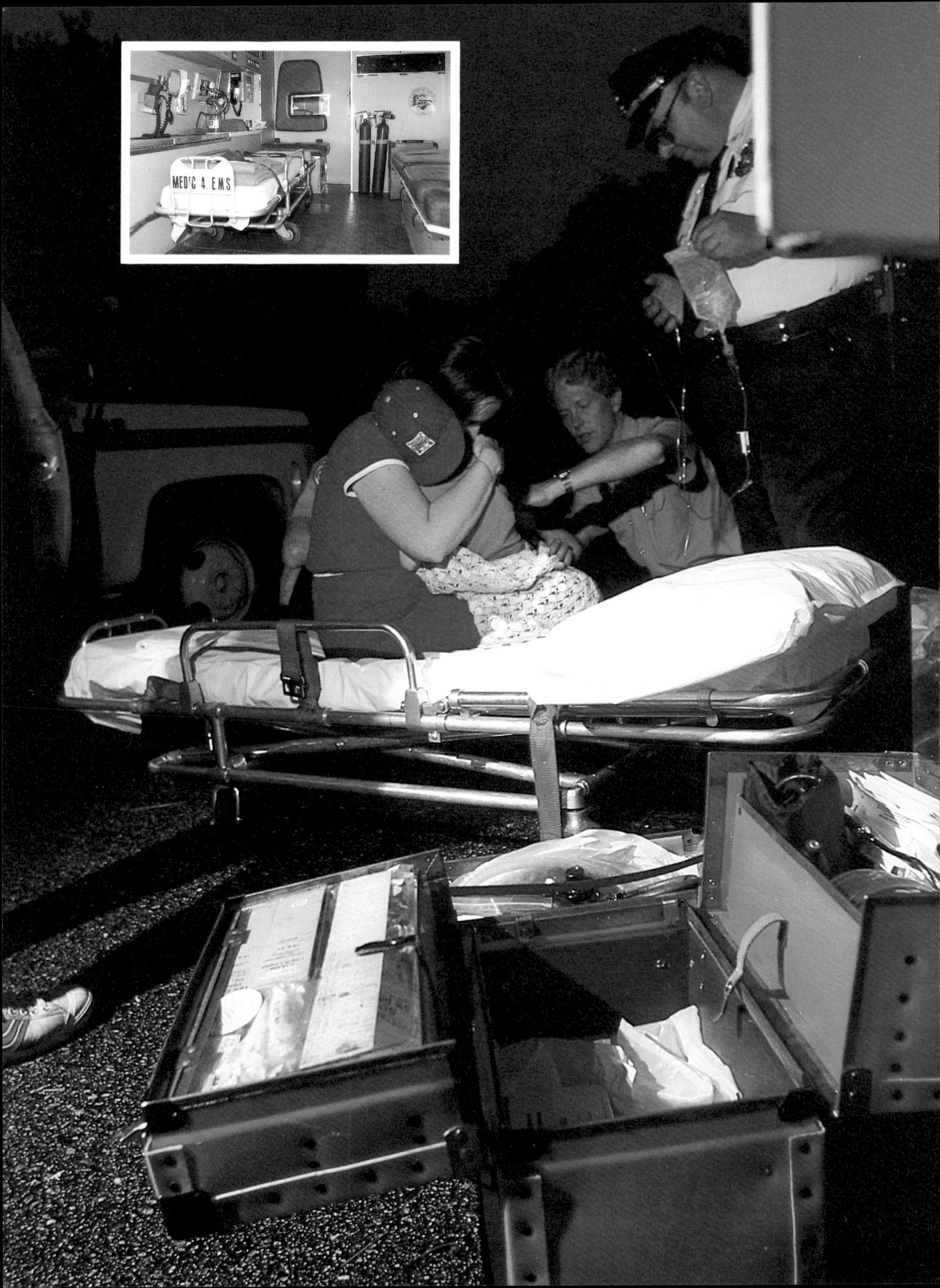
MEDIC 4 EMS

UNIT 8

Paramedic

Bud Rimel, paramedic, and his partner jump into the van and speed to the accident site. Approaching the wreck, Rimel sees the smashed front end of a sports car. The driver, obviously shaken, is leaning against his car.

"How're you doing, son?"

"Okay, I guess. Just a little shaken up. Must've dozed off. Sure didn't see the truck ahead of me. Had to swerve to miss him, and I ended up face-to-face with that embankment."

"Do you have pain anywhere? Did you bump your head?"

"I don't think so. I'm probably okay."

Rimel takes the victim's vital signs. "Blood pressure 126/76, pulse 84, respiration 18. All normal." Glancing inside the car, he notices that the steering wheel is bent upward. "Do you remember hitting the steering wheel?"

"Well, I did get my breath knocked out."

"I think we'd better take you to the hospital for a checkup before you go home. Brian, bring that stretcher over, would you?"

Rimel keeps close tabs on the accident victim's vital signs as they head for the hospital. He notices that the young man is starting to sweat. "Respiration 28, pulse 132, blood pressure 80/40. Afraid you may have some internal bleeding, son." He calls the hospital and is advised to start a trauma IV using a large bore catheter and Ringer's Lactate, a blood volume expander. The victim needs lots of fluid. As Rimel inserts an IV into each arm, he takes note of the victim's vital signs again. When the young man's blood pressure reaches 100, Rimel begins tapering off the amount of fluid flowing through the IV. Reaching the hospital, Rimel transfers care of the young man to the doctors and nurses trained to treat him. He has done his part—and well.

Emergency medical personnel face a myriad of situations. They must be alert and quick to respond with accurate and scrupulously monitored attention to the victim's needs. The paramedic must be prepared to read the gauge on a blood pressure cuff and evaluate that reading for indications of abnormality; administer carefully measured doses of medicine; calculate the amount of oxygen needed for transporting a patient; or work with numerous metric measurements to determine such things as the number of drips per minute needed in an IV and the size of tubing to use in administering it.

Any work involving medicines and injections requires meticulous attention to cleanliness. Our task of applying the medicine of the Scriptures to sin-wounded souls requires a clean heart and life. Just as an unclean needle will cause serious harm to the patient, so an impure life will impair our relationship with God and hurt others. Only the blood of Jesus Christ, claimed in the confessing and forsaking of sin, is powerful "to cleanse us from all unrighteousness" and to restore the purity of soul required of God's servants (I John 1:7, 9).

Customary Units of Measurement

Length

1 foot (ft.) = 12 inches (in.)
1 yard (yd.) = 3 feet
1 mile (mi.) = 1,760 yards

Weight

1 pound (lb.) = 16 ounces (oz.)
1 ton (t.) = 2,000 pounds

Liquid Volume

1 cup (c.) = 8 fluid ounces (fl. oz.)
1 pint (pt.) = 2 cups
1 quart (qt.) = 2 pints
1 gallon (gal.) = 4 quarts

What do you think?

Which unit would you use to report
the length of a pencil?
the width of a room?
the length of a football field?
the distance from your house to school?

Which unit would you use to report the weight
of a pencil?
of a piano?
of an aircraft carrier?

Which unit would you use to report the volume
of a glass?
of a bucket?
of a swimming pool?

22 yards equal how many feet?
Since 1 yd. = 3 ft.,
then 22 yd. = $(22 \cdot 3)$ ft. = 66 ft.

156 inches equal how many feet?
Since 1 ft. = 12 in.,
then 156 in. = $(156 \div 12)$ ft. = 13 ft.

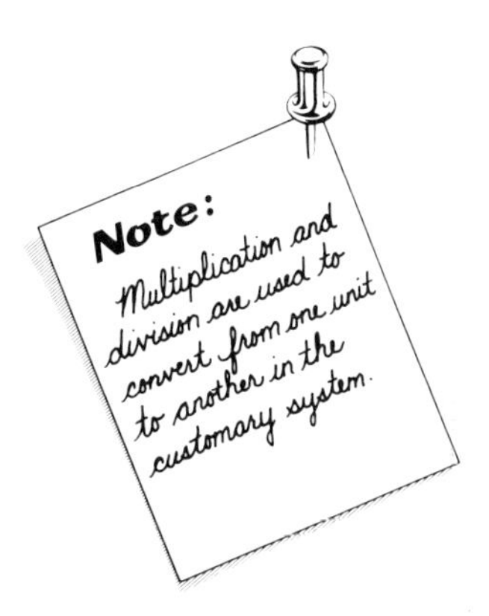

9 pounds equal how many ounces?
Since 1 lb. = 16 oz.,
then 9 lb. = $(9 \cdot 16)$ oz. = 144 oz.

192 ounces equal how many pounds?
Since 1 lb. = 16 oz.,
then 192 oz. = $(192 \div 16)$ lb. = 12 lb.

2 gallons equal how many cups?
Since 1 gal. = 4 qt.,
then 2 gal. = $(2 \cdot 4)$ qt. = 8 qt.

Since 1 qt. = 2 pt.,
then 8 qt. = $(8 \cdot 2)$ pt. = 16 pt.

Since 1 pt. = 2 cups,
then 16 pt. = $(16 \cdot 2)$ cups = 32 cups

Practice

Fill in the blanks with the correct conversions.

1. 3 ft. = ___ in.
2. 6 c. = ___ fl. oz.
3. 3 t. = ___ lb.
4. 12 ft. = ___ yd.
5. 7 qt. = ___ pt.
6. 80 oz. = ___ lb.
7. 12 gal. = ___ qt.
8. 6 lb. = ___ oz.
9. 2,640 ft. = ___ yd.
10. 6 pt. = ___ c.
11. 1 mi. = ___ ft.
12. 10 t. = ___ lb.
13. 1 pt. = ___ fl. oz.
14. 276 in. = ___ ft.
15. 1 gal. = ___ fl. oz.

Metric Units of Measurement

The Standard Metric Units
The *meter* is used to measure distances. (symbol: m)
The *gram* is used to measure weight and mass. (symbol: g)
The *liter* is used to measure liquid volume. (symbol: ℓ)

Keys to Understanding

Prefix	Meaning	Symbol
milli-	one-thousandth (0.001 or $\frac{1}{10^3}$)	m
centi-	one-hundredth (0.01 or $\frac{1}{10^2}$)	c
deci-	one-tenth (0.1 or $\frac{1}{10}$)	d
deka-	ten (10 or 10^1)	dk
hecto-	one hundred (100 or 10^2)	h
kilo-	one thousand (1,000 or 10^3)	k

What do you think?

What is a millimeter? a kilometer? a centimeter?
What is a dekagram? a decigram? a hectogram?
What is a centiliter? a milliliter? a dekaliter?

How many milliliters are in a liter? 1 ℓ = ? ml
How many dekameters are in a kilometer? 1 km = ? dkm
How many centigrams are in a decigram? 1 dg = ? cg

Practice

Find the measurements of these lines, using metric measures.

1. ______________

3. ______________

5.

2.

4. ______________

Find the measurements of these lines.

6. __________

___ mm
___ cm

8. ______________________________

___ cm ___ dm

7. ________________

___ mm
___ cm

9. ______

___ mm
___ dm

10. ______________________

___ cm
___ m

Metric Units Illustrated

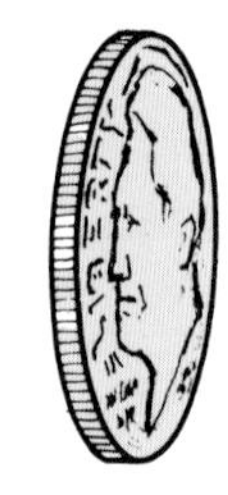

One *millimeter:*
about the thickness of
a dime

One *centimeter:*
about the width of a paper
clip

One *meter:*
about the length of four of
these books placed end
to end

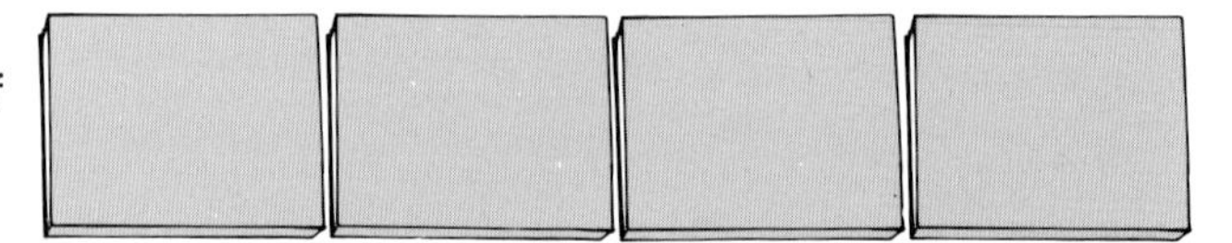

One *kilometer:*
about the length of
five city blocks

One *gram:*
about the weight of two paper
clips

One *kilogram:*
about the weight of two of
these books

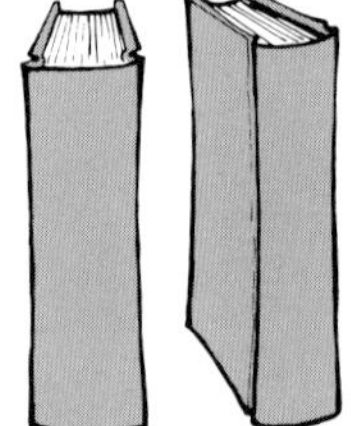

One *liter:*
about the volume of $2\frac{3}{4}$
cans of soda pop

Metric Units Charted

Units of Length

1 kilometer (km)	= 1,000 meters
1 hectometer (hm)	= 100 meters
1 dekameter (dkm)	= 10 meters
1 meter (m)	= 1 basic unit
1 decimeter (dm)	= .1 ($\frac{1}{10}$) meter
1 centimeter (cm)	= .01 ($\frac{1}{100}$) meter
1 millimeter (mm)	= .001 ($\frac{1}{1,000}$) meter

Units of Weight

1 kilogram (kg)	= 1,000 grams
1 hectogram (hg)	= 100 grams
1 dekagram (dkg)	= 10 grams
1 gram (g)	= 1 basic unit
1 decigram (dg)	= .1 ($\frac{1}{10}$) gram
1 centigram (cg)	= .01 ($\frac{1}{100}$) gram
1 milligram (mg)	= .001 ($\frac{1}{1,000}$) gram

Units of Liquid Volume

1 kiloliter (kl)	= 1,000 liters
1 hectoliter (hl)	= 100 liters
1 dekaliter (dkl)	= 10 liters
1 liter (ℓ)	= 1 basic unit
1 deciliter (dl)	= .1 ($\frac{1}{10}$) liter
1 centiliter (cl)	= .01 ($\frac{1}{100}$) liter
1 milliliter (ml)	= .001 ($\frac{1}{1,000}$) liter

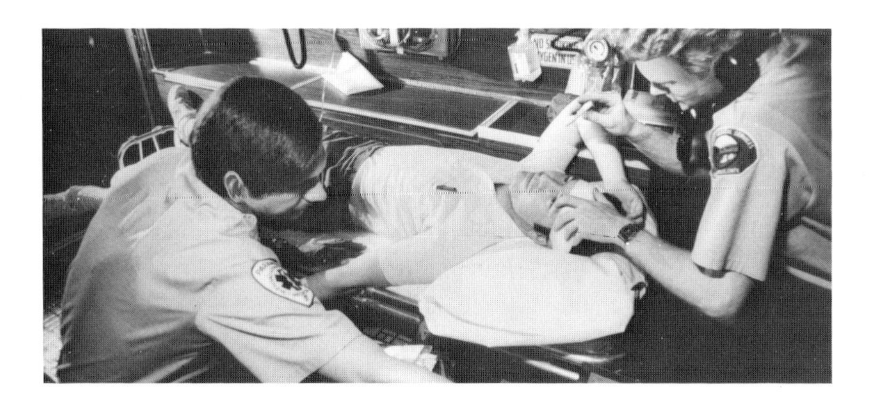

Metric Conversion

This class is learning how to do measurement conversions. It is much easier to convert within the metric system than within the customary system. All you have to do is multiply or divide by a power of 10.

1 kilometer = 1,000 meters
4.3 kilometers (4.3 · 1,000) meters = 4,300 m
100 grams = 1 hectogram
453.5 grams = $\left(\frac{453.5}{100}\right)$ hectograms = 4.535 hg
1 liter = 100 centiliters
1.7 liters = (1.7 · 100) centiliters = 170 cl

Remember the fast way to multiply and divide by powers of 10.

When changing from one unit to another in the metric system, what must we do with the decimal point?

Practice

Fill in the blanks with the correct conversions.

1. 1 m = ____ mm
2. 1 m = ____ km
3. 1 m = ____ cm
4. 1 g = ____ dkg
5. 1 g = ____ dg
6. 1 ml = ____ cl
7. 1 kl = ____ ℓ
8. 1 cm = ____ m
9. 4 kg = ____ g
10. 500 cm = ____ m
11. 3 cm = ____ mm
12. 25 cg = ____ g
13. 29 dl = ____ ℓ
14. 6.3 km = ____ hm
15. 8.39 hm = ____ m

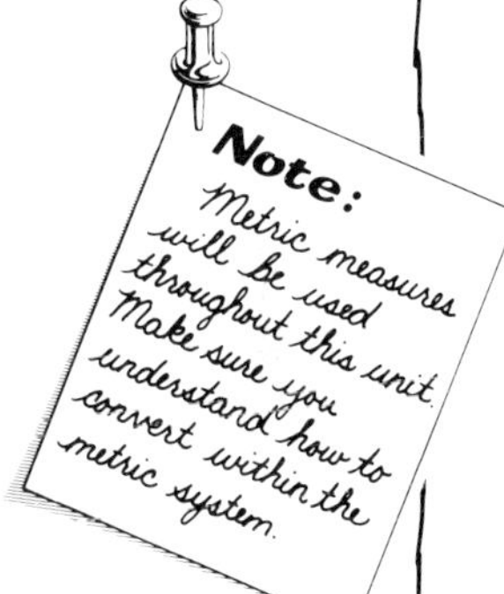

Convert these measures to meters.

16. 2.3 km **17.** 516.1 cm **18.** 0.83 hm **19.** 177 mm

Convert these measures to kilograms.

20. 2,781 g **21.** 18.1 dkg **22.** 122,680 mg **23.** 896 cg

Convert these measures to milliliters.

24. 6.1ℓ **25.** 0.43 cl **26.** 2 kl **27.** 1.85 dl

Convert these measures to centimeters.

28. 4.7 m **29.** 0.6 hm **30.** 21.2 mm **31.** 0.03 km

DEAR MR. COMPUTER,
PRINT THE METRIC EQUIVALENT FOR 38 FEET.

Metric Conversions Made Simple

The "staircase metric converter" is an easy method of converting in the metric system.

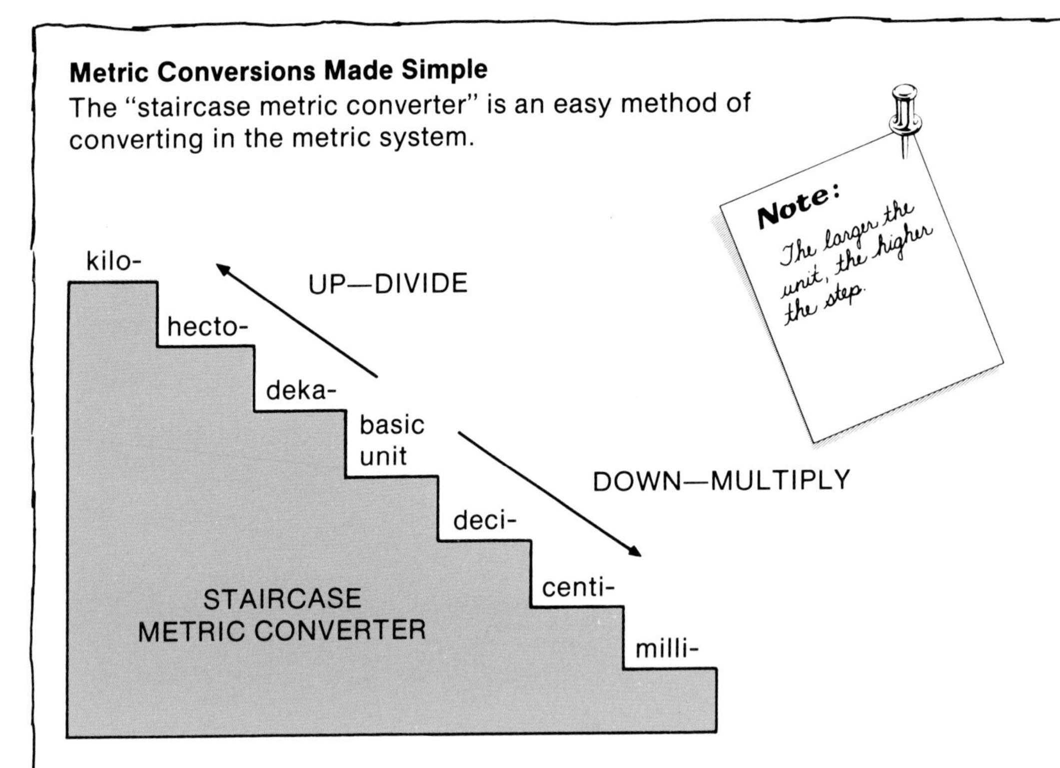

Examples:

3.75 km = ____ dkm

3.75. km = 375 dkm

To move from km to dkm, you multiply (go down two steps).

Move the decimal point two places to the right.

121 ml = ____ dl

1.21. ml = 1.21 dl

To move from ml to dl, you divide (go up two steps).

Move the decimal point two places to the left.

Practice

Fill in the blanks with the correct conversions.

1. 0.03 m = ____ cm
2. 2.06 dm = ____ mm
3. 349 m = ____ km
4. 1.645 mm = ____ m
5. 69.3 km = ____ dkm
6. 3.61 cm = ____ mm
7. 0.48 dkm = ____ cm
8. 63.4 mm = ____ dm
9. 5.83 hm = ____ m
10. 862 mm = ____ km
11. 4.3 g = ____ mg
12. 0.3 kg = ____ g
13. 8 dkl = ____ dl
14. 96.1 cl = ____ ℓ
15. 6.15 mg = ____ cg
16. 1,362 dg = ____ hg
17. 0.67 ℓ = ____ ml
18. 5,482 cg = ____ g
19. 95.6 cl = ____ dkl
20. 0.027 mg = ____ kg

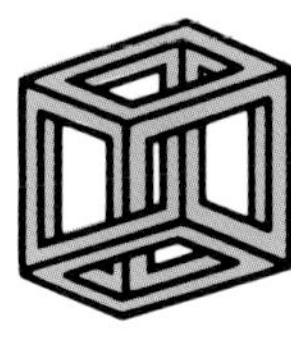

MIND BOGGLER

A solid one-cubic-meter wooden block is painted black on all faces. It is then cut into twenty-seven equal-sized smaller cubes. What size are the smaller cubes? How many of the smaller cubes are painted on three faces? two faces? one face? no face?

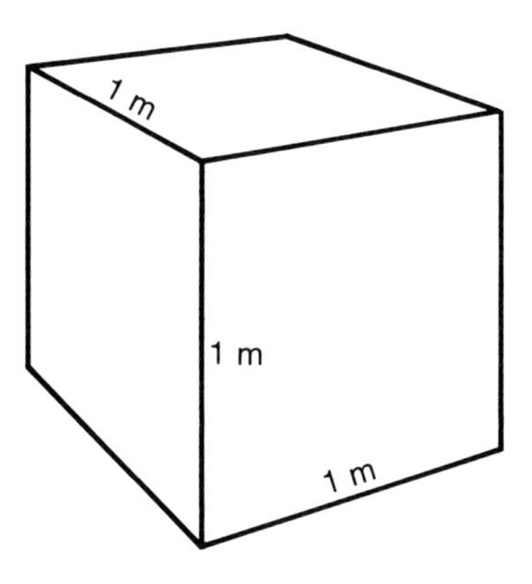

Math in Action

1. Mr. Bryson, a paramedic, has been authorized to give an accident victim a certain amount of medication. He knows that the amount of medication he administers depends on how many kilograms the victim weighs. To find the victim's weight in kilograms, he uses the following formula:

$$\text{weight in kg} = \frac{\text{weight in lb.}}{2.2}$$

   What is the weight in kg of a man who weighs 209 pounds?

2. Dr. Kerin has ordered that a patient be given 600 milligrams of a certain medicine. The paramedic knows that this drug is dispensed in 0.3-gram tablets. How many tablets should he give?
   If the patient is given a prescription containing 20 tablets to be taken over a period of time, how many milligrams of the medicine will he eventually take?

3. Mr. Landis has 6.25 liters of cough syrup to fill 25 bottles. How many milliliters of cough syrup should he pour into each bottle?

4. If Mrs. Sanders requires an injection of 2 ml of a prescribed drug each 12 hours, how many days will she receive injections if she must receive 76 ml of the drug all together?

5. A person's pulse rate is the number of pulses per minute. A normal adult has a rate of 60 to 80; a child, 80 to 100. If Shane's heart beats 23 times in 15 seconds, what is his pulse rate?

Perimeter

Jared jogs around a square block every morning. How far does he jog if the block measures 500 meters on a side?

A formula for the perimeter of a square is

$P = s + s + s + s$

$P = 4s$

(s = length of a side)

Keys to Understanding

The perimeter of a figure is the distance around the figure. The perimeter of a polygon is the sum of the lengths of its sides.

Write an equation for the perimeter of a rectangle.

Write an equation for the perimeter of a parallelogram.

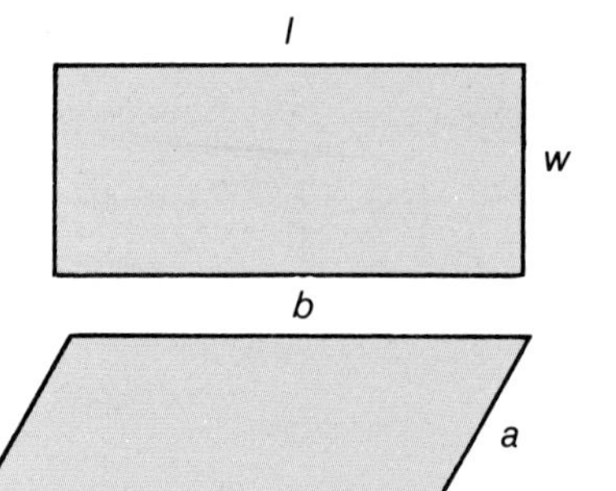

Write an equation for the perimeter of a triangle.

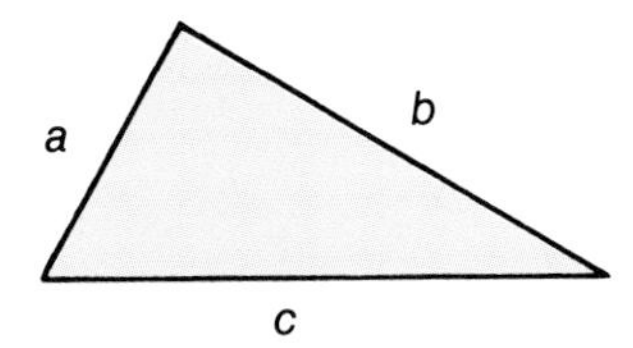

What would be the equation for the perimeter of an equilateral triangle?

Practice

Measure the lengths of the sides of these polygons and then write the perimeters.

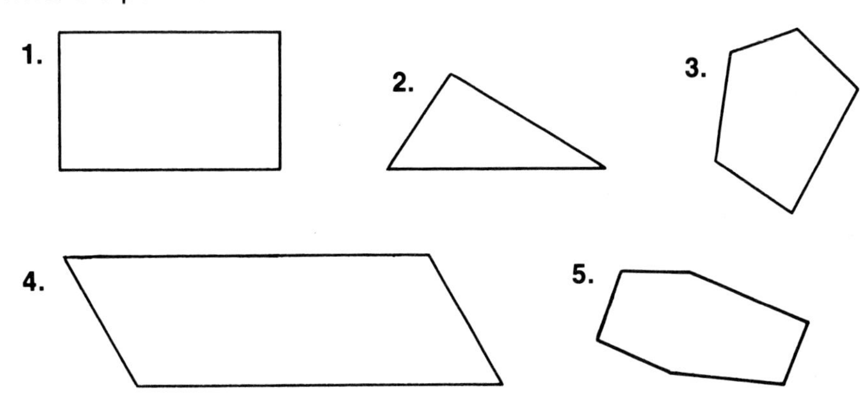

Find the perimeters of each of these rectangles.

	length	width
6.	2.8 cm	1.4 cm
7.	3.1 m	10.6 dm
8.	1.3 cm	22 mm
9.	1.6 km	37 hm
10.	0.01 km	10 m

Find the perimeters of each of these regular polygons.

	number of sides	length of each side
11.	3	6.3 cm
12.	5	3.21 m
13.	6	1.41 mm
14.	4	2.8 km
15.	8	0.15 dm

Area of Polygons

How would you find out how much carpet this man will use to cover the living room floor?

You must find the *area* of the room.

Keys to Understanding

Area is the amount of surface in a closed region.
It is measured in square units.
Example: the symbol m^2 means "square meter."

Square units

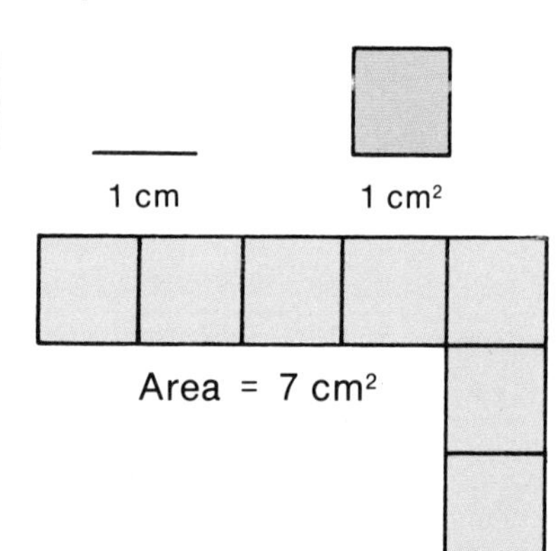

The unit 1 cm^2 (square centimeter) is the area enclosed by a square having sides that measure 1 cm each. What is the unit 1 m^2? 1 $yd.^2$? 1 $in.^2$?

Note:
The area of a polygon is the amount of surface enclosed by the polygon.

What do you think?

How was the area of this polygon found?

Is there an easier way?

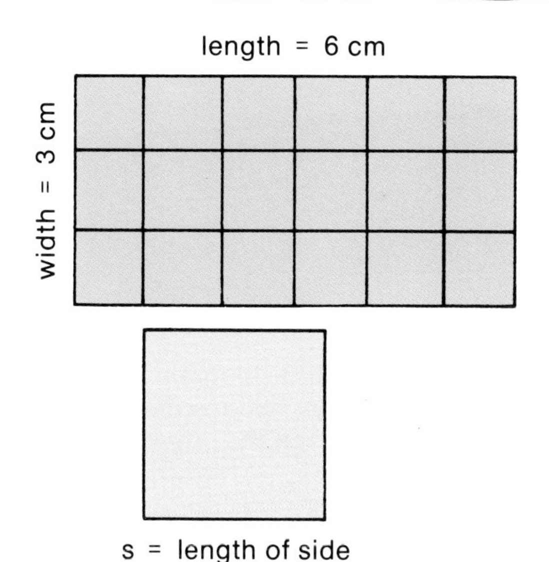

What is the easy way to find the area of a rectangle?

Write an equation for the area of a rectangle.
Why does it work?

Write an equation for the area of a square.
Why does it work?

Practice

Find the areas of each of these polygons.

1.
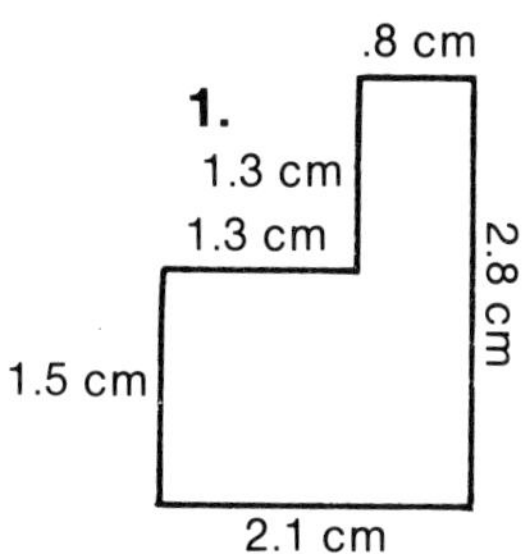

2.
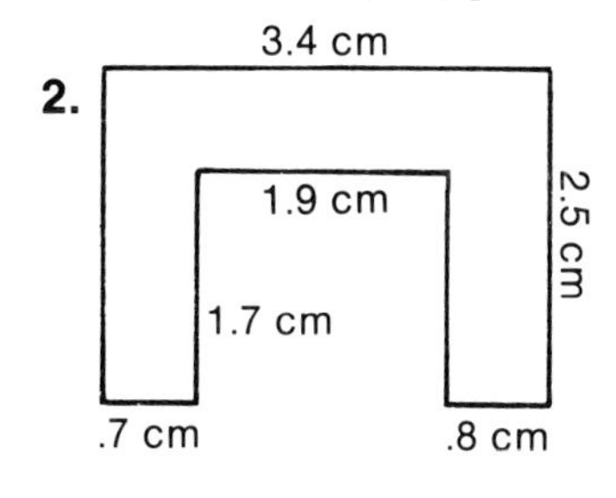

3.
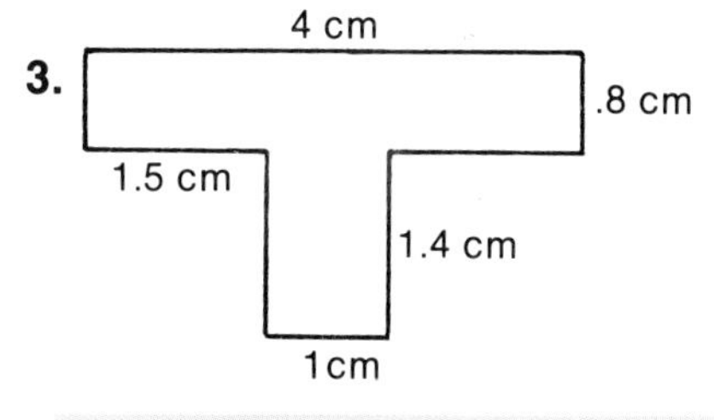

Find the areas of each of these rectangles.

	length	width
4.	2.3 cm	1.8 cm
5.	0.6 km	0.3 km
6.	5.2 in.	4 in.
7.	3.15 dm	1.2 dm
8.	5.4 ft.	4.9 ft.

Remember, when finding areas by multiplying, make sure that the length and width are expressed in the same units.

9. What is the area of a square if one side is 7.2 cm long?

10. What is the area of a rectangle with a length of 3.2 m and a width of 21.3 dm?

Area of Parallelograms

Now you can use what you already know about measuring the area of a rectangle to find the equation for the area of a parallelogram.

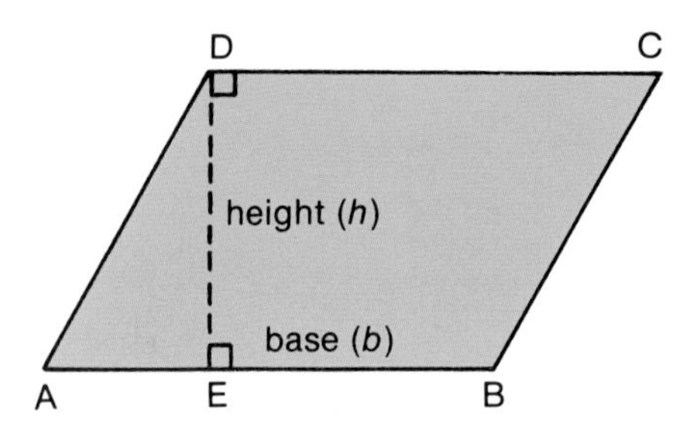

Consider parallelogram ABCD. What relationship is there between the opposite sides?

$\overline{AB}$ and $\overline{CD}$ are parallel lines.
So are $\overline{AD}$ and $\overline{BC}$.
Consider $\overline{AB}$ the *base* of parallelogram ABCD. $\overline{AB} = b$

Remember the definition of a parallelogram.

Consider any line perpendicular to $\overline{AB}$ and $\overline{CD}$ (the length of the distance between them) the *height* (h).
$DE = h$

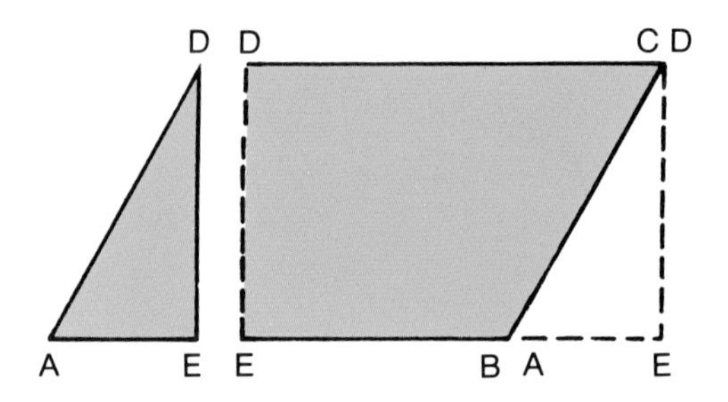

Remove Δ ADE and place it at the other end of the parallelogram so that $\overline{AD}$ lies on $\overline{BC}$.

What do you think?

Are $\overline{AD}$ and $\overline{BC}$ the same length? How do you know?
By moving Δ ADE, what kind of figure have you made?
Does the figure you made have the same area as ▱ABCD?
Write an equation for the area of a parallelogram, using b as the base and h as the height.

Keys to Understanding

Area of a rectangle

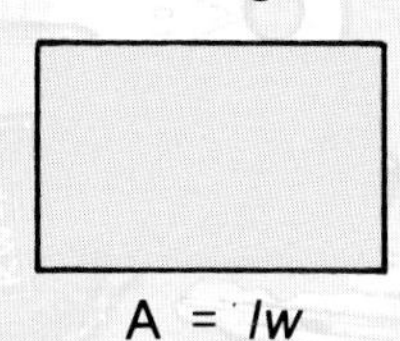

$A = lw$

Area of a square

$A = s^2$

Area of a parallelogram

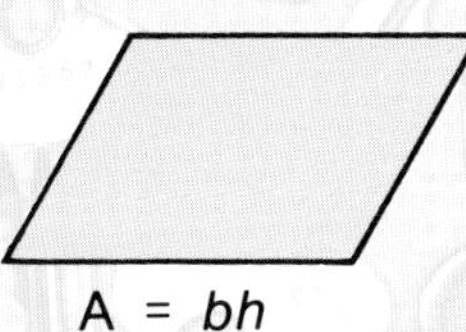

$A = bh$

Note: When two letters that represent numbers are written next to each other, they are to be multiplied. ($A = bh = b \cdot h$)

Practice

Find the areas of these parallelograms.

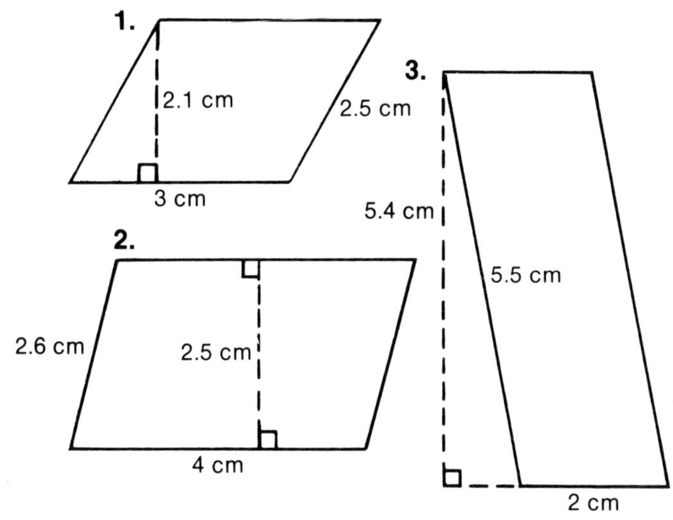

Find the areas of these parallelograms.

	base	height
4.	2.1 cm	4.8 cm
5.	1 ft.	3 in.
6.	1.5 m	2 dm
7.	0.3 km	21 hm
8.	12 yd.	$5\frac{1}{4}$ yd.
9.	3.5 cm	20.5 mm

10. Write an equation for the area of a rhombus.

Remember what a rhombus is.

Area of Triangles

Now you can use what you know about measuring the area of a parallelogram to find the equation for the area of a triangle.

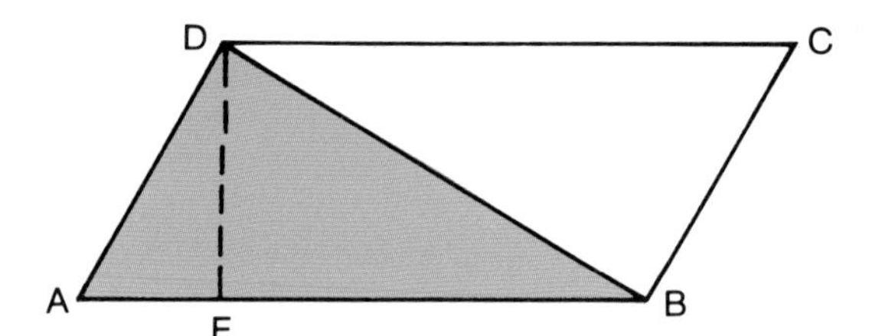

Consider parallelogram ABCD with height $\overline{DE}$ and diagonal $\overline{BD}$.

Remember what a diagonal is.

What do you think?

What kind of figures are ABD and BCD?
Are the two figures congruent?
The area of the two figures together equals the area of what figure?
How much of the area of parallelogram ABCD is ABD?

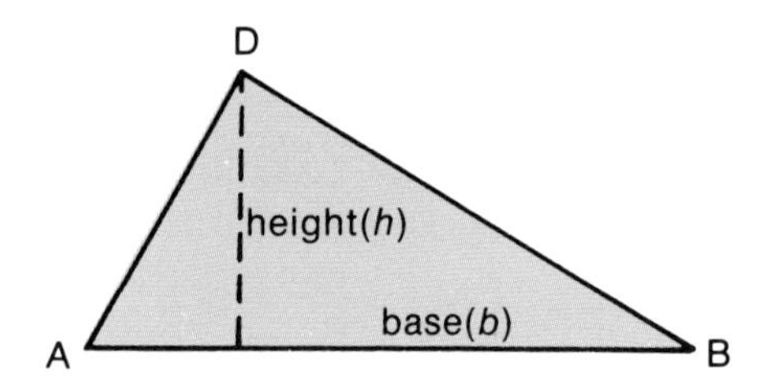

Write an equation for the area of a triangle, using b as base and h as height.

The *height* (h) of a triangle is a line segment drawn from any vertex perpendicular to the opposite side (or opposite side extended). The opposite side is the *base* (b) of the triangle.

Every triangle has three possible heights and three possible bases.

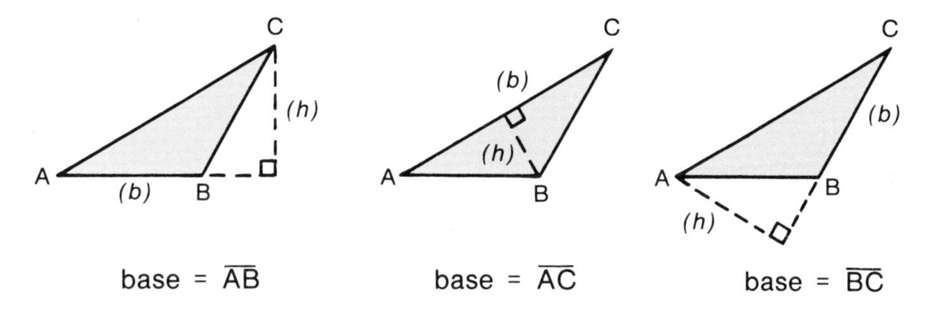

The height may be inside or outside the triangle.

Practice

Find the areas of these triangles.

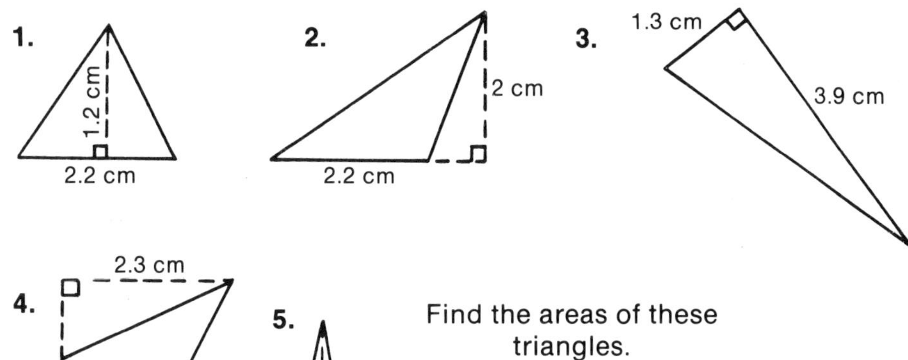

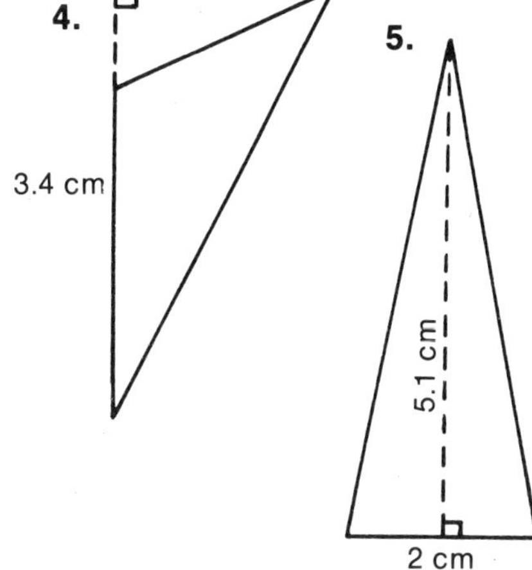

Find the areas of these triangles.

	base	height
6.	1.6 cm	0.3 cm
7.	2.1 dm	4.4 mm
8.	$2\frac{1}{3}$ ft.	6 in.
9.	0.013 hm	5.7 m
10.	261 dm	3.6 hm

Area of Trapezoids

Now you can use what you know about measuring the area of a triangle to find the equation for the area of a trapezoid.

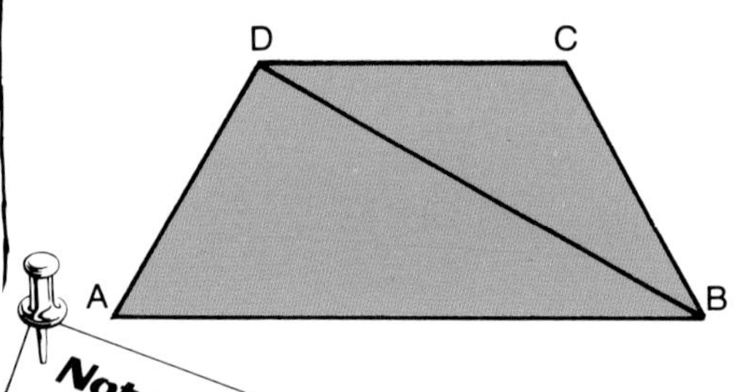

Consider trapezoid ABCD with diagonal $\overline{BD}$. What relationship is there between opposite sides $\overline{AB}$ and $\overline{DC}$?

Note:

Area of $\triangle ABD$ + area of $\triangle BCD$ = area of trapezoid ABCD.

Remember the definition of a parallelogram.

$\overline{AB}$ is the base (b_1) of ΔABD.
$\overline{CD}$ is the base (b_2) of ΔBCD.

The heights *(h)* of the two triangles are equal. Why?

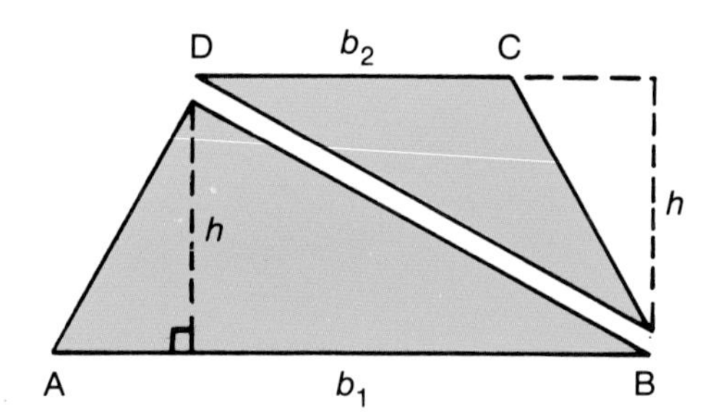

Area of trapezoid ABCD = Area of ΔABD + Area of ΔBCD

$$A = \frac{1}{2} b_1 h + \frac{1}{2} b_2 h$$

$$A = \frac{1}{2} h (b_1 + b_2)$$

What mathematical property tells us that $\frac{1}{2} b_1 h + \frac{1}{2} b_2 h = \frac{1}{2} h (b_1 + b_2)$?

Keys to Understanding

Area of a triangle

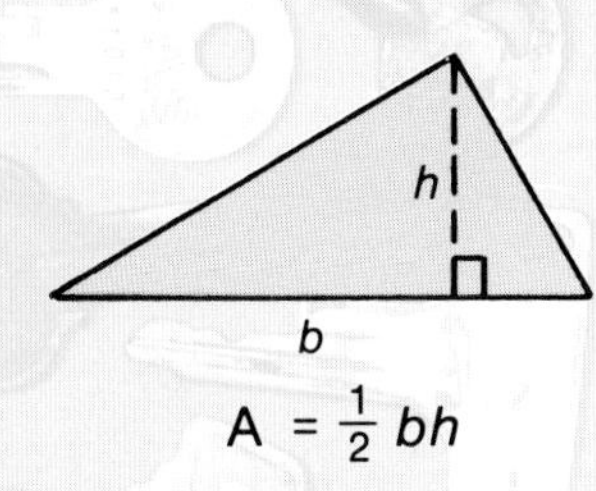

$A = \frac{1}{2}bh$

Area of a trapezoid

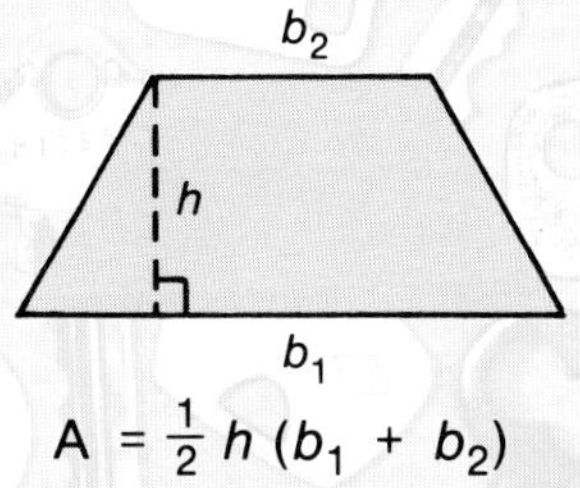

$A = \frac{1}{2}h(b_1 + b_2)$

Practice

Find the areas of these trapezoids.

1.

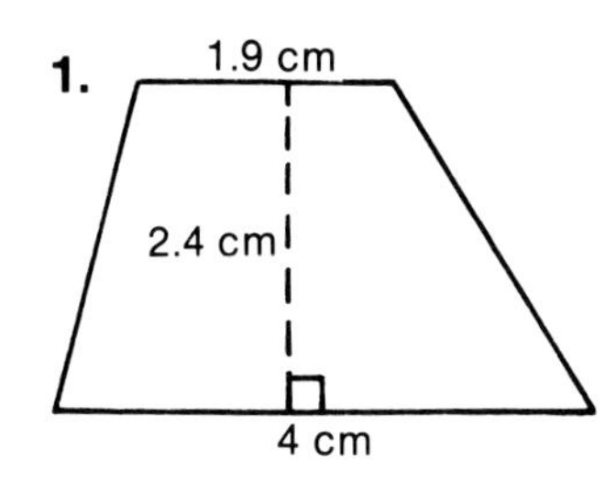

2. **3.**

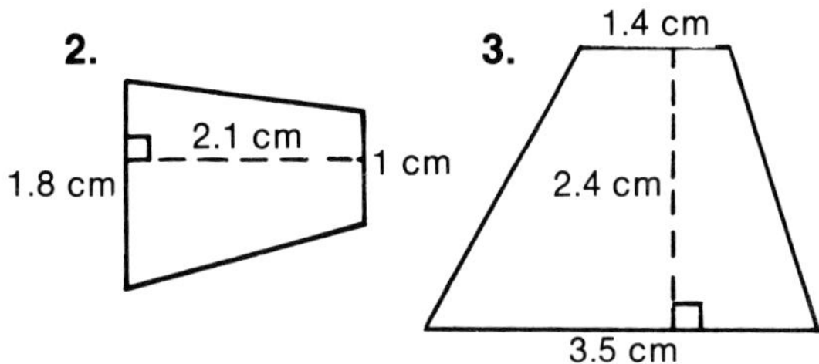

4.

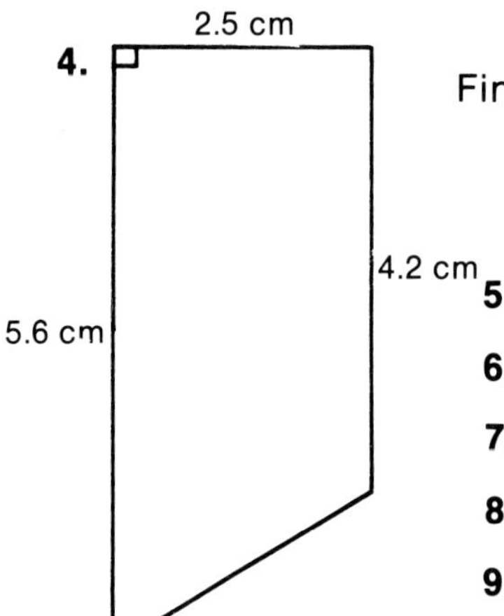

Find the areas of these trapezoids.

	height	base 1	base 2
5.	3.1 m	2 m	5 m
6.	1 ft.	13 in.	8 in.
7.	2.4 mm	0.7 mm	1.6 mm
8.	1.5 m	2 m	11 dm
9.	6 in.	1.5 ft.	$2\frac{1}{4}$ ft.
10.	112 mm	0.06 dm	1.8 cm

Circles

Keys to Understanding

A *circle* is a set of all the points that are equidistant from a center point.

A *diameter* of a circle is a line segment that goes through the center point and has its endpoints on the circle.

A *radius* of a circle is a line segment with one endpoint at the center of the circle and the other endpoint on the circle.

The *circumference* of a circle is the distance around the circle.

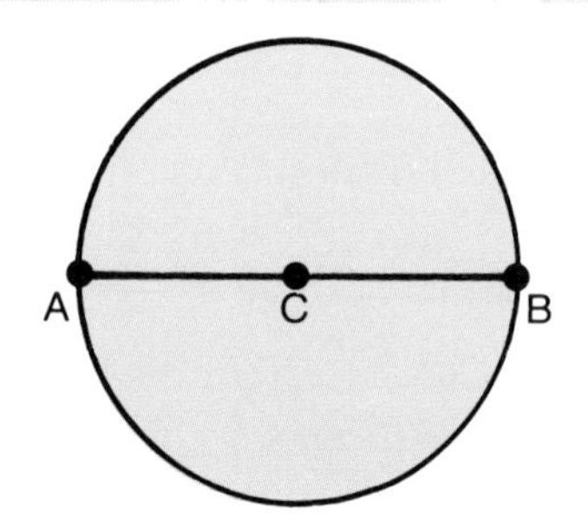

If C is the center point, then $\overline{AB}$ is a *diameter,* $\overline{AC}$ is a *radius,* and $\overline{BC}$ is a *radius.*

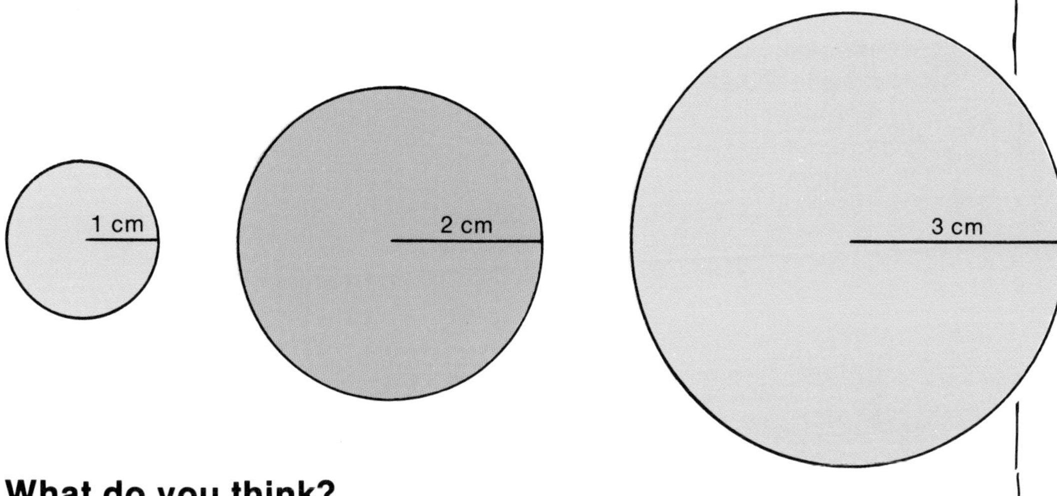

What do you think?

What is the diameter of each of the circles pictured above?

Write an equation showing the relationship between the diameter *(d)* and the radius *(r)* of a circle.

Construct three circles the same size as the ones pictured above (with radii of 1 cm, 2 cm, and 3 cm). Cut out each circle and fill in the chart. How can you measure to find the circumference of the circles?

	radius (r)	diameter (d)	circumference (c)	$c \div d$
Circle 1	1 cm			
Circle 2	2 cm			
Circle 3	3 cm			

What do you notice about $c \div d$?

Remember, a constant number is a number that does not change.

For each of the circles you constructed, the length of the circumference divided by the length of the diameter is a constant number: π *(pi)*.

$$\pi \doteq \frac{22}{7} \text{ or } 3.14$$

Remember what the symbol $\doteq$ means.

Keys to Understanding

The equation for the circumference of a circle with diameter d is

$$C = \pi d$$

The equation for the circumference of a circle with radius r is

$$C = \pi \cdot 2r$$
$$C = 2\pi r$$

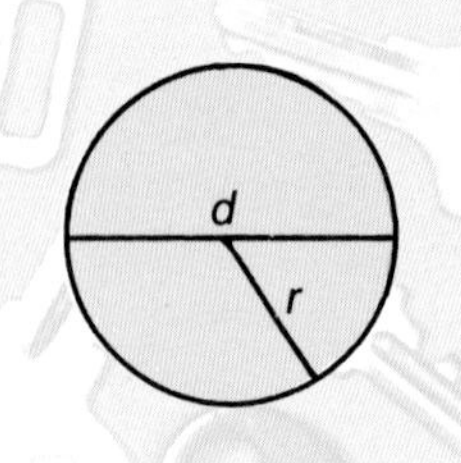

Practice

Find the circumferences of circles with these diameters. Use 3.14 for π.

1. 8 mm	**3.** 11 in.	**5.** 1.5 ft.	**7.** $4\frac{1}{2}$ yd.	**9.** 2.7 mm
2. 5 km	**4.** 2.2 cm	**6.** 0.6 dm	**8.** 3.1 m	**10.** $6\frac{1}{4}$ in.

Find the circumferences of circles with these radii. Use 3.14 for π.

11. 1 in.	**13.** 6 ft.	**15.** 2.4 km	**17.** $2\frac{3}{4}$ ft.	**19.** 6.1 hm
12. 3 mm	**14.** 1.6 cm	**16.** $1\frac{1}{2}$ yd.	**18.** 3.5 m	**20.** 0.11 cm

Solve these problems.

21. Mrs. Miller has planted a circular flower bed with a diameter of 9 feet. If she wishes to put wire fencing around the flower bed, how many feet of fencing should she buy?

22. The pilot of an airplane was asked to circle the airfield to wait for clearance to land. The pilot estimated the radius of the circular path made by the plane to be 3.5 kilometers. How many kilometers did the plane travel in one complete circle?

23. If the diameter of the earth is 7,918 miles, what is the length of the equator?

24. The glass lens of the great Palomar telescope located in California is 200 inches in diameter. What is the circumference of this lens?

25. A bicycle wheel has a 30-centimeter radius. How many *meters* does the bicycle go when the wheel revolves one time? two times? five times?

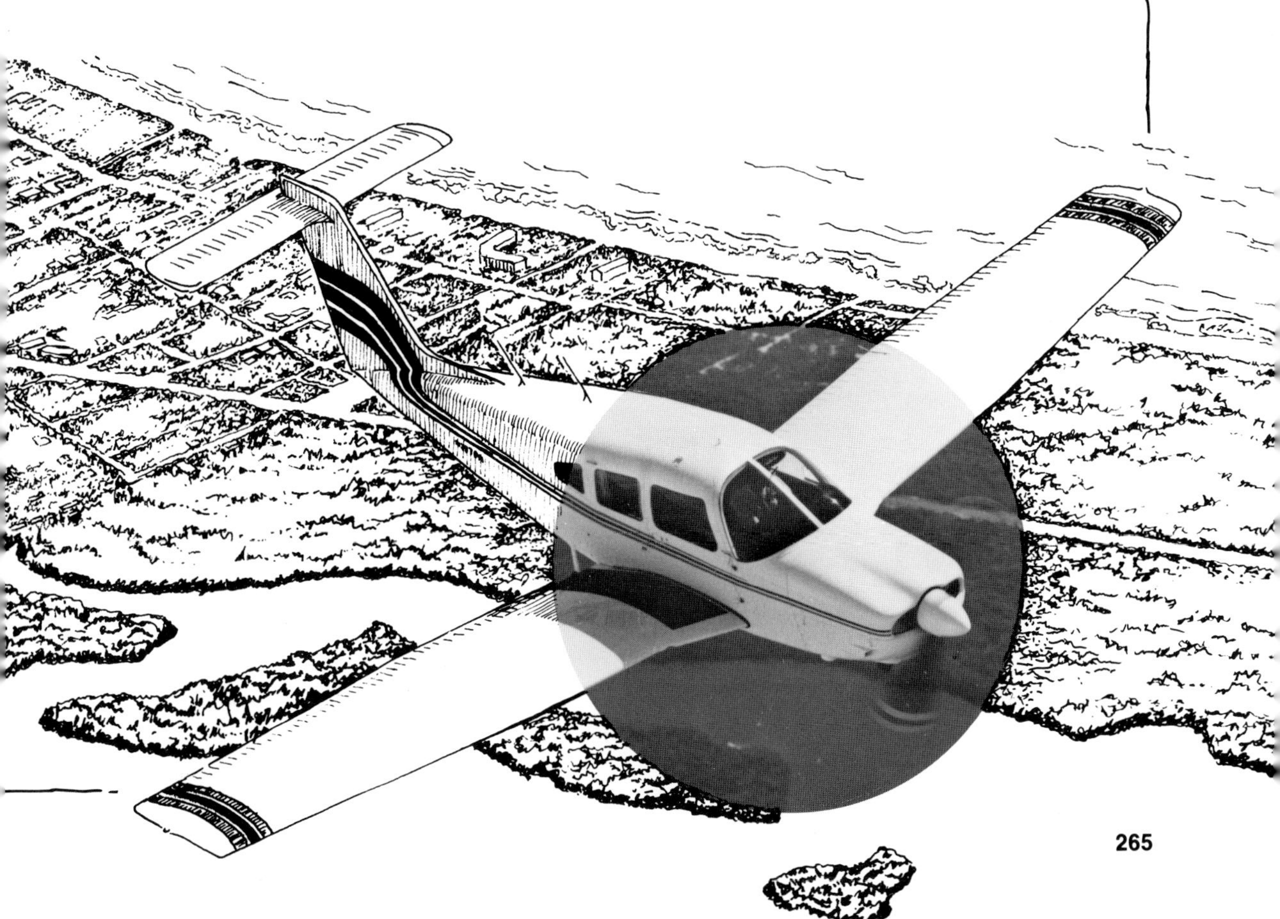

Area of a Circle

Now you can use what you know about the circumference of a circle and the area of a parallelogram to find the equation for the area of a circle.

Consider this circle, which has a radius of r.
Divide the circle into sections and put the sections together to form a figure like a crooked parallelogram.

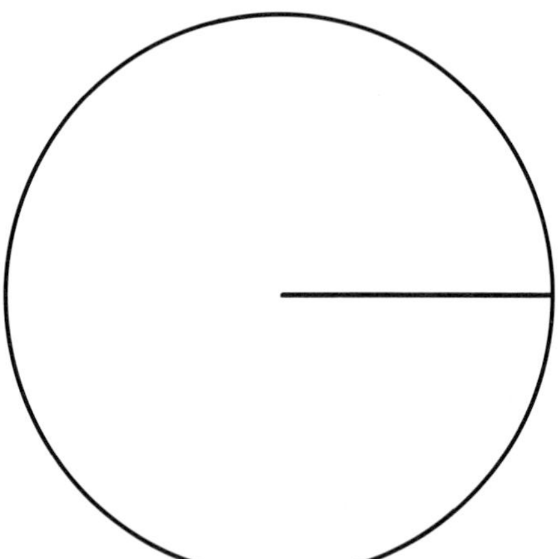

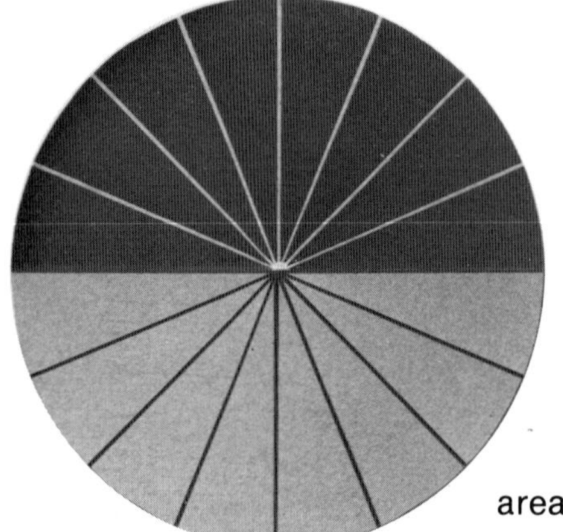

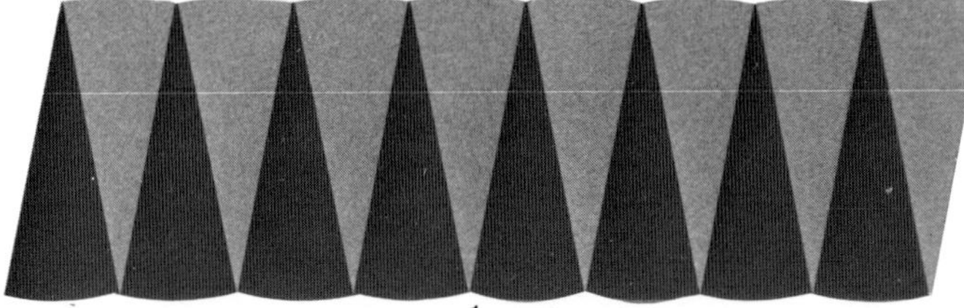

area of the circle = area of the crooked parallelogram

Can you explain how this was done? Can you explain why it works?

$$\begin{aligned}\text{Area of the circle} &= b \cdot h \\ &= (\tfrac{1}{2} c) \cdot r \\ &= \tfrac{1}{2}(2\pi r) \cdot r \\ &= \pi r \cdot r \\ &= \pi r^2\end{aligned}$$

Keys to Understanding

The equation for the area of a circle that has a radius of *r* is

$A = \pi r^2$

Practice

Find the areas of circles with these radii.

1. 2 in. **2.** 3 cm **3.** 5 m **4.** 0.4 dm **5.** $1\frac{1}{2}$ ft.

Find the areas of circles with these diameters.

6. 2 in. **7.** 8 mm **8.** 1.4 cm **9.** 5 yd. **10.** 4.2 m

Solve these problems.

11. Susan is making a circular flower bed that is 10 feet across. How much area will she have to dig up?

12. The range of a circular weather radar is 100 km. In what amount of area will the radar detect a thunderstorm?

13. Larry brought a 16-inch pizza to the party. Miguel brought two 10-inch pizzas. Who brought more pizza? How much more?

14. What is the area of a circular skating rink with a radius of 30 meters?

15. A circular tabletop has a diameter of 24 decimeters. What is the area of the tabletop expressed in meters?

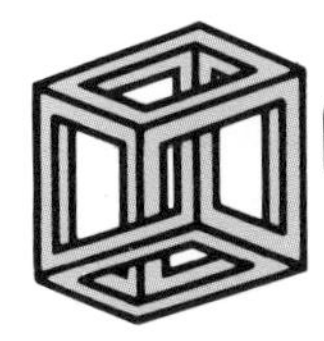

MIND BOGGLER

A construction company has been hired to build a 10-meter-wide circular sidewalk around the athletic stadium. If the stadium has a diameter of 0.5 km, how much area will the sidewalk cover?

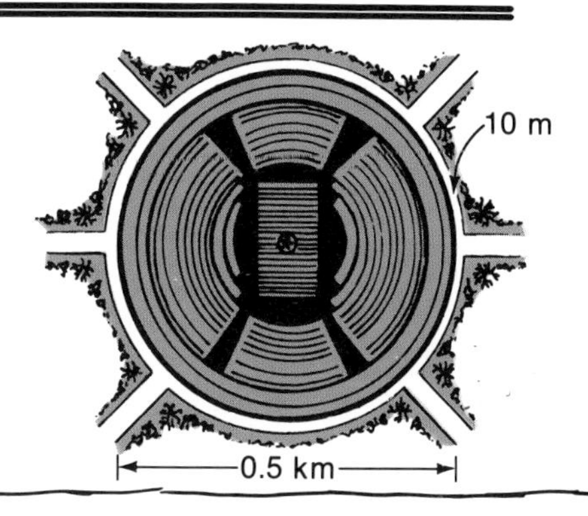

Surface Area

The girls are going to wrap their brother's birthday present. How can they find out how much paper it will take to cover the surface of the box?

The girls must find the *surface area* of the box.

Keys to Understanding

The *surface area* of a prism equals the sum of the areas of all the faces (the surfaces of the prism).

What do you think?

How many faces does a rectangular prism have?

How many faces does a triangular prism have?

What is the surface area of the box pictured?

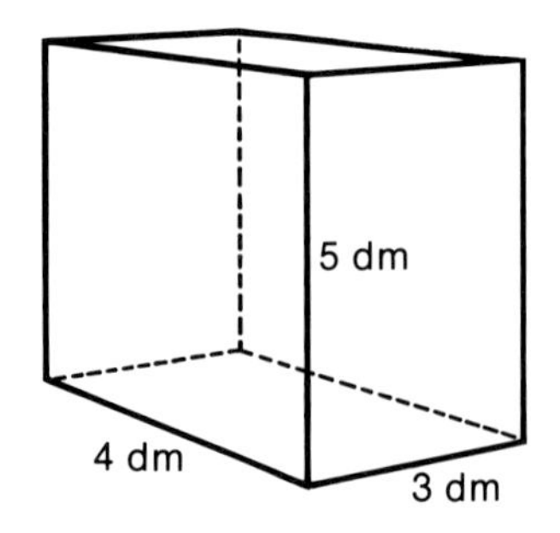

$$\begin{aligned} SA &= (2 \cdot 12)\ dm^2 + (2 \cdot 15)\ dm^2 + (2 \cdot 20)\ dm^2 \\ &= 24\ dm^2 + 30\ dm^2 + 40\ dm^2 \\ &= 94\ dm^2 \end{aligned}$$

Can you explain how the surface area was found?

What if the girls had bought their brother a can of tennis balls for his birthday? How could they find the surface area of the can?

Imagine cutting the can apart.

This kind of solid is called a *cylinder.*

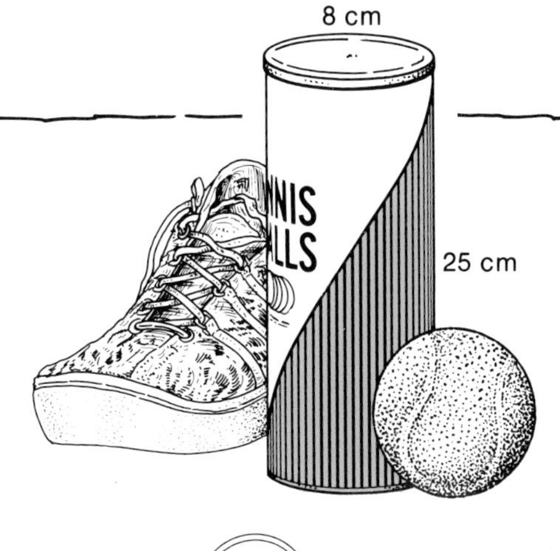

$C = \pi d = 8\pi$

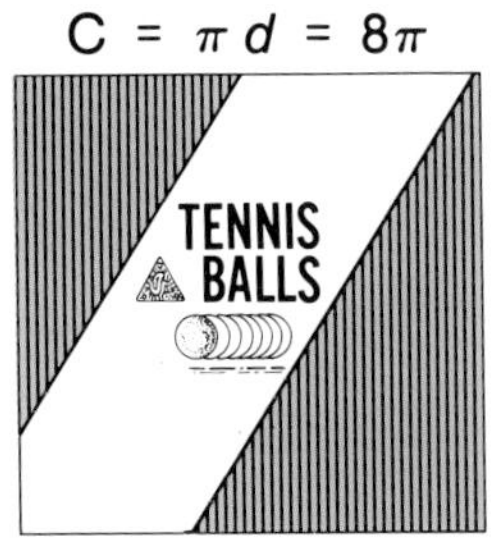

Curved face flattened

$h = 25$ cm

8 cm

bases

$A = 2 \cdot \pi r^2$
$= 2 \cdot 16\pi \text{ cm}^2$
$= 32\pi \text{ cm}^2$

Once the curved face is spread open, it forms a rectangle. The width of the rectangle is equal to the height of the cylinder and the length is equal to the circumference of the base.

$A = \pi d \cdot h$

$$\begin{aligned} SA &= (2 \cdot \pi r^2) + (\pi d \cdot h) \\ &= (2 \cdot 16\pi) \text{ cm}^2 + (8\pi \cdot 25) \text{ cm}^2 \\ &= 32\pi \text{ cm}^2 + 200\pi \text{ cm}^2 \\ &= 232\pi \text{ cm}^2 \\ &= 728.48 \text{ cm}^2 \end{aligned}$$

Why did this work?

Practice

Find the surface area of each of these solids.

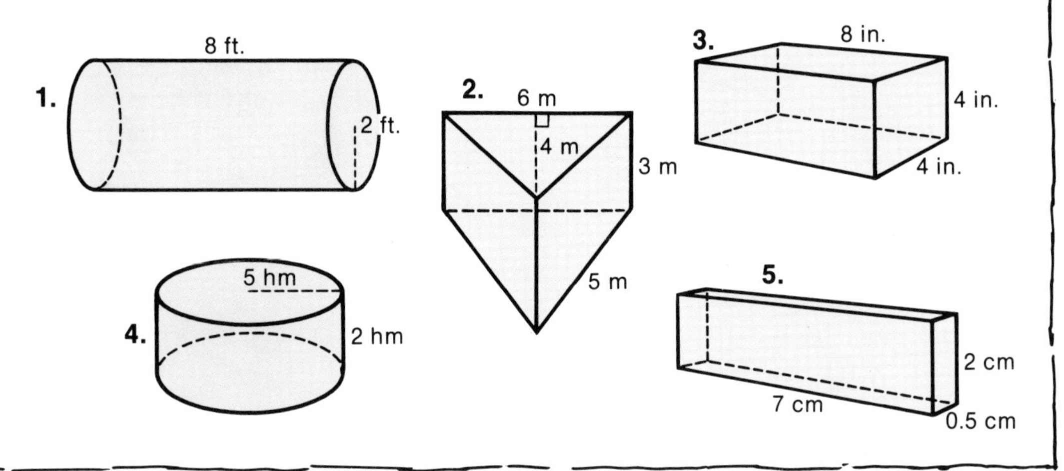

Volume

How would you find out how much concrete it would take to fill a level space?

You must find the *volume* of the space.

Keys to Understanding

Volume is the amount of space in a solid figure.

It is measured in cubic units.

Example: the symbol m^3 means "cubic meter."

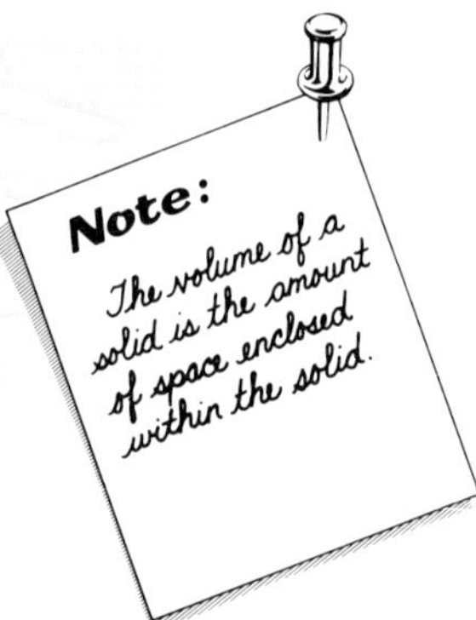

Cubic units

1 cm   1 cm^2 1 cm^3

The unit 1 cm^3 (cubic centimeter) is the space within a solid having a base of 1 cm^2 and a height of 1 cm. What is the unit 1 m^3? 1 $in.^3$? 1 $ft.^3$?

Note:
Volume is the amount of cubic units it takes to fill a given space.

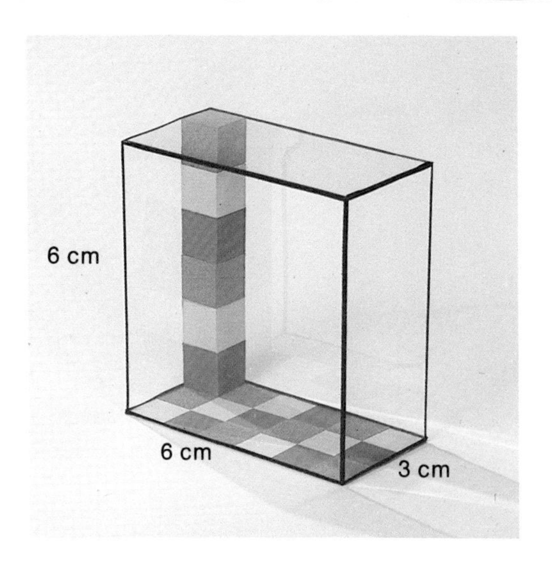

Find out how many cubic centimeters it will take to fill this prism.

How many cubic centimeters are in each stack?

How many stacks will it take to fill the prism?

How do you find the total number of cubic centimeters it will take to fill the prism?

The height *(h)* tells how many cubic units are in each stack. The area of the base (B) tells how many stacks. The volume equals the number of stacks times the number in each stack.

Write an equation for the volume of a prism.

Will your equation work for the volume of a cylinder?

$$
\begin{aligned}
V &= B \cdot h \\
&= (\pi r^2) \cdot h \\
&= 16\,\pi\ m^2 \cdot 9\ m \\
&= 144\,\pi\ m^3 \\
&= 452.16\ m^3
\end{aligned}
$$

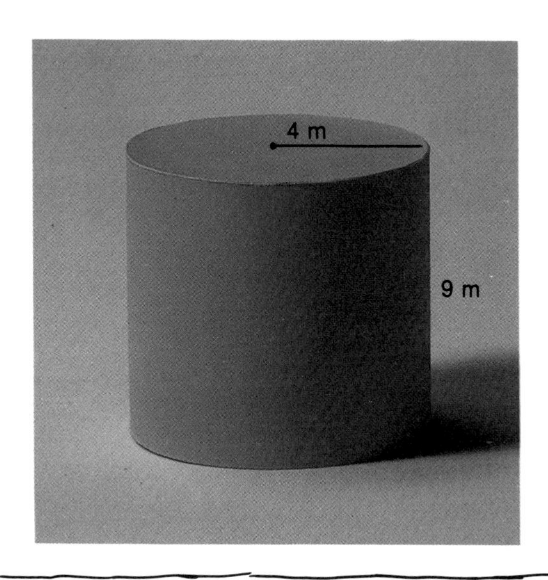

Keys to Understanding

The equation for the volume of a prism or a cylinder is

$V = Bh$ B = area of the base
h = height

Prism

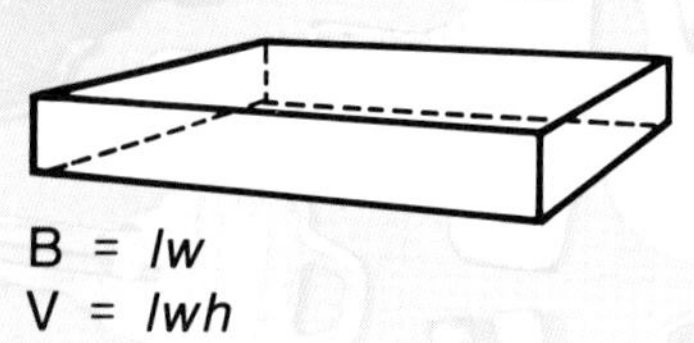

$B = lw$
$V = lwh$

Cylinder

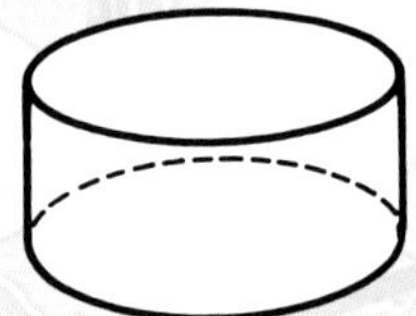

$B = \pi r^2$
$V = \pi r^2 h$

Practice

Find the volume of each of these solids.

1.

2.

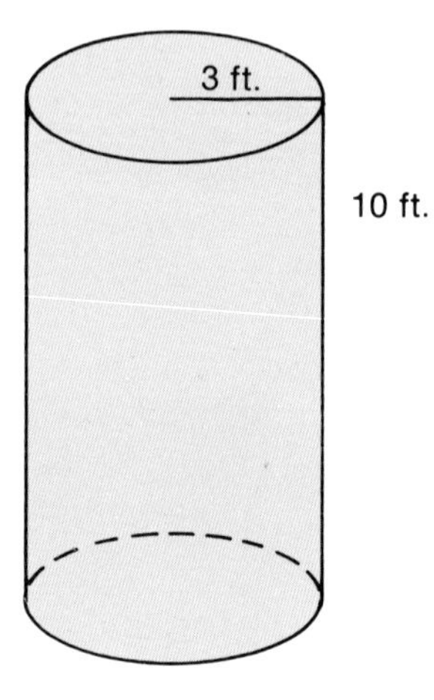

3.

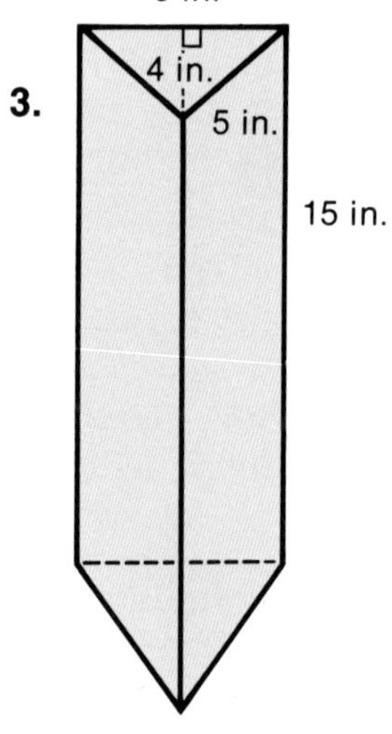

4.

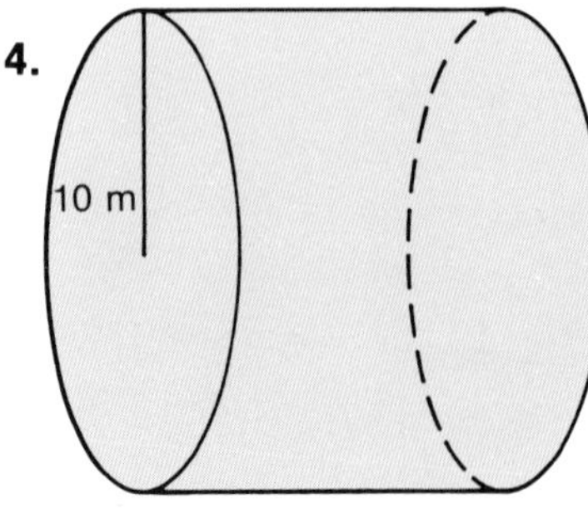

5.

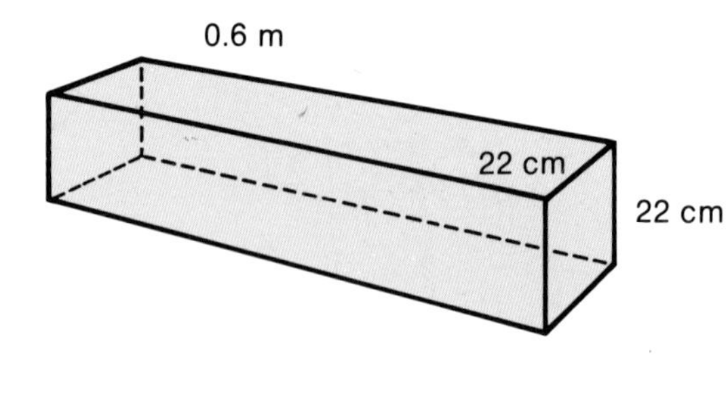

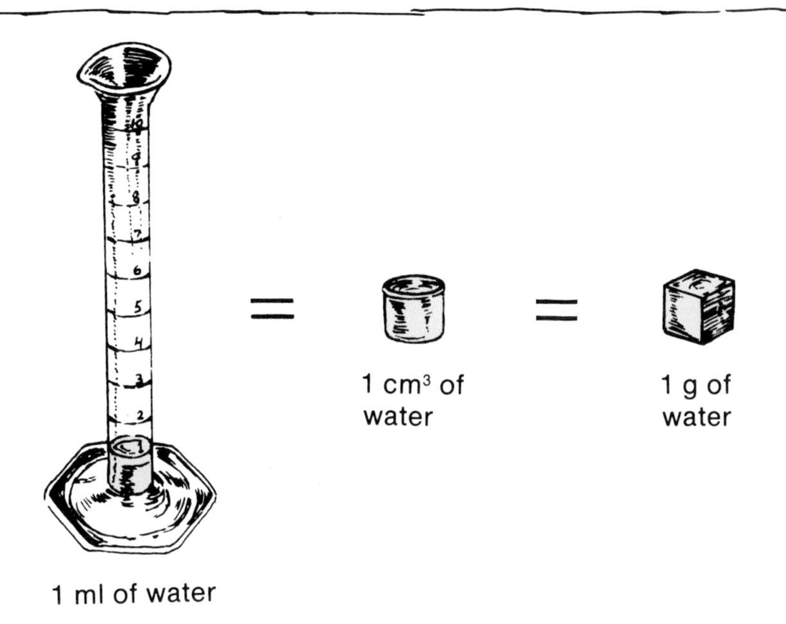

1 ml of water

The relationship of 1 ℓ of water to the other measures is

1ℓ of water = 1,000 g of water = 1,000 cm^3 of water = 1 dm^3 of water

1,000 ℓ = 1,000 dm^3 = 1m^3

Practice

Solve these problems.

1. A swimming pool is 5 m wide, 10 m long, and 3 m deep. What is the volume of the pool? How many liters of water would it take to fill the pool completely full?
2. If you drank 0.5 ℓ of water, how many grams of water did you drink?
3. A water glass has a diameter of 10 cm and a height of 1.5 dm. If the water is 2 cm from the top of the glass, how many milliliters of water are in the glass?
4. John used 9,983 cm^3 of water on his grass. How many liters did he use?
5. Tim's sandbox is 4 ft. by 5 ft. by 8 in. deep. How many cubic feet of sand will it hold when leveled off?

Unit Review

Fill in the blanks with the correct conversions.

1. 1 g = ______ mg	**5.** 13.2 dm = ______ m	**9.** 3.9 cg = ______ g
2. 1 g = ______ kg	**6.** 248 m = ______ km	**10.** 0.15 hm = ______ dm
3. 2.6 m = ______cm	**7.** 1,680 ml = ______ ℓ	**11.** 1.3 ℓ = ______ cl
4. .8 ℓ = ______ hl	**8.** 14.3 mm = ______ dm	**12.** 12 kg = ______ dg

Measure and find the perimeters of these figures.

13. **14.** **15.**

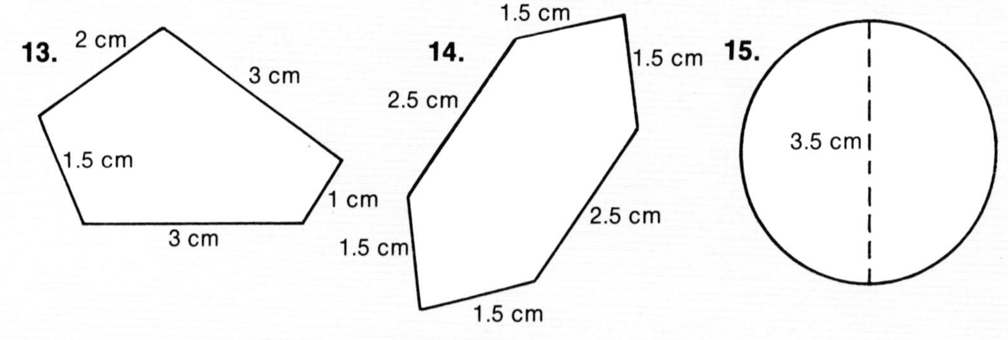

Find the area of each of these figures.

16.

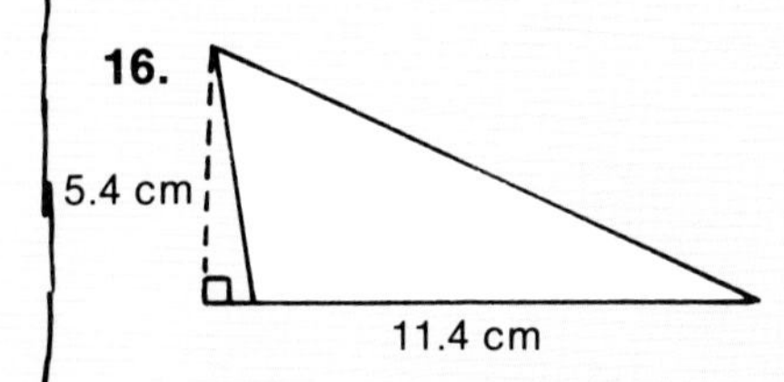

17.

8 in.

10 in.

16 in.

18.

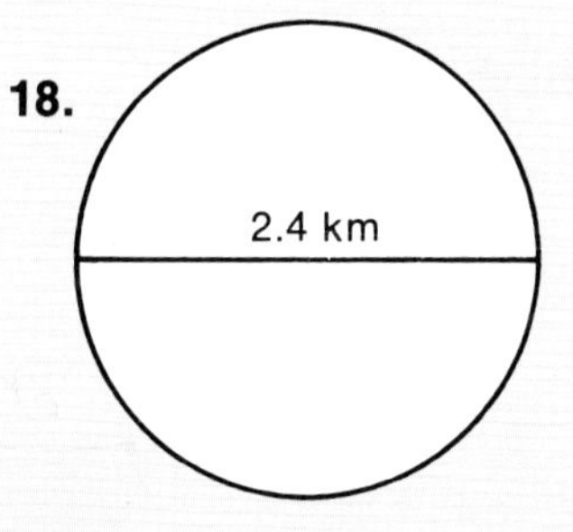

Find the surface area and volume of each of these solids.

19.

1.2 m

0.8 m

2 dm

20.

16 ft.

6 ft.

20 ft.

10 ft.

Give the letter of the answer that *best* matches each of the following expressions. (No letter is used more than once.)

21. $2r$	**a.** trapezoid
22. $\frac{1}{2} h (b_1 + b_2)$	**b.** circumference
23. bh	**c.** perimeter
24. πr^2	**d.** volume
25. Bh	**e.** diameter
26. lw	**f.** rectangle
27. πd	**g.** surface area
28. $\frac{1}{2} bh$	**h.** parallelogram
29. s^2	**i.** triangle
30. $\frac{d}{2}$	**j.** radius
	k. square
	l. circle

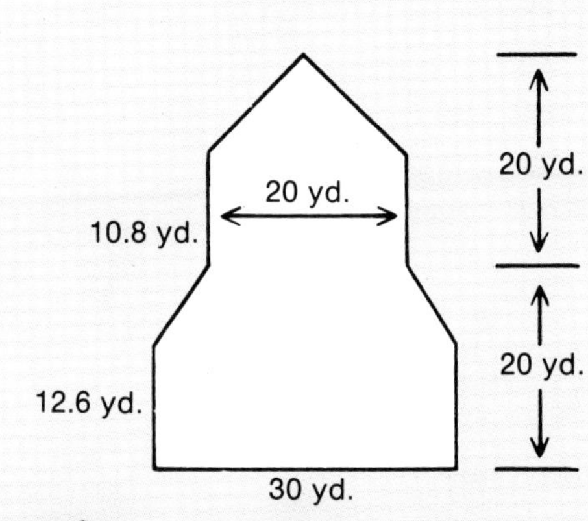

31. The members of a church are planning to recarpet their auditorium. Using the scale drawing of the auditorium floor, determine how many square yards of carpet they need. If the carpet costs $18 per square yard, how much money will they have to spend?

MIND BOGGLER

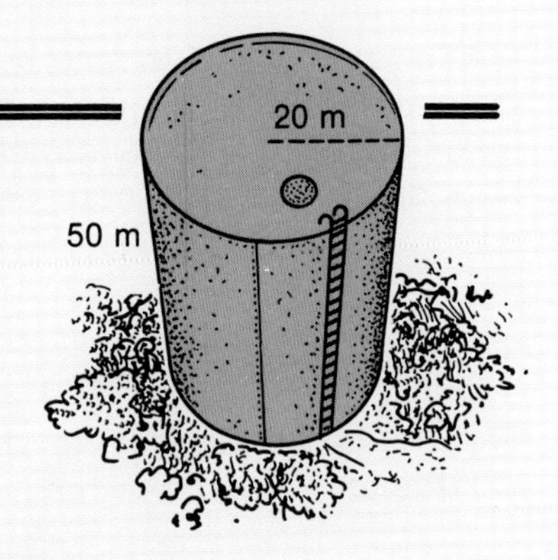

The town of Lakeville is going to paint the outside of a tank and then fill it with water. How much surface will need to be painted? How many liters of water will the tank hold? (The bottom of the tank will not be painted since it is fastened to the ground.)

Skills Checkup

1. 410,221 + 31,856 + 200 + 8,953 + 215,273 + 352,495 + 208 + 29,001

2. 52,314 - 41,698
3. 976,300 - 244,527
4. 157,408 - 34,109
5. 4,567,604 × 308
6. 368 × 5,679
7. 146 × 5,389
8. 237,372 ÷ 569
9. 5,535 ÷ 41
10. 31,000 ÷ 30

11. $3\frac{3}{4} + \frac{1}{2} + \frac{3}{20}$
12. $1\frac{7}{15} + 3\frac{2}{3}$
13. $4\frac{5}{8} + \frac{5}{6} + 3\frac{7}{24}$
14. $6\frac{7}{8} - 2\frac{1}{4}$
15. $9\frac{3}{10} - \frac{17}{20}$
16. $2\frac{3}{5} - \frac{7}{8}$
17. $\frac{2}{5} \times 3\frac{1}{4}$
18. $3\frac{1}{4} \times 2\frac{1}{5}$
19. $6\frac{3}{4} \times 2\frac{1}{2}$
20. $2\frac{1}{3} \div 3\frac{1}{2}$
21. $\frac{5}{6} \div \frac{1}{8}$
22. $2\frac{3}{4} \div \frac{3}{4}$

23. 0.9 + 3.6 + 10.9 + 17.04 + 8.36
24. 35.4179 + 8.3 + 6.5 + 9.253
25. 6.3758 - 2.8136
26. 7 - 0.783
27. 34,005 - 23.99
28. 34.86 × 0.234
29. 87.01 × 0.45
30. 0.123 × 33.4
31. 706.8 ÷ 9.3
32. 2.632 ÷ 0.47
33. 1.1778 ÷ 0.453

34. Karen bought a pair of shoes for $19.95, a sweater for $17.98, a skirt for $11.50, and a purse for $13.45. How much did she spend in all? If Karen saved $2.62 every week to buy these new things, how long did it take her to save the money?
35. Meg earned $33.75 in nine hours. How much did she make per hour? If she got a raise of $.15 an hour, how much would she make in nine hours? in three nine-hour days? in a forty-hour work week?
36. If Meg rents an apartment that costs $250 per month, is her salary from one week enough to pay a month's rent? Her salary for one week is how much more or less than necessary?
37. The church parking lot can hold as many as 320 cars. If $\frac{7}{8}$ of the lot is filled, how many cars are in the lot?

1. 30,216 + 256 + 16,945 + 2,142 + 11,281 + 327 + 115,394 + 253

2. 3,142,251 - 2,256,143
3. 6,042,751 - 4,215,816
4. 70,532 - 65,763
5. 4,142 × 623
6. 786 × 4,173
7. 753 × 328
8. 87 × 82
9. 85,094 ÷ 271
10. 9,676 ÷ 417
11. 2,232 ÷ 18
12. 5,130 ÷ 15

13. $6\frac{3}{8} + 3\frac{5}{16} + 1\frac{3}{4}$
14. $5\frac{1}{6} + 7\frac{2}{5} + 3\frac{1}{3}$
15. $8\frac{3}{8} + 7\frac{1}{8}$
16. $19\frac{5}{7} - 12\frac{2}{5}$
17. $4\frac{7}{10} - 2\frac{19}{20}$
18. $8 - 5\frac{5}{6}$
19. $4 \times 3\frac{3}{4}$
20. $\frac{6}{7} \times \frac{2}{3}$
21. $1\frac{1}{2} \times 3\frac{5}{6}$
22. $2\frac{1}{2} \div \frac{2}{3}$
23. $7\frac{3}{8} \div 3$
24. $1\frac{1}{2} \div 1\frac{1}{8}$

25. 3.4 + 89.31 + 8.245
26. 6.7 + 8.3 + 52.71 + 7
27. 27 + 0.63 + 9.2 + 1.4
28. 0.7537 - 0.1243
29. 53.034 - 6.917
30. 7.3 - 3.4125
31. 53.9 × 6.3
32. 2.47 × 0.32
33. 0.0004 × 0.03
34. 10.92 ÷ 0.52
35. 2.001 ÷ 8.7
36. 76.22 ÷ 0.74

37. Jerry has a board 3.75 meters long. He wants to cut the board in half. How long will each piece be? How long would each piece be if he cut the board into three pieces? five pieces?
38. One sheet of paper is 0.08 millimeters thick. How many millimeters high is a stack of 2,500 sheets of paper? How many meters high is the same stack?
39. Mr. Martin's backyard is 50 meters long and 40 meters wide. How much fence would it take to enclose his yard? How much sod would it take to cover his yard?
40. Mr. Block found tires for sale at $39.95 each at one store and "4 for $150" at another store. If he needs four new tires, which is the better buy? How much less is the better buy?
41. A plumber earns $35.50 an hour. If it took him $2\frac{1}{2}$ hours to fix some pipes and faucets, how much did he make on the repair?

yellow

+ magenta

+ cyan

+ black

math...

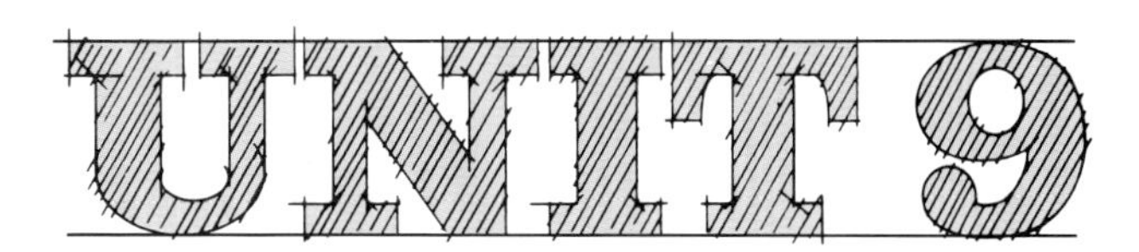

Printer

From the writing on your toothpaste tube to the tag inside your shoe, printing plays a part in your life. Most of us would have a hard time getting along without printed materials. Textbooks would be handwritten; scribes would be overworked, to say the least.

Every aspect of the printing process, from composition to camera, from platemaking to the press, requires close attention to detail. If the typesetter produces bad type, the camera will pick it up, and the press will print the defect. Images that the camera does not pick up are lost on film, and the press cannot recover them. Each part of the process of printing depends on each of the others.

Many large printing companies use multicolor perfectors, which print up to four colors at once on one side of a sheet of paper. Because of their size, these presses require at least two pressmen to operate them.

Math 7 for Christian Schools was printed by a multicolor perfector. During one eight-hour shift, the press used forty pounds of ink, twenty gallons of water, and three skids of paper. Each skid contains 24,000 sheets of paper, each large enough for 16 pages in the finished book.

After the paper rolls through the press, the pressmen check the product to be sure that the color is properly aligned and the print is clear. While working, the pressmen must set their minds on the goal of printing a flawless book rather than just watching the presses roll.

Printing is a day-by-day process that results in a book that many people see. Our lives are shaped day by day into forms that bear testimony to Christ's work in us. One day the "book" of our lives will be completed. "He which hath begun a good work in you will perform it until the day of Jesus Christ" (Philippians 1:6).

Ratios

A baseball player has made 3 hits for every 10 times at bat.

His *ratio* of hits to times at bat is 3 to 10.

Keys to Understanding

A *ratio* is a comparison of two sets, expressed with numbers.
The ratio of *a* to *b* can be written *a*:*b*.

Ratios are often expressed in fractional form, because in most situations, operating with ratios follows fractional procedures.

Note:
The ratio of a to b (a:b) can also be written $\frac{a}{b}$.

Remember how to find equivalent fractions.

What do you think?

How would you express the ratio 3 to 10 in fractional form?
How do you think you could find equivalent ratios?
Is the ratio 3:10 in simplest form?
How would you determine the number of hits the baseball player made if he batted 40 times?

Jessica makes punch by mixing three cups of orange juice with two cups of ginger ale. How much ginger ale would she mix in if she had six cups of orange juice? nine cups? twelve cups? fifteen cups?

A chart might be helpful in solving this problem.

Cups of orange juice	Cups of ginger ale
3	2
6	4
9	?
12	?
15	?

Could you have solved the problem without a chart? How? Which method is quicker and easier?

Practice

Write a ratio for each statement in two different ways, comparing the first item to the second.

1. A ruler is 1 foot long, and a yardstick is 3 feet long.

2. There are 11 girls and 13 boys in the math class.

3. You can buy 2 book covers for 25 cents.

4. In each package you receive 5 pencils and 2 pens.

5. Phil answered 8 out of 10 questions on the test correctly.

Tell whether each of the following fractional forms is equivalent to the ratio 5:7.

6. $\frac{15}{21}$ **7.** $\frac{3}{5}$ **8.** $\frac{30}{42}$ **9.** $\frac{45}{63}$ **10.** $\frac{42}{49}$

Write each ratio as an equivalent ratio in simplest fractional form.

11. 12:30 **12.** 25:9 **13.** 14:49 **14.** 15:15 **15.** 55:100

16. What will 8 items cost if you can buy 2 for 15 cents?

17. What will 16 items cost if you can buy 4 for 3 dollars?

18. What will 15 items cost if you can buy 3 for 59 cents?

19. What will 49 items cost if you can buy 7 for $1.50?

20. What will 111 items cost if you can buy 3 for 25 cents?

Comparing Ratios

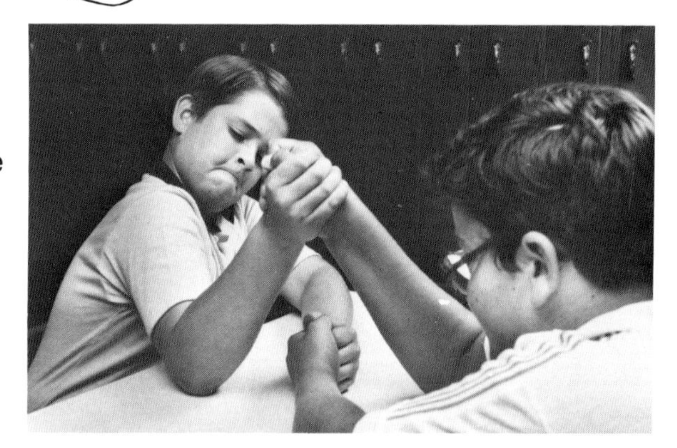

There are still three possible outcomes. What are they?

What three possibilities are there when we compare numbers?

Is the ratio 2:3 equal to, greater than, or less than 12:18?

To compare ratios, first express them in fractional form. Then compare them as you would fractions.

Remember the easy way to compare fractions.

$\frac{2}{3} \stackrel{?}{=} \frac{12}{18}$	Write as fractions.
$2 \cdot 18 \stackrel{?}{=} 3 \cdot 12$	Cross multiply.
$36 = 36$ $2:3 = 12:18$	The ratios are equal. We say that they are *proportional*.

Keys to Understanding

A *proportion* is an equation that states that two ratios are equal.

$$3:5 = 6:10 \quad \text{or} \quad \frac{3}{5} = \frac{6}{10}$$

The two end numbers in a proportion are called the *extremes*.

The two middle numbers in a proportion are called the *means*.

The product of the extremes is equal to the product of the means.

extremes
$3:5 = 6:10$
means

$3 \cdot 10 = 5 \cdot 6$

$\frac{3}{5} \times \frac{6}{10}$
cross multiplication

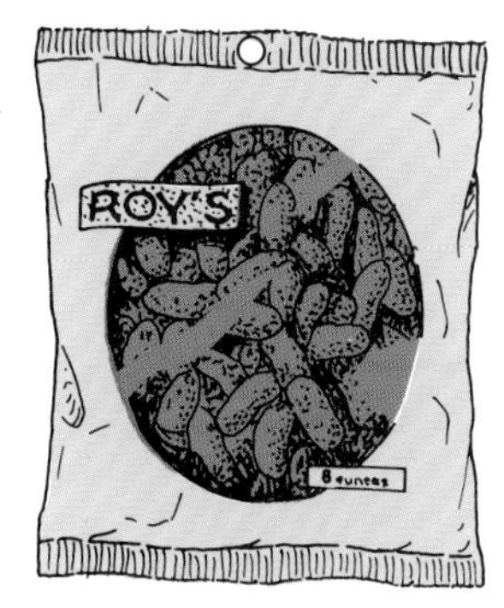

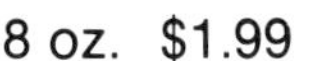
8 oz. $1.99

2 oz. $.49

Paul wants to buy some peanuts at the store. He notices two sizes of packages at different prices. How can he figure out which package is the better buy?

Note: *The larger package is not always the better deal.*

Set up a ratio for each package, comparing ounces to costs.

$8:199$ and $2:49$, or $\frac{8}{199}$ and $\frac{2}{49}$

These ratios express the number of ounces that can be bought for 1 cent.

Compare the ratios by multiplying the extremes and the means (cross multiplication).

$$2 \cdot 199 \stackrel{?}{=} 8 \cdot 49$$

$$392 < 398, \text{ so } 8:199 < 2:49$$

Are the ratios proportional? Which package contains more peanuts for the money?

Remember the proper procedure for cross multiplication.

Practice

Compare these ratios, using the correct symbol $(<, >, =)$.

1. 6:5 and 3:1

2. 11:12 and 18:21

3. 15:9 and 20:12

4. 3:5 and 12:20

5. 5:3 and 100:55

6. 4:6 and 40:72

Solve these problems.

7. One car traveled 260 miles on 15 gallons of gas. Another car traveled 100 miles on 7 gallons of gas. Which car got the better gas mileage?

8. There are 2 sizes of peanut butter jars at the store. The 18-ounce jar costs $1.89, and the 8-ounce jar costs $.89. Which is the better buy?

9. One team has *won* 11 of 20 games. Another team has *lost* 8 of 18 games. Which team has the better record?

10. The seventh grade has 3 boys for every 5 girls. The eighth grade has 15 girls for every 12 boys. Which class has the higher ratio of girls?

Using Proportions

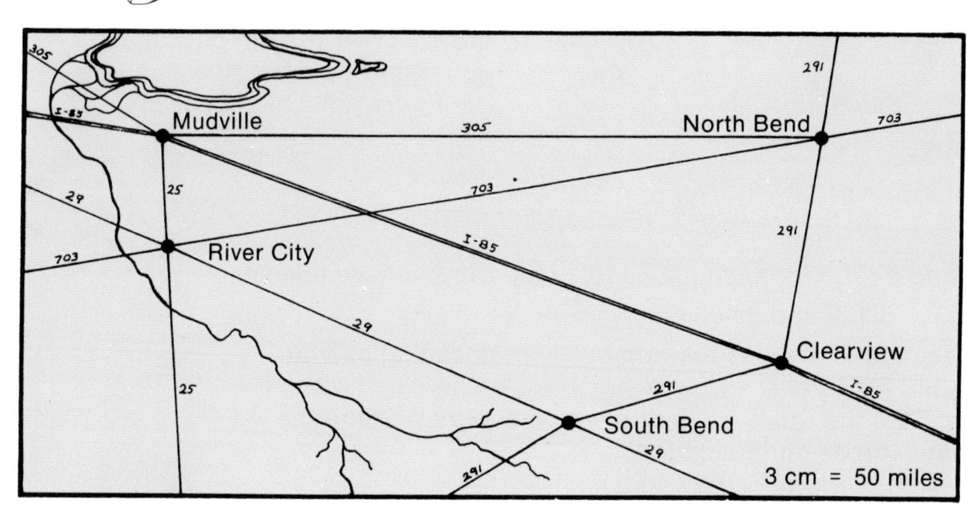

How many miles is it from Mudville to Clearview?

You can solve this problem by using a proportion.

First write a proportion in fractional form.	$\frac{3}{50} = \frac{9}{n}$
Then cross multiply.	$3n = 450$
Now find the solution.	$n = \frac{450}{3}$
	$n = 150$

The distance from Mudville to Clearview is 150 miles.

Remember, divide to find the missing factor.

What do you think?

How many miles is it from Mudville to North Bend? to River City?
How many miles is it from North Bend to Clearview? to River City?
How many miles is it from South Bend to North Bend? to River City?
Which two cities are the same distance from Clearview?

Practice

Use cross multiplication to find the solution for each problem.

1. $\frac{4}{n} = \frac{2}{9}$
2. $\frac{2}{3} = \frac{a}{12}$
3. $\frac{6}{8} = \frac{9}{b}$
4. $\frac{4}{16} = \frac{3}{x}$
5. $\frac{n}{3} = \frac{8}{12}$
6. $\frac{a}{5} = \frac{3}{5}$
7. $\frac{3}{8} = \frac{n}{16}$
8. $\frac{10}{a} = \frac{2}{5}$
9. $\frac{5}{11} = \frac{10}{x}$

Solve these problems, using proportions.

10. A class went to the state capital in a bus that used 2 gallons of gas to travel 25 miles. How much gas would the bus use to travel 175 miles?
11. The school booster club is selling 1 dozen school pennants for $6. How much would 4 pennants cost?
12. A sloppy-joe recipe calls for 3 pounds of hamburger to feed 9 people. How much hamburger would be needed to feed sloppy joes to 27 people?
13. The Sunday school had a ratio of 2 adults for every 3 children. If the Sunday school had 88 adults in attendance, how many children were present?
14. A baseball player's ratio of hits to times at bat is 3 to 8. How many times has he batted if he has made 15 hits?
15. The ratio of boys to girls in a senior choir is 2 to 3. There are 24 boys in the choir. How many girls are in the choir?

BUT BOB, JUST THINK OF THE GAS WE'RE SAVING!

Percent

The percent symbol (%) is used to show a ratio of a given number to 100.

51% = 51:100

49% = 49:100

The word *percent* comes from the Latin phrase *per centum* and means "for each hundred."

For every 100 students who voted in the school election, 51 voted for Paul Lyda (51%), and 49 voted for Peter Lynch (49%).

Keys to Understanding

Percent (%) is the ratio of a given number to 100.

35 for each 100 = 35% = $\frac{35}{100}$ = .35

Any ratio that compares a number n to 100 can be expressed as a percent.

$\frac{n}{100} = n\%$

What do you think?

Can any ratio be expressed in fractional form?
Can any fraction be expressed as a percent?
Can any ratio be expressed as a percent?
Can any mixed number be expressed as a percent?
Can any decimal fraction be expressed as a percent?

To write a fraction as a percent, find an equivalent fraction with a denominator of 100.

Write $\frac{1}{4}$ as a percent:

Set up a proportion. $\frac{1}{4} = \frac{n}{100}$

Cross multiply. $100 = 4n$

Solve. $25 = n$

$\frac{1}{4} = \frac{25}{100} = 25\%$

Percents may be greater than 100%.

Write $2\frac{1}{2}$ as a percent:

$\frac{5}{2} = \frac{n}{100}$

$500 = 2n$

$250 = n$

$2\frac{1}{2} = \frac{5}{2} = \frac{250}{100} = 250\%$

Percents may be equal to 100%.

Write $\frac{3}{3}$ as a percent:

$\frac{3}{3} = \frac{n}{100}$

$300 = 3n$

$100 = n$

$\frac{3}{3} = \frac{100}{100} = 100\%$

Practice

Write each fraction as a percent.

1. $\frac{15}{100}$	**6.** $\frac{2}{5}$	**11.** $1\frac{1}{2}$	**16.** $\frac{3}{100}$	**21.** $\frac{18}{25}$
2. $\frac{67}{100}$	**7.** $\frac{1}{25}$	**12.** $\frac{7}{7}$	**17.** $1\frac{1}{5}$	**22.** $\frac{81}{81}$
3. $\frac{9}{10}$	**8.** $1\frac{2}{10}$	**13.** $\frac{3}{5}$	**18.** $\frac{1}{50}$	**23.** $\frac{19}{20}$
4. $\frac{1}{2}$	**9.** $\frac{3}{4}$	**14.** $\frac{3}{50}$	**19.** $\frac{6}{25}$	**24.** $2\frac{1}{5}$
5. $\frac{5}{4}$	**10.** $\frac{11}{20}$	**15.** $\frac{3}{10}$	**20.** $1\frac{3}{4}$	**25.** $\frac{23}{50}$

Write each percent as a fraction in lowest terms.

26. 32%	**27.** 5%	**28.** 50%	**29.** 63%	**30.** 150%

Percents and Decimal Numbers

Ratio	Fraction	Equivalent Fraction (denominator of 100)	Decimal	Percent
40:100	$\frac{40}{100}$	$\frac{40}{100}$	.40	40%
3:5	$\frac{3}{5}$	$\frac{60}{100}$	.60	60%
6:25	$\frac{6}{25}$	$\frac{24}{100}$	.24	24%
5:4	$\frac{5}{4}$	$\frac{125}{100}$	1.25	125%

In order to solve problems, it is often necessary to change decimal numbers to percents and percents to decimal numbers.

Decimal Numbers to Percents

$.80 = \frac{.80}{1} \times \frac{100}{100} = \frac{80}{100} = 80\%$ $\quad .80 \times 100 = 80\%$

$1.34 = \frac{1.34}{1} \times \frac{100}{100} = \frac{134}{100} = 134\%$ $\quad 1.34 \times 100 = 134\%$

$.7 = \frac{.7}{1} \times \frac{100}{100} = \frac{70}{100} = 70\%$ $\quad .7 \times 100 = 70\%$

$.0045 = \frac{.0045}{1} \times \frac{100}{100} = \frac{.45}{100} = .45\%$ $\quad .0045 \times 100 = .45\%$

Converting decimal numbers to percents is simple. Just multiply the decimal number by 100 and annex the percent symbol (%).

When you follow this rule, what are you actually doing?

Remember the fast way to multiply a decimal by 100.

You can write a fraction as a percent by first writing it as a decimal and then converting the decimal to a percent.

$\frac{1}{2} = .5 = 50\%$ $\quad \frac{13}{20} = .65 = 65\%$

Remember how to convert a fraction to a decimal.

Percents to Decimal Numbers

$75\% = \frac{75}{100} = .75$ $\quad 75 \div 100 = .75$

$182\% = \frac{182}{100} = 1.82$ $\quad 182 \div 100 = 1.82$

$.9\% = \frac{.9}{100} = .009$ $\quad .9 \div 100 = .009$

$.16\% = \frac{.16}{100} = .0016$ $\quad .16 \div 100 = .0016$

Remember the fast way to divide a decimal by 100.

Converting percents to decimal numbers is simple. Just divide the percent number by 100 and omit the percent symbol (%).

Practice

Write each decimal as a percent.

1. 0.63	**5.** 1.18	**9.** 0.47	**13.** 0.4	**17.** 3.15
2. 0.33	**6.** 0.03	**10.** 0.002	**14.** 0.01	**18.** 1
3. 0.16	**7.** 0.2	**11.** 2.8	**15.** 0.007	**19.** 2.136
4. 0.80	**8.** 1.09	**12.** 0.05	**16.** 0.0001	**20.** 0.1198

Write each fraction as a decimal and then as a percent. (If you divide to find the decimal, round to the nearest thousandth.)

21. $\frac{1}{2}$	**23.** $\frac{1}{4}$	**25.** $\frac{1}{6}$	**27.** $\frac{1}{8}$	**29.** $\frac{1}{10}$
22. $\frac{1}{3}$	**24.** $\frac{1}{5}$	**26.** $\frac{1}{7}$	**28.** $\frac{1}{9}$	**30.** $\frac{1}{11}$

Write each percent as a decimal.

31. 33%	**35.** 107%	**39.** 6.3%	**43.** 4.2%	**47.** 1.8%
32. 67%	**36.** 8%	**40.** 0.1%	**44.** .015%	**48.** 0.001%
33. 48%	**37.** 218%	**41.** 23.3%	**45.** 0.5%	**49.** 2.23%
34. 25%	**38.** 5%	**42.** 118%	**46.** 73%	**50.** 100%

Finding Percents of Numbers

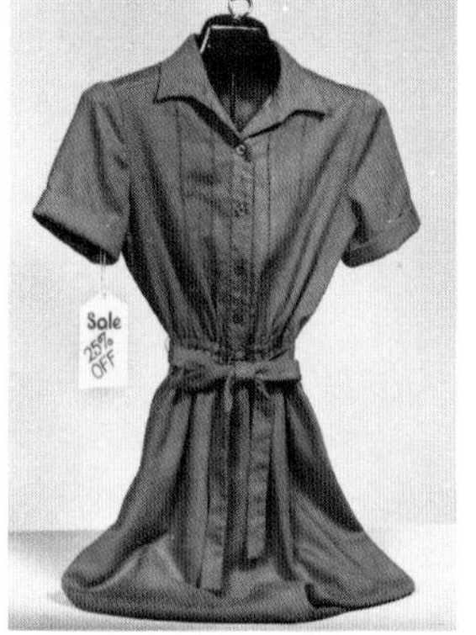

Diane wants to buy a dress that usually costs $28.60. There is now a sale, and the dress is marked 25% off. How much will Diane save if she buys the dress now? What is the sale price of the dress?

The percent of a number can be found by changing the percent to a fraction or a decimal and then multiplying.

Change the percent to a fraction and multiply.

$$25\% \text{ of } \$28.60 = n$$
$$\frac{1}{4} \text{ of } \$28.60 = n$$
$$\frac{1}{4} \times \$28.60 = n$$
$$\$7.15 = n$$

Change the percent to a decimal and multiply.

$$25\% \text{ of } \$28.60 = n$$
$$.25 \text{ of } \$28.60 = n$$
$$.25 \times \$28.60 = n$$
$$\$7.15 = n$$

How much money can Diane save by buying the dress on sale?

What is the sale price of the dress? How did you find it?

Remember why "of" is replaced by the multiplication symbol (×).

What do you think?

Which of the two methods above do you think is easier? Why?
What is 100% of a number? How do you know?
What will be true about the answer if it is more than 100% of a number? less than 100%?
What is 0% of a number? How do you know?
Could you find the percent of a number by using a proportion? How?

Practice

Solve each of these problems by first replacing each percent with a fraction.

1. 75% of 16 =
2. 25% of 20 =
3. 20% of 75 =
4. 15% of 80 =
5. 50% of 120 =
6. 80% of 150 =
7. $33\frac{1}{3}$% of 45 =
8. $12\frac{1}{2}$% of 64 =
9. $16\frac{2}{3}$% of 24 =

Solve each of these problems by first replacing each percent with a decimal.

10. 20% of 80 =
11. 6% of 18 =
12. 72% of 70 =
13. 34% of 226 =
14. 42% of 68 =
15. .3% of 5 =
16. 21.3% of 11 =
17. 8.4% of 14.3 =
18. .13% of 187 =

Solve each of these problems using either method.

19. 35% of 16 =
20. 110% of 8 =
21. 4.1% of 20 =
22. 100% of 123 =
23. 325% of 2.7 =
24. 56% of 14 =
25. 17.1% of 23 =
26. 8.1% of 21.8 =
27. 522% of 1.3 =

Solve these problems.

28. The school baseball team won 75% of their games. They played sixteen games during the year. How many games did they win?
29. There are 225 students enrolled in Grace Schools. Forty-eight percent of the students bring their lunches from home. What percent of the students do not bring their lunches? How many students bring their lunches?
30. Mr. Mason earns $325 a week. He wants to give at least a tithe (10%) to his local church. What is 10% of his weekly earnings?

Finding the Total Number

The honor roll has just been posted, and eight students in Miss Sawyer's class are on it. They represent 25% of the total class. How many students are in Miss Sawyer's class?

This problem can be expressed in this way:
25% of what number is 8?

$25\% \times b = 8$	Write a math sentence. (Let b = the number in the class.)
$.25 \times b = 8$	Change the percent to a decimal.
$b = \frac{8}{.25}$	Find the solution.

Answer: Miss Sawyer's class has 32 students.

Remember how to find the missing factor.

A school raised the price of its yearbook to \$20. The new price is 150% of last year's price. What was the cost of the yearbook last year?

What do you think?

What math sentence would you write to express this problem?
Will the answer be greater than or less than \$20? How do you know?
What operation will you use to solve the problem? Solve the problem.
What was the amount of increase in the price of the book?
What was the percent of increase in the price of the book?
Could you have solved the problem using a proportion? How?

Practice

Solve these problems.

1. 50% of what number is 4?
2. 15% of what number is 45?
3. 125% of what number is 55?
4. 65% of what number is 65?
5. 300% of what number is 21?
6. 2.5% of what number is 5?
7. 100% of what number is 163?
8. 0.9% of what number is 18?
9. 10% of what number is 12.5?
10. 0.19% of what number is 2.7?
11. There are 20 boys on the school's baseball team. They represent 5% of the boys in the junior high. How many boys are in the junior high altogether?
12. Rick bought a new suit on sale and saved $36. All the suits were on sale for 70% of the original price. What was the original price of Rick's suit?
13. Angie spent 45% of her allowance to buy a school banner. The banner cost $1.80. How much money does Angie receive for her allowance?
14. Eighty-five percent of the student body at Christian Academy are going on a field trip to the hydroelectric generating plant. That means that 221 of the students are going. How many students attend the academy?
15. The price for a school jacket is 125% of last year's price. If the current price is $32, what was last year's price?

Finding Percents

On a math test, Frank answered 36 of the 40 problems correctly. What is his percent grade? (What percent of the problems did he answer correctly?)

MATH TEST — Frank Smith

1. 8	11. 20	21. 93	31. .5
2. 4	12. 31	22. 76	32. 27
3. 11	13. 25	23. 54	33. 88
4. 5	14. 28	24. 13	34. 43
5. 16	15. 101	25. 212	35. 31
6. 23	16. 7	26. 234	36. 82
7. 54	17. 3	27. 81	37. 2
8. 12	18. 21	28. 0	38. -3
9. 36	19. 29	29. .9	39. .1
10. 44	20. 67	30. 71	40. 99

This problem can be expressed in this way:

What percent of 40 is 36?

$P \times 40 = 36$	Write a math sentence.
$P = \frac{36}{40}$	(Let P = percent correct.)
$P = .90$	Find the solution.
$P = 90\%$	Change the decimal to a percent.

Answer: Frank's percent grade is 90%.
Do you think he received a good grade?

The price of a chicken dinner has gone up from $2 to $3.
What percent of the old price is the new price?

What do you think?

What math sentence would you write to express this problem?
Will the percent be greater than or less than 100%? How do you know?
What operation will you use to solve the problem? Solve the problem.
The new price is what percent of the old price?
What was the percent of increase in the price of the dinner?
Could you have solved the problem using a proportion? How?

Practice

Solve these problems. Round to the nearest tenth of a percent.

1. What percent of 18 is 9?
2. What percent of 12 is 8?
3. What percent of 11 is 11?
4. What percent of 5 is 8?
5. What percent of 500 is 125?
6. What percent of 4 is 0.8?
7. What percent of 10 is 0.05?
8. What percent of 96 is 4.8?
9. What percent of 0.9 is 1.8?
10. What percent of 44 is 1.1?

11. In a class of 25 students, 4 were absent. What percent of the class were absent?
12. The discount store is having a big sale on tennis shoes. The sale price on any pair of tennis shoes is $12.50. The normal price is $20.00. What percent of the original price is the sale price?
13. Wayne batted 48 times during the baseball season. He made 16 hits. What percent of times at bat did he make a hit?
14. The junior high's record for the inner-tube distance throw was 20 feet. This year on field day Jim threw the inner tube 35 feet. What percent of the record distance did Jim throw the inner tube?
15. Carla's dad gave her $30.00 to spend at camp. She spent $21.30. What percent of her money did she spend?

Solving Problems

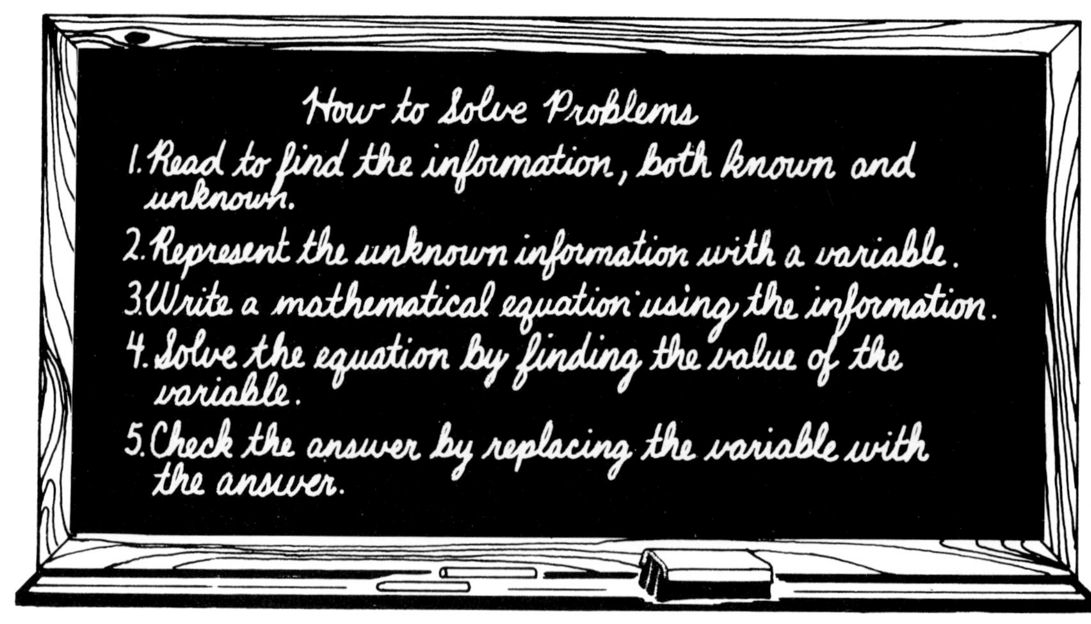

Practice

Solve these problems.

1. There were 60 questions on the English test. Jane missed 15% of them. How many questions did she get wrong? How many questions did she get right?
2. Yesterday there were 21 students in Mrs. Kelley's class. They represented 70% of her entire class. How many students are enrolled in Mrs. Kelley's class?
3. The school's basketball team has won 6 games, which is 75% of the games played so far. How many games have been played?
4. Carolyn bought a skirt on sale for $12. The original price of the skirt was $15. What percent of the original price did she pay?
5. Mr. and Mrs. Myers are buying a house that sells for $68,500. They must make a down payment of 20%. How much will the down payment be?

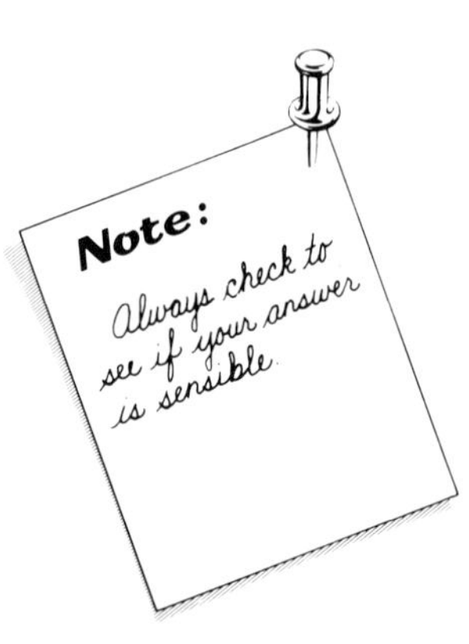

6. Kevin's father saved $475 last year. If his yearly salary was $14,250, what percent of his earnings did he save?
7. The school's record for the soccer season was 5 wins and 3 losses. What percent of their games did they lose?
8. This year Mike's church increased $8\frac{1}{2}$% in attendance over last year's average attendance of 240. How much of an increase did the church have? What was the church's average attendance this year?
9. Theodore bought a camera on sale for 20% off. If he paid $100 for it, what was the original price of the camera?
10. Sharon correctly solved 8 out of the 9 word problems on her math assignment. What percent of the problems did she solve correctly? (Round to the nearest whole percent.)

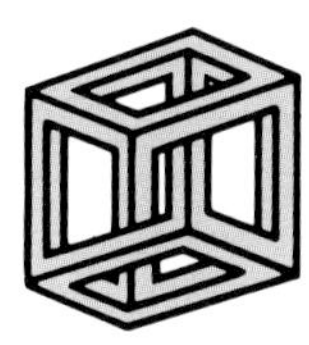

MIND BOGGLER

Thirty-seven and one-half percent of a group of young people at camp were boys. After a week, 24 girls left camp and 24 more boys came to camp. Now $37\frac{1}{2}$% of the group are girls. How many boys and how many girls were at camp the first week?

Percent Change

Last year there were 200 students enrolled at Greenwood Academy. This year there are 240 enrolled. What was the *percent change* from last year to this year?

What do you think?

How can you find the amount of change in student enrollment?
What is the amount of change from last year?
Is the change an increase or a decrease from last year?
What was the original enrollment before the change?
How can you find the percent change in enrollment?

Keys to Understanding

Percent change is a ratio comparing the amount of change to the original amount.

To find percent change, find what percent of the original amount is represented by the amount of change.

The percent change can be either an increase or a decrease.

240 - 200 = 40
Find the change.
Is the change an increase or a decrease?

What percent of the original figure is the amount of change?

$$P \times 200 = 40$$

$$P = \frac{40}{200}$$

Find the solution. $P = .2 = 20\%$
Percent change = 20% increase

The increased number (240) is equal to 100% of the original number (100% of 200) plus the percent increase of the original number (20% of 200).

$(100\% \times 200) + (20\% \times 200) = 240$, or $120\% \times 200 = 240$

Therefore the increased number is 120% of the original figure.

Find the percent change from $2.50 to $1.50.

What is the amount of change?
Is this change an increase or a decrease?
What percent of the original figure is the amount of change?

$$P \times \$2.50 = \$1.00$$

Percent change = 40% decrease

The decreased number is 60% of the original figure.

60% × $2.50 = $1.50

Practice

Find the percent change to the nearest tenth of a percent for each problem. Specify increase or decrease.

1. From 50 to 70
2. From 42 to 28
3. From 60 to 120
4. From \$1.00 to \$1.75
5. From 25 to 15
6. From \$5.00 to \$5.20
7. From 4 to 5.2
8. From \$28.00 to \$26.60
9. From 1.2 to 0.4
10. From 410 to 492

Solve these problems.

11. The temperature in the morning was 40 degrees. In the middle of the afternoon the temperature had gone up to 65 degrees. What was the percent increase in the temperature?
12. Mr. Cook's heating bill last month was \$120. This month the bill dropped to \$102. What was the percent decrease in Mr. Cook's bill?
13. Gordon bought a can of tennis balls for \$3.50. Later, when he went back to buy another can of balls, the price was \$3.92. What was the percent increase in the price?
14. Carol was earning \$1.25 an hour helping Mrs. Craig. Mrs. Craig then gave Carol a \$.50 raise. What percent increase did she receive?
15. The city zoo had five gorillas. The manager traded one of the gorillas for an aardvark, a chimp, and a baby rhinoceros. What was the percent decrease in the gorilla population at the zoo?

Calculate the percent change in the price of each item to the nearest tenth of a percent.

Item	Last year's price	This year's price	Percent change
5 lb. sugar	$2.75	$3.25	18.2%
5 lb. flour	1.33	1.50	12.8%
1 lb. coffee	2.89	3.15	
1 doz. eggs	.99	1.09	
1 qt. mayonnaise	1.50	1.75	
3 lb. shortening	2.10	2.25	
1 can peaches	.99	1.10	
1 loaf bread	.80	.95	
1 cake mix	.75	1.00	
1 lb. ground beef	1.69	1.95	
1 lb. pork chops	1.39	1.57	
1 gal. milk	2.25	2.49	
1 head lettuce	.69	.89	
12 oz. peanut butter	1.35	1.67	
12 oz. cereal	1.27	1.55	

What was the average percent change for the year?

What do you think?

Do you know what inflation in prices is?
What would be the year's percent of inflation shown by these prices?
What percent more money would a person have to earn this year to keep up with the rate of inflation?

Math in Action

1. Your math book contains a total of 352 pages, or 22 large sheets of paper. Each skid of paper contains 24,000 of these large sheets. What percentage of the skid would be used to print 750 *Math 7* books?
2. A ream of paper contains 500 sheets of printing-size paper. How many reams are on a skid?
   If a skid weighs 2400 lbs., how much does a ream weigh?
3. Mr. Barrett was mixing the ink for a color run. He mixed 12 parts warm red with 4 parts rubine red and $\frac{1}{4}$ part black. About what percent of the color was made up of warm red? rubine red? black? (Round to the nearest 0.01%.)
4. During one eight-hour shift Mr. Barrett's press uses 39 pounds of ink, 19.5 gallons of water, and 3 skids of paper. How much ink, water, and paper will the press use to produce an order of books that takes 18 hours to print?
5. To get a desired shade of green, Mr. Barrett had to mix yellow, black, and blue. He mixed 12 times as much blue as black, and twice as much yellow as blue. If he used 6 parts of blue ink, how many parts of black did he use? how many parts of yellow?

Operating with Percents

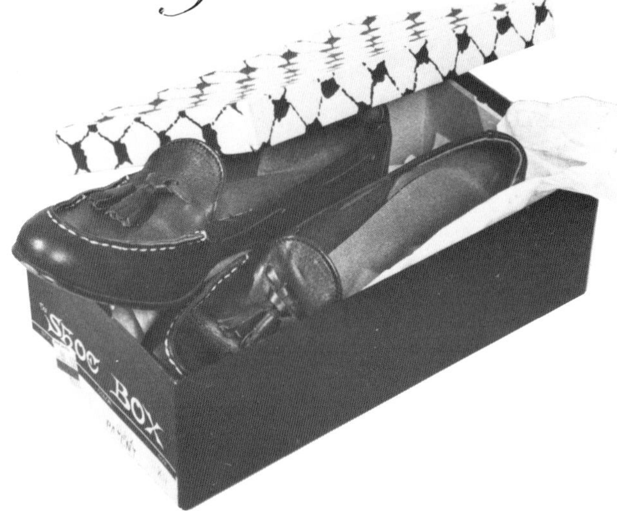

The regular price of a pair of shoes is $28.50.
Find the sale price if the shoes are marked down 20%.

First, find the amount of discount.

Discount = (rate of discount) × (regular price)
Discount = 20% × $28.50
Discount = .2 × $28.50
Discount = $5.70

Now find the sale price.

Sale price = (regular price) - (discount)
Sale price = $28.50 - $5.70
Sale price = $22.80

Practice

25% OFF

Find the sale price of a—

1. Notebook for $2.80
2. Gym bag for $6.00
3. Pen for $1.28
4. Book cover for $.20
5. Jacket for $22.60

30% DISCOUNT

Find the discounted price of a—

6. Basketball for $21.50
7. Baseball bat for $7.50
8. Pair of track shoes for $31.80
9. Soccer ball for $18.25
10. Golf glove for $5.80

Kent earns a 20% commission on his newspaper sales. He sells each newspaper for \$.30.

How much money does he make on each paper he sells?

Commission = (rate of commission) × (sales)
Commission = 20% × \$.30
Commission = .2 × \$.30 = \$.06

Practice

Solve these problems.

1. Mr. Duncan receives a 7% commission for selling houses. He just sold a house for \$68,300. How much commission did he earn?
2. Mr. Fremont sells new cars. He earns 5% commission on his sales. Last week he sold a car for \$6,500 and another for \$8,900. How much did he earn in commissions?
3. Mrs. Rheinhardt is selling cosmetics. She makes 35% commission on all that she sells. How much commission will she make if she sells a lipstick for \$3.20?
4. Luis is being paid 40% commission for selling magazine subscriptions. So far he has sold \$58.60 worth of magazines. How much money has he made?
5. A lawyer earns a 2.5% commission for drawing up the legal papers on the sale of a house. How much would he receive for a \$76,000 house?

Unit Review

Write a ratio for each statement in two different ways, comparing the first item to the second.

1. There are 2 boys for every 3 girls in the school.

2. You can buy 3 hamburgers for $2.

3. George shot the basketball and made 7 out of 10.

Compare these ratios, using the correct symbol ($<$, $>$, =).

4. 3:5 and 7:10 **5.** 11:4 and 25:7 **6.** 9:13 and 4:7

Find the solution to each of these proportions.

7. $\frac{5}{6} = \frac{n}{54}$ **8.** $\frac{8}{7} = \frac{40}{n}$ **9.** $\frac{n}{350} = \frac{2}{7}$

10. The ratio of the number of foreign cars to American cars sold is 5:2. If 1,200 American cars were sold, how many foreign cars were sold during the same time period?

Write each fraction as a percent.

11. $\frac{11}{100}$ **12.** $\frac{7}{10}$ **13.** $\frac{3}{25}$ **14.** $\frac{17}{17}$ **15.** $2\frac{3}{5}$

Write each percent as a fraction in lowest terms.

16. 19% **17.** 40% **18.** 75% **19.** 138% **20.** 89%

Write each decimal as a percent.

21. 0.73 **22.** 1.24 **23.** 0.015 **24.** 0.8 **25.** 3.875

Write each percent as a decimal.

26. 28% **27.** 0.6% **28.** 1.4% **29.** 35.6% **30.** 0.15%

Write each fraction as a decimal and then as a percent. Express each percent to the nearest tenth of a percent.

31. $\frac{2}{5}$ **32.** $\frac{3}{8}$ **33.** $1\frac{1}{4}$ **34.** $\frac{2}{3}$ **35.** $2\frac{5}{6}$

Solve these problems. Round to the nearest tenth of a percent.

36. What is 25% of 120?
37. What percent of 32 is 8?
38. 10% of what number is 16?
39. What is the percent change from 6 to 70?
40. What percent of 63 is 70?
41. 100% of what number is 7.1?
42. 8.9% of 18.1 =
43. What is the percent change from 120 to 102?
44. 4.5% of what number is 3.6?
45. What is the percent change from 3 to 3.5?

Solve these problems.

46. Sweaters that normally cost $25 are on sale for 25% off. What is the sale price?
47. Dave sold 10 posters for $1.50 each. He made 40% profit on each poster. How much money did he make?
48. In a country town, 1 out of every 4 persons works at a nearby textile manufacturing plant. What percent of the people work at the plant?
49. The tuition for school went up from $1,000 to $1,200 per year. What was the percent increase?
50. Linda bought a ticket to the circus from a friend and saved 15%. The ticket cost her $2.55. What was the original price of the ticket?

MIND BOGGLER

A rectangle is 12 cm long and 5 cm wide. Find the dimensions of another rectangle such that the ratio of the perimeter of the second rectangle to the first is 2:1, and the ratio of the area of the second rectangle to the first is also 2:1.

12 cm

5 cm

Skills Checkup

1. 91,015,918 + 2,223,549 + 13,634,777
2. 2,867,413 + 913,024 + 758
3. 3,462,713 - 683,449
4. 4,009,001 - 2,195,093
5. 4,030 - 2,816
6. 18,394 × 804
7. 17,463 × 560
8. 6,412 × 352
9. 3,648 ÷ 64
10. 182,342 ÷ 346
11. 625,570 ÷ 655
12. $7\frac{2}{5} + 6\frac{2}{3} + 3\frac{5}{6}$
13. $3\frac{1}{4} + 6\frac{1}{12}$
14. $5\frac{7}{12} + 7\frac{5}{8}$
15. $8\frac{2}{3} - 1\frac{1}{5}$
16. $6\frac{1}{4} - 2\frac{3}{4}$
17. $9 - 3\frac{5}{7}$
18. $1\frac{2}{3} \times \frac{3}{4}$
19. $6\frac{2}{3} \times 1\frac{1}{2}$
20. $5\frac{1}{5} \times 3$
21. $1\frac{1}{2} \div \frac{1}{3}$
22. $5\frac{1}{6} \div 2\frac{2}{3}$
23. $\frac{5}{6} \div 2\frac{1}{2}$
24. 3.561 + 1.08 + 17.34
25. 8.371 + 2.04 + 7.7
26. 16.3579 + 9.78
27. 17.356 - 2.14
28. 6.3758 - 2.8136
29. 53.034 - 6.917
30. 8.745 × 0.023
31. 0.6539 × 0.83
32. 6.047 × 0.55
33. 255.75 ÷ 3.41
34. 169.12 ÷ 2.8
35. 1.6856 ÷ 6.02
36. The Southside Sabres won 6 of their first 7 games. If their winning percentage was the same at the end of the season, how many games did they win of the 35 that they played?
37. A baseball pitcher won 15 of the 17 games that he played, while another pitcher won 49 of the 55 games that he played. Which pitcher had the better record? What percent did the first pitcher win? the second pitcher?
38. During a fifteen-minute period at a gas station, several customers made purchases: 17.6 gallons, 9.5 gallons, 12.9 gallons, 20 gallons, 18.35 gallons, 4.5 gallons, and 13.45 gallons. How many gallons of gas were sold altogether? If gasoline costs $1.40 a gallon, how much did the proprietor take in during the time?
39. Miss Riley sold $360,000 worth of real estate in one year. Her rate of commission is 7%. How much of the $360,000 is her income for the year? What would be her average monthly income?

1. 3,251,176 + 76,450 + 341,210 + 12 + 4,158,260 + 23,251 + 709

2. 6,413,001 - 2,937,674
3. 456,891 - 316,041
4. 35,016 - 28,345
5. 17,463 × 560
6. 2,059 × 7,854
7. 546 × 372
8. 923,100 ÷ 510
9. 93,818 ÷ 643
10. 27,618 ÷ 16

11. $3\frac{2}{3} + 7\frac{5}{6}$
12. $7\frac{2}{5} + 4\frac{1}{4}$
13. $6\frac{1}{7} + 5\frac{3}{8}$
14. $8\frac{1}{12} - 3\frac{2}{3}$
15. $8\frac{3}{8} - 2\frac{5}{6}$
16. $9\frac{3}{8} - 3\frac{7}{10}$
17. $2\frac{1}{2} \times \frac{7}{8}$
18. $5\frac{2}{5} \times 2\frac{1}{4}$
19. $6\frac{3}{8} \times 5$
20. $\frac{1}{3} \div 1\frac{1}{4}$
21. $\frac{6}{7} \div \frac{5}{6}$
22. $7\frac{1}{2} \div 3\frac{3}{5}$

23. 56.791 + 15.24 + 28.567
24. 0.3567 + 0.8199
25. 0.81 + 9.3 + 0.005
26. 0.7358 - 0.2609
27. 4.19378 - 2.08
28. 53.034 - 6.917
29. 5.642 × 0.871
30. 3.9678 × 0.406
31. 8.74 × 0.023
32. 91.8 ÷ 2.7
33. 2.144 ÷ 3.2
34. 169.12 ÷ 2.8

35. Employees at Steve's Stereo Store receive a 15% discount on their purchases. How much would an employee pay for a console stereo that sells for $589.95? There is also a 4% sales tax on the cost to the employee after the discount has been figured. What is the total cost of the stereo and tax?
36. Jerry bought a new sweater for $15.50. He also had to pay $.77 sales tax. What percent tax was charged on the sweater? What was the total that Jerry had to pay?
37. A new washing machine costs $480. The Jantzes bought one on sale for $336. What percent of the original cost did they pay? What percent did they save? How much money did they save?
38. At Harbor Christian Academy $\frac{5}{7}$ of the student body came to the soccer game. If there are 420 in the student body, how many students were at the game? How many did not attend? What percent of the student body came? (to the nearest whole percent)

Bonds	Cur Yld	Vol	High	Low	Close	Net Chg.
AbbtL 6⅝93	9.8	1	64	64	64	+2
AetnLf 8⅛07	14.	10	58½	58½	58½	+½
AlaP 9s2000	16.	32	56⅛	56	56	-1¼
AlaP 8⅞s03	16.	21	54⅞	54¾	54¾	-¼
AlaP 8¼s03	16.	12	53	52⅝	52⅝	+¼
AlaP 9¾s04	16.	5	59⅛	59⅛	59⅛	-1¾
AlaP 10⅝05	17.	5	64½	64½	64½	+⅜
AlaP 9⅛07	16.	10	56⅝	56⅝	56⅝	-¼
AlaP 9⅛08	16.	10	58	58	58	.....
AlaP 9⅝08	16.	31	59	57½	58⅞	+1⅛
AlaP 12⅝10	16.	9	79⅝	77⅛	77⅛	+⅜
AlaP 14⅜91	16.	20	94	93½	94	+¼
AlaP 17⅜11	17.	16	100⅞	100	100	.....
AlaP 18¼89	17.	5	105	105	105	-1
AlskH 16¼94	16.	5	102	102	102	+5
AlskH 17⅜91	17.	10	105	105	105	.....
AlskH 15¼92	16.	1	98	98	98	.....
AlldC 87s	..	4	49⅝	49⅝	49⅝	+⅛
AlldC 92s	..	31	25	25	25	-¼
AlldC 2000s	..	94	10¼	10	10¼	.....
Alcoa 9s95	14.	5	63½	63½	63½	-½
AMAX 8s86	10.	23	79½	79⅛	79⅛	-1⅛

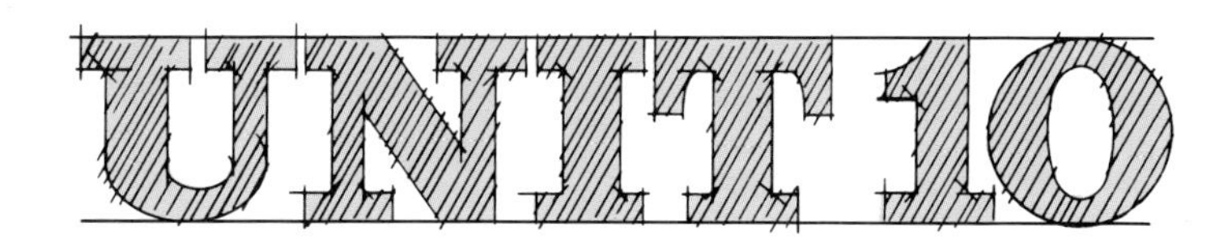

Broker

"Good morning, Robertson-Westmeyer Company."

"Hello, this is Jarod Steiner. I'd like to speak to one of your brokers about purchasing some stock."

"Fine, Mr. Steiner. I'll connect you with Mr. Yoder."

"Dan Yoder here."

"Yes, this is Jarod Steiner. I'd like to invest in some Melville Corporation stock. Two hundred shares at 49, or as close as possible, but not over 51."

"Okay, Mr. Steiner. I'll see what I can get for you and give you a call back. Please leave your number with my secretary."

Dan Yoder wires the information of Mr. Steiner's order to Michael Rodriguez, Robertson-Westmeyer's member on the floor of the New York Stock Exchange. Mr. Rodriguez goes to a station on the floor where a specialist, another type of broker, deals in Melville stock.

"What's the current price of Melville?" he asks.

"I can give it to you at $49\frac{5}{8}$."

"Okay, I might need that. I'll get back to you." Mr. Rodriguez questions other brokers around the station to see if any of them is selling Melville stock at a lower price than $49\frac{5}{8}$, or \$49.625. Since none is, he returns to the specialist.

"Looks like I'll need 200 shares at $49\frac{5}{8}$."

"All right, Mike. I'll take care of that right away. Who is the purchaser?"

After giving the broker the information he needs, Rodriguez sends a ticket with details of the sale to the computer operators at the Exchange. They key these details into the computer, which continuously flashes them overhead on video screens to keep brokers aware of trading and current market prices. Brokerage firms all over the nation have immediate access to current trading information by means of computer systems.

Although Mr. Steiner's purchase has been arranged, closing details follow. Mr. Yoder figures his commission, based upon the total value of the transaction. Mr. Steiner has five business days to pay for the stock.

Mr. Steiner has made a purchase through the efforts of several brokers, men acting in his stead. Brokers function not only in stock trading, but also in other areas, such as real estate and insurance. Some markets are more "liquid," or fast moving, than others. For example, you can buy or sell stock much more quickly than you can buy or sell a piece of real estate. Any one stock price can change in a matter of minutes. The stock market changes because it is controlled by the dealings of men. God, however, never changes. He is immortal and immutable; His love and care for His children never diminish. We can depend on Him (Malachi 3:6).

Opposites and Order

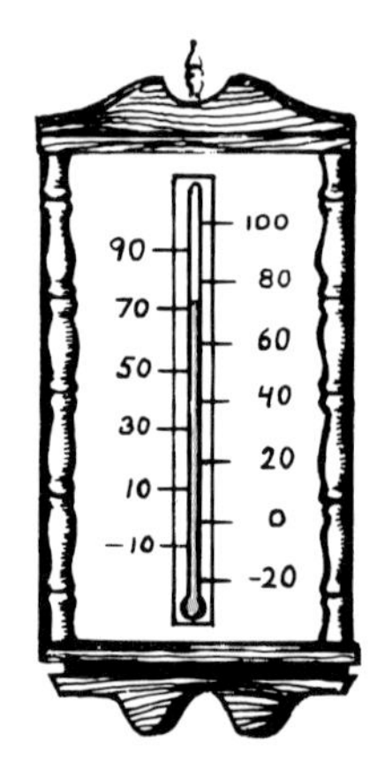

Business Statement			
Date	Debits Checks written	Credits Payments received	Balance
3-28	$28.50		-$28.50
4-2	56.70		-85.20
4-4		242.00	156.80
4-5	223.68		-66.88
4-7		84.00	17.12

Both the thermometer and the business statement illustrate measurement in *opposite directions.*
A thermometer may indicate temperatures above zero or below zero.
A business may show a loss or a profit.
These illustrations require the use of *integers.*

Remember which numbers are included in the set of numbers called *integers*.

Integers can be placed on a number line.

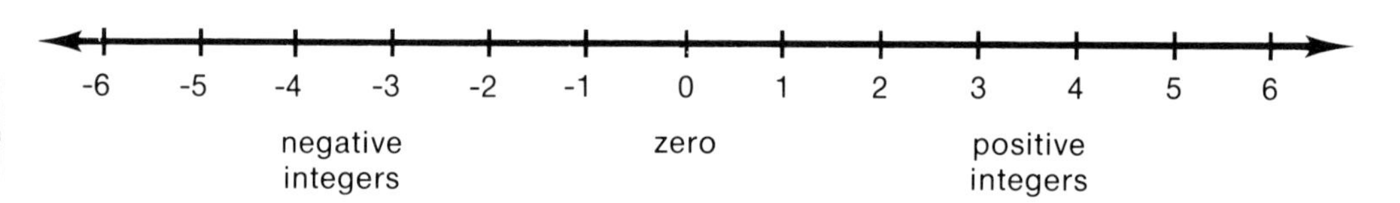

What do you think?

How many units are there from zero to positive 1?
  negative 1?
How many units are there from zero to positive 2?
  negative 2?
How many units are there from zero to positive 3?
  negative 3?
How many units are there from zero to positive 5?
  negative 5?
How many units are there from zero to positive 30?
  negative 30?

Keys to Understanding

On a number line, numbers that are the same distance from zero, but on opposite sides of it, are called *opposites*.

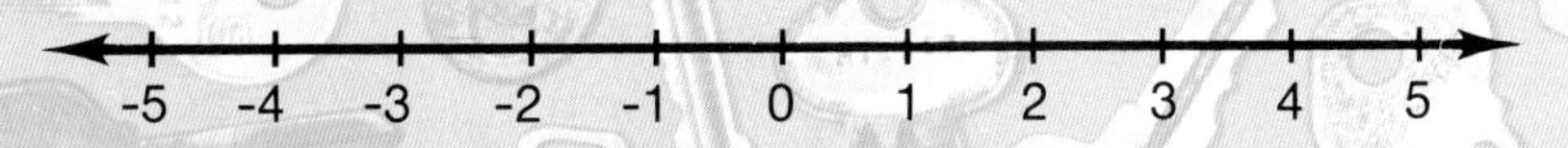

-1 and 1 are opposites.
-5 and 5 are opposites.

The larger of two numbers is the one farther to the right.

$5 > 1 > -1 > -5$

The smaller of two numbers is the one farther to the left.

$-5 < -1 < 1 < 5$

Practice

Write the opposite of each integer.

1. 9	**3.** -18	**5.** 125	**7.** -148	**9.** 419
2. -7	**4.** 6	**6.** -89	**8.** 24	**10.** -637

Compare each of these pairs of integers, using $<$ or $>$.

11. 3 and 7	**16.** -8 and -6	**21.** 2 and -16
12. -3 and -7	**17.** 5 and -11	**22.** -19 and 22
13. 0 and -2	**18.** -8 and -9	**23.** 49 and -49
14. -8 and 1	**19.** -16 and 48	**24.** -162 and -158
15. 6 and 0	**20.** -87 and -63	**25.** 463 and -485

"BIGGER THAN" IS NOT ALWAYS "GREATER THAN."

Math in Action

1. Jason Smythe bought 200 shares of stock at $36\frac{1}{2}$ (\$36.50) per share. He later sold the same stock for $39\frac{3}{4}$ (\$39.75) per share. How much profit did he make?
2. Mark Westerville bought 100 shares of stock at $34\frac{5}{8}$ (\$34.625), 50 shares of another stock at $29\frac{7}{8}$ (\$29.875), and 200 shares at $42\frac{1}{8}$ (\$42.125). How much money did his purchase cost?
3. In one day of trading, Block Corporation stock sold for as much as $44\frac{3}{4}$ and as little as $31\frac{1}{8}$. How much did its price vary during the day?
   What is the dollar equivalent of the highest price, lowest price, and the difference between the two?
4. In its stock-market columns a newspaper usually gives a "net change" figure, which tells the difference between the closing price for one day and the closing price for the preceding day. If it is a positive amount, the stock's price increased from the previous day. If it is a negative amount, the price decreased. If the closing price of a stock was $18\frac{1}{4}$ on Tuesday and the net change figure is $+\frac{3}{8}$, what was its closing price on Monday?
   If the same stock closed at $18\frac{1}{4}$ and showed a net change figure of $-\frac{1}{4}$ on Thursday, what was its closing price on Wednesday?
   If a stock's closing price on Wednesday is $31\frac{1}{8}$ and its closing price on Thursday is $29\frac{5}{8}$, what is its net change?
5. Warren Ellis made a 6% commission on a transaction totaling \$5,884.50. What was his commission?

Absolute Value

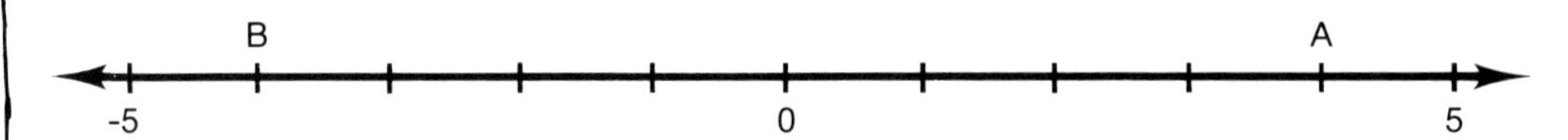

How many units are there from zero to point A?
How many units are there from zero to point B?
The absolute value of both point A and point B is 4.

Keys to Understanding

The *absolute value* (| |) of an integer is the number of units the integer is from zero, regardless of the direction.

| 7 | = 7 means "The absolute value of positive 7 is 7."
| -7 | = 7 means "The absolute value of negative 7 is 7."

What do you think?

What is the absolute value of zero?
Are the absolute values of opposite integers equal?
Does direction from zero affect absolute value?

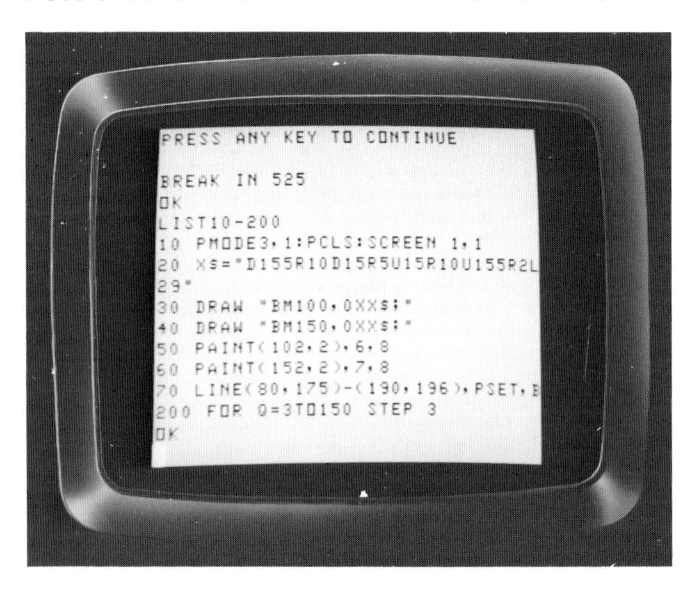

Practice

Write each absolute value.

1. $|7|$
2. $|-3|$
3. $|-11|$
4. $|18|$
5. $|0|$
6. $|21|$
7. $|-34|$
8. $|-51|$
9. $|381|$
10. $|-156|$
11. $|-1|$
12. $|17|$
13. $|1{,}310|$
14. $|1|$
15. $|-3{,}481|$
16. $|-99|$

Compare each of these pairs of numbers, using the appropriate sign ($>$, $<$, $=$).

17. $|7|$ and $|9|$
18. $|-8|$ and $|-6|$
19. $|-16|$ and $|12|$
20. $|-21|$ and $|21|$
21. $|9|$ and $|-11|$
22. $|25|$ and $|-13|$
23. $|118|$ and $|-118|$
24. $|0|$ and $|-6|$
25. $|72|$ and $|56|$
26. $|-121|$ and $|-99|$
27. $|227|$ and $|312|$
28. $|1{,}610|$ and $|-1{,}610|$

Find each sum.

29. $|6| + |5| =$
30. $|5| + |-7| =$
31. $|4| + |0| =$
32. $|-6| + |-8| =$
33. $|-20| + |5| =$
34. $|-11| + |11| =$
35. $|-9| + |-9| =$
36. $|-33| + |21| =$
37. $|-2| + |130| =$
38. $|-78| + |-22| =$
39. $|0| + |-861| =$
40. $|127| + |-127| =$

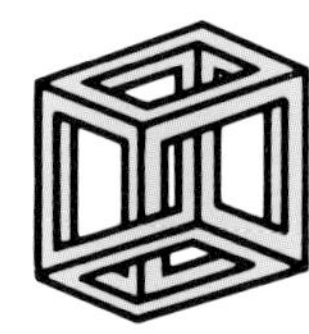

MIND BOGGLER

$a \times b = 12{,}802$

$a(b + 1) = 13{,}148$

Find the values of a and b.

Adding Integers on a Number Line

Adding a positive number means a move to the right on the number line.
Adding a negative number means a move to the left on the number line.

Integers with the Same Sign

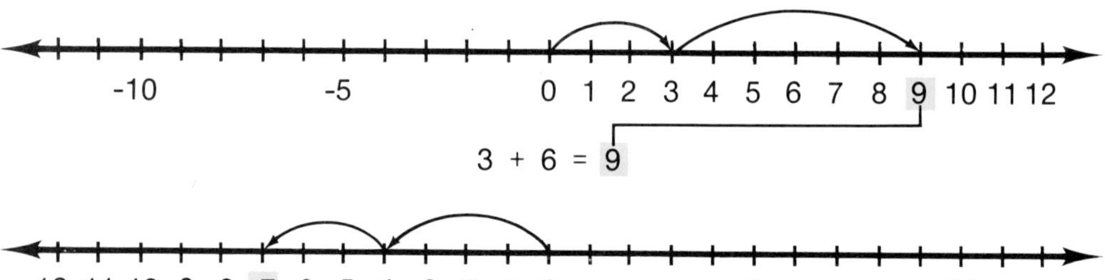

The sum of two positive integers is a positive integer.
The sum of two negative integers is a negative integer.

Integers With Different Signs

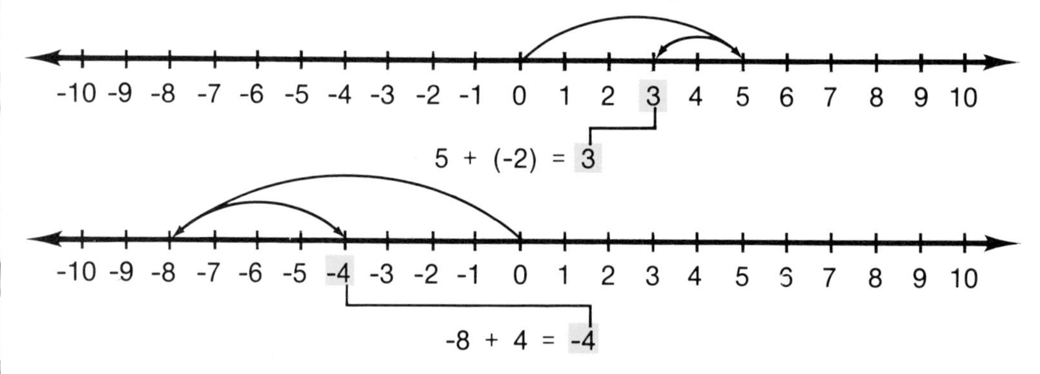

The sum of a positive integer and a negative integer has the sign of the integer with the greater absolute value.

Practice

Draw number lines to illustrate these sums.

1. 4 + 4 =
2. -3 + (-6) =
3. -2 + (-1) =
4. 1 + 7 =
5. -1 + (-1) =
6. 5 + 2 =

Note:
It is important to be able to add integers mentally.

Find each sum.

7. -11 + (-22) =
8. -28 + (-36) =
9. 123 + 64 =
10. -6 + (-5) + (-12) + (-3) =

Draw number lines to illustrate these sums.

11. -7 + 1 =
12. -2 + 8 =
13. 3 + (-1) =
14. 8 + (-9) =
15. -14 + 6 =
16. 12 + (-3) =

Find each sum.

17. -12 + 6 =
18. 8 + (-7) =
19. -13 + 30 =
20. -8 + 16 =
21. 12 + (-12) =
22. -75 + 50 =
23. 9 + (-21) =
24. -33 + 18 =
25. -111 + 123 =

Add these integers mentally and write only the answers.

26. -6 + 10 =
27. 1 + (-9) =
28. -8 + 3 =
29. -8 + (-9) =
30. 2 + (-1) =
31. 12 + (-15) =
32. -18 + 8 =
33. -4 + (-6) =
34. 20 + (-25) =
35. 13 + (-6) =
36. -7 + (-3) =
37. -8 + 9 =
38. 2 + (-15) =
39. -11 + 11 =
40. 40 + (-15) =

Rules for Adding Integers

Keys to Understanding

Rules for Adding Integers

1. If the signs of two integers are the same, add the absolute values and use the same sign.

2. If the signs of two integers are different, find the difference between the two absolute values and use the sign of the integer that has the larger absolute value.

Integers With the Same Sign

Find the sum of the absolute values.

$3 + 6 = ?$

$|3| + |6| = 3 + 6 = 9$

Therefore $3 + 6 = 9$.

The sum is positive because both the addends are positive.

$-4 + (-3) = ?$

$|-4| + |-3| = 4 + 3 = 7$

Therefore $-4 + (-3) = -7$

The sum is negative because both the addends are negative.

Integers With Different Signs

Find the difference between the absolute values.

$5 + (-2) = ?$

$|5| - |-2| = 5 - 2 = 3$

Therefore $5 + (-2) = 3$.

The sum is positive because 5 has the larger absolute value.

Remember, to find the difference between two numbers, subtract the smaller number from the larger number.

$-8 + 4 = ?$

$|-8| - |4| = 8 - 4 = 4$

Therefore $-8 + 4 = -4$.

The sum is negative because -8 has the larger absolute value.

$3 + (-9) = ?$

$|-9| - |3| = 9 - 3 = 6$

Therefore $3 + (-9) = -6$.

The sum is negative because -9 has the larger absolute value.

What do you think?

Is the commutative property true for addition of integers?
Is the associative property true for addition of integers?
What is the sum of an integer and zero?
What is the additive identity element for integers?
What is the sum of an integer and its opposite?

Practice

Tell which sign each of these sums will have.

1. -48 + 15
2. -12 + (-21)
3. 22 + (18)
4. 128 + 93
5. -16 + 41
6. -17 + (-14)
7. 240 + (-518)
8. -18 + 0
9. -15 + 8 + 9

Find each sum.

10. -15 + 2 =
11. 33 + (-20) =
12. -11 + (-14) =
13. -7 + 25 =
14. -49 + 49 =
15. 118 + (-76) =
16. 7 + (-45) =
17. -181 + 0 =
18. -92 + (-10) =
19. -28 + 59 =
20. 20 + (-23) =
21. -89 + 112 =
22. 419 + 183 =
23. 8 + 6 + (-3) =
24. -4 + (-5) + (-8) =
25. -11 + 2 + 5 =
26. 6 + 2 + (-8) =
27. -13 + 16 + 21 =
28. 25 + (-11) + (-12) + 7 + (-9) + 17 =

Solve these problems.

29. Juanita is keeping a record of her weight. One week she lost six pounds. The next week she gained two pounds. What was her total weight change after these two weeks?

30. Mrs. Stump was playing shuffleboard. If her four discs were positioned as shown, how many points did she score?

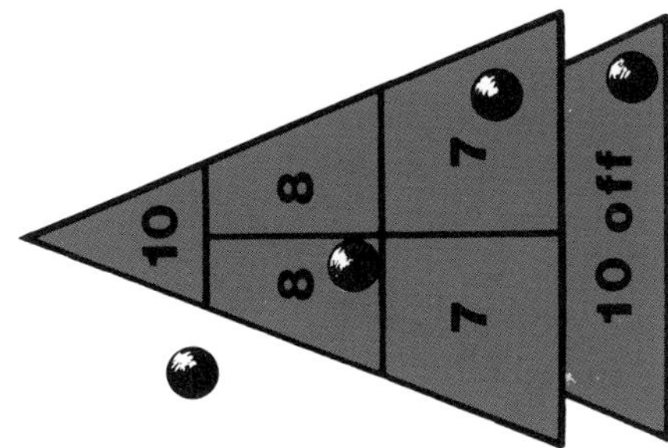

Subtracting Integers

Note: *To subtract two integers, find the sum of the first integer and the opposite of the second integer.*

Study the number patterns to determine which numbers should be in the blanks.
By looking at the patterns, you can see that subtracting an integer is the same as adding its opposite.

Keys to Understanding

Subtracting an integer is the same as adding its opposite.
For any integer a and b:

$$a - b = a + (\text{opposite of } b)$$

Examples:

	add opposites	answers
8 - 5 =	8 + (-5)	= 3
-7 - 3 =	-7 + (-3)	= -10
4 - (-6) =	4 + 6	= 10
-9 - (-2) =	-9 + 2	= -7

Practice

Subtract by adding the opposites.

1. 5 - 2 =

2. 2 - 5 =

3. 6 - (-4) =

4. -2 - (-8) =

5. -3 - 7 =

6. 9 - 0 =

7. 0 - 9 =

8. 11 - (-11) =

9. -12 - (-13) =

10. -50 - 20 =

11. 18 - 21 =

12. -73 - 48 =

13. 0 - (-125) =

14. 215 - 215 =

15. -15 - (-31) =

Subtract these integers mentally and write only the answers.

16. 5 - 2 =

17. -3 - (-5) =

18. -6 - 4 =

19. 9 - (-1) =

20. 6 - 8 =

21. -11 - (-9) =

22. -10 - 15 =

23. 1 - 9 =

24. 10 - (-10) =

25. -12 - (-14) =

26. -15 - 0 =

27. 3 - 10 =

28. -8 - (-8) =

29. -11 - 9 =

30. -10 - (-15) =

Solving Multi-step Problems

These problems may appear to be difficult. However, they can be easily solved if the operations in the parentheses are done first.

$-18 + 7 = -11$
$13 + -21 = -8$

Therefore $(-18 - 7) + (13 + -21) = ?$
$-11 + -8 = -19$

$21 - 6 = 15$
$-11 + 3 = -8$

Therefore $(21 - 6) - (-11 + 3) = ?$
$15 - -8 = 23$

Practice

Add.

1. -5 + (-3 + -2) =
2. (-7 + 8) + -6 =
3. 21 + (-16 + 3) =
4. -25 + (47 + 18) =
5. (-90 + 100) + (-34 + 17) =

Remember, do the work in the parentheses first.

Subtract.

6. -16 - (-4 - 3) =
7. 48 - (15 - 18) =
8. (30 - 17) - (-12) =
9. (-27 - 18) - 41 =
10. (-9 + 6) - (16 - 25) =

Do the indicated operations mentally and write only the answers.

11. (8 - 6) + 3 =
12. -12 + (3 - 6) =
13. (8 - 3) - (-7) =
14. (-10 + 12) - 3 =
15. 5 - (12 + 4) =
16. -10 + (6 - 8) =
17. (8 - 15) - (-3) =
18. -9 + (-1 - 2) =
19. (-3 + 9) - 6 =
20. (2 - 5) + (-3 + 3) =

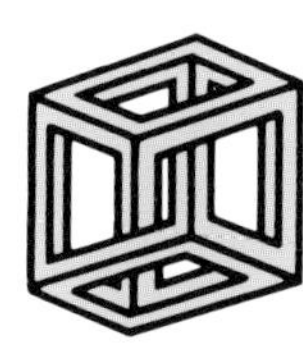

MIND BOGGLER

Terry has a box full of apples. When he counts the apples by 2s, 3s, 5s, or 7s, he has one apple left over each time. What is the least number of apples that could be in the box?

Multiplying Integers

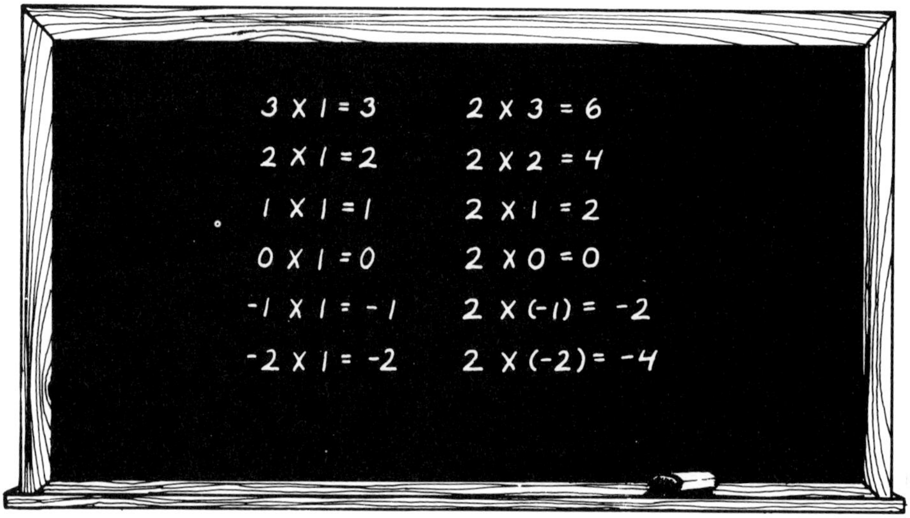

3 × 1 = 3	2 × 3 = 6
2 × 1 = 2	2 × 2 = 4
1 × 1 = 1	2 × 1 = 2
0 × 1 = 0	2 × 0 = 0
-1 × 1 = -1	2 × (-1) = -2
-2 × 1 = -2	2 × (-2) = -4

When multiplying two integers, first multiply the absolute values of the integers just as you would whole numbers. Then use rules to determine the correct sign of the product.

Complete the patterns to help discover the rules.

2 × 3 = _____	4 × 2 = _____
1 × 3 = _____	4 × 1 = _____
0 × 3 = _____	4 × 0 = _____
-1 × 3 = _____	4 × (-1) = _____
-2 × 3 = _____	4 × (-2) = _____
-3 × 3 = _____	4 × (-3) = _____

What do you think?

Is the product of two positive integers positive or negative?

When multiplying a positive and a negative integer, what will be the sign of the answer?

What rule will help to determine the sign of the product of a positive and a negative integer?

Practice

Find each product.

1. $7 \times 4 =$
2. $-4 \times 7 =$
3. $3 \times (-5) =$
4. $-5 \times 3 =$
5. $-6 \times 8 =$
6. $-8 \times 10 =$
7. $5 \times (-12) =$
8. $-11 \times 0 =$
9. $9 \times 8 =$
10. $-5 \times 6 =$
11. $4 \times (-9) =$
12. $-8 \times 4 =$
13. $7 \times (-1) =$
14. $-6 \times 6 =$
15. $-12 \times 5 =$

Find each product.

16. $-8 \times (5 \times 2) =$
17. $(-8 \times 5) \times 2 =$
18. $(3 \times 4) \times (-3) =$
19. $-6 \times (5 \times 4) =$
20. $6 \times (-2 \times 5) =$
21. $(-7 \times 5) \times 2 =$

Solve these problems.

22. $6 \times (-8 - 3) =$
23. $(-7 + 7) \times 6 =$
24. $-5 \times (-6 + 7) =$
25. $(-3 \times 4) - 8 =$
26. $(-4 \times 4) - (-9) =$
27. $-12 + (-3 \times 4) =$

28. On New Year's Day the temperature in northern Indiana was -3 degrees. At the same time, the temperature in northern Minnesota measured 12 degrees colder than in Indiana. What was the temperature in Minnesota?
29. Jim had an average weight change of -2 pounds a week for a period of 14 weeks. What was his total weight change?
30. An iceberg is 3,109 meters from top to bottom. If 813 meters of the iceberg is above sea level, how far below sea level is the bottom of the iceberg?

$3 \times (-1) = -3$
$2 \times (-1) = -2$
$1 \times (-1) = -1$
$0 \times (-1) = 0$
$-1 \times (-1) = 1$
$-2 \times (-1) = 2$

$-2 \times 3 = -6$
$-2 \times 2 = -4$
$-2 \times 1 = -2$
$-2 \times 0 = 0$
$-2 \times (-1) = 2$
$-2 \times (-2) = 4$

Complete the patterns.

$2 \times (-3) =$ _____
$1 \times (-3) =$ _____
$0 \times (-3) =$ _____
$-1 \times (-3) =$ _____
$-2 \times (-3) =$ _____
$-3 \times (-3) =$ _____

$-4 \times 2 =$ _____
$-4 \times 1 =$ _____
$-4 \times 0 =$ _____
$-4 \times (-1) =$ _____
$-4 \times (-2) =$ _____
$-4 \times (-3) =$ _____

Is the product of two negative integers positive or negative?

Keys to Understanding

Rules for Multiplying Integers

1. The product of two positive integers is positive.
2. The product of two negative integers is positive.
3. The product of one positive integer and one negative integer is negative.

What do you think?

Is the commutative property true for multiplication of integers?
Is the associative property true for multiplication of integers?
What is the product of an integer and 1?
What is the multiplicative identity element for integers?
What is the product of an integer and negative 1?

Practice

Find each product.

1. -2 × (-9) =
2. -5 × (-7) =
3. -8 × (-8) =
4. -6 × (-3) =
5. -10 × (-5) =
6. -4 × (-11) =
7. -20 × (-6) =
8. -15 × (-2) =
9. -18 × (-1) =
10. 0 × (-22) =
11. -5 × (-12) =
12. -15 × (-8) =
13. -11 × (-10) =
14. -16 × (-12) =
15. -20 × (-15) =

Find each product.

16. -2 × (-3 × 4) =
17. (-10 × 1) × -5 =
18. -6 × (-18) =
19. -9 × (-12) =
20. (-2 × 3) × (-4 × 2) =
21. (-5 × 1) × (-1 × 6) =

Solve these problems.

22. (-3 × 2) + (2 × 5) =
23. (-5 × 3) - (-6 × 3) =
24. (-10 × 8) + (-7 × 8) =
25. (-3 × 11) - (6 × 5) =

Dividing Integers

Since $2 \times 4 = 8$,
then $8 \div 2 = 4$
and $8 \div 4 = 2$.

Since $-5 \times 3 = -15$,
then $-15 \div 3 = -5$
and $-15 \div (-5) = 3$.

Remember the relationship between multiplication and division.

When dividing two integers, divide the absolute values of the integers just as you would whole numbers.

Keys to Understanding

Rules for Dividing Integers

1. The quotient of two positive integers is positive.
2. The quotient of two negative integers is positive.
3. The quotient of one positive integer and one negative integer is negative.

Practice

Find each quotient.

1. $-16 \div 2 =$
2. $21 \div 3 =$
3. $-42 \div (-6) =$
4. $-48 \div 8 =$
5. $-28 \div (-7) =$
6. $49 \div (-7) =$
7. $0 \div (-8) =$
8. $-25 \div 5 =$
9. $56 \div 7 =$
10. $-98 \div (-1) =$
11. $-24 \div 6 =$
12. $-35 \div (-7) =$
13. $200 \div (-5) =$
14. $-144 \div 12 =$
15. $196 \div 14 =$

Find each quotient.

16. $\frac{-21}{-7} =$
17. $\frac{-36}{6} =$
18. $\frac{-8}{-8} =$
19. $\frac{45}{-5} =$
20. $\frac{81}{9} =$
21. $\frac{-32}{-4} =$
22. $\frac{-54}{6} =$
23. $\frac{0}{-11} =$
24. $\frac{147}{7} =$

Solve these problems.

25. $(-28 \div 4) \div (-7) =$
26. $(-3 \times 8) \div 12 =$
27. $(-15 \div 5) + (-24 \div 4) =$
28. $(-3 \times 8) \div (-3 \times 2) =$
29. $(-6 - 4) \div (2 \times 5) =$
30. $(-16 \div 2) \times (-20 \div 4) =$

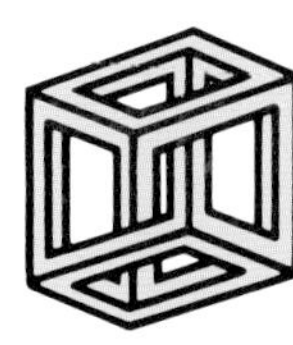

MIND BOGGLER

Mr. Key weighs twice as much as his wife. His wife weighs twice as much as their son. If their total weight is 399 pounds, how much does each person weigh?

Graphing Ordered Pairs

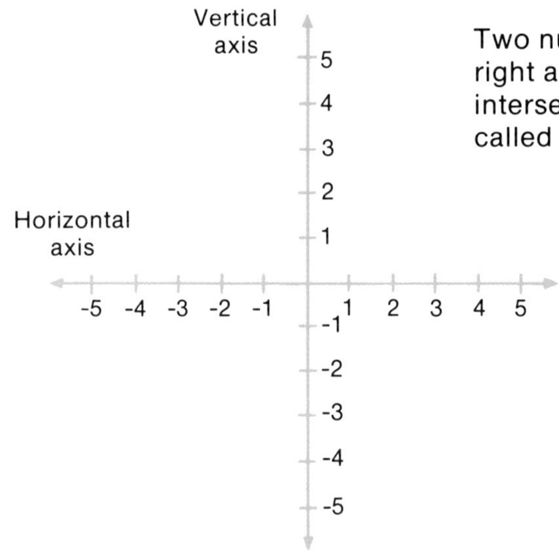

Two number lines drawn at right angles to each other and intersecting at 0 form what is called the *coordinate plane.*

Remember that two lines determine a plane.

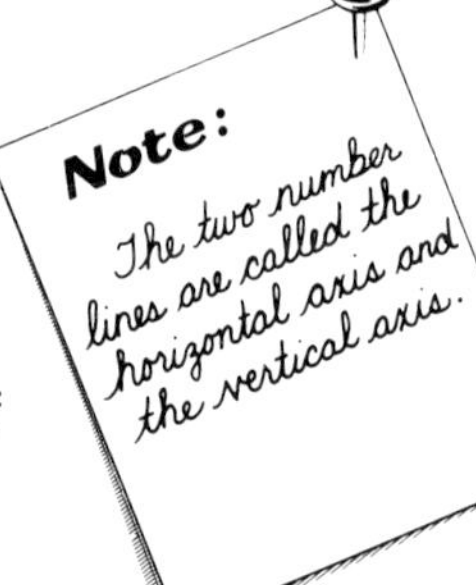

On the horizontal axis, positive numbers are to the right of 0, and negative numbers are to the left of 0.
On the vertical axis, positive numbers are above 0, and negative numbers are below 0.

To locate a point on a coordinate plane, we use pairs of numbers, such as (3, 2), (-3, 1) (-1, -2), and (1, -3). These pairs are called *ordered pairs,* because the order of the numbers is important.

In the ordered pair, the first number tells the distance to the right or left of 0. The second number tells the distance above or below 0.

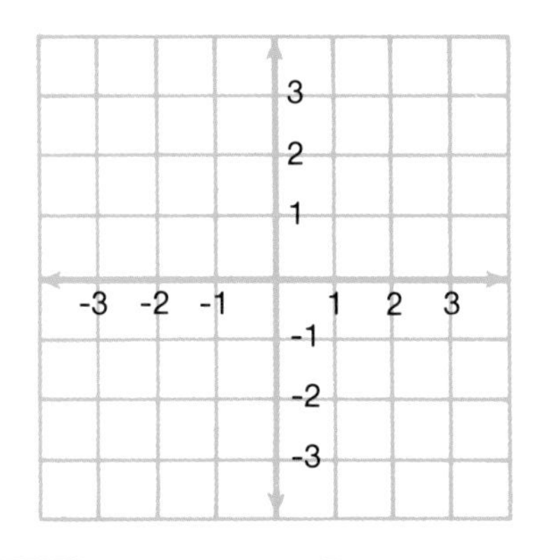

Point	Ordered Pair	Position
M:	(4, 1)	4 units to the right 1 unit up
A:	(-2, 2)	2 units to the left 2 units up
T:	(-3, -4)	3 units to the left 4 units down
H:	(1, -3)	1 unit to the right 3 units down

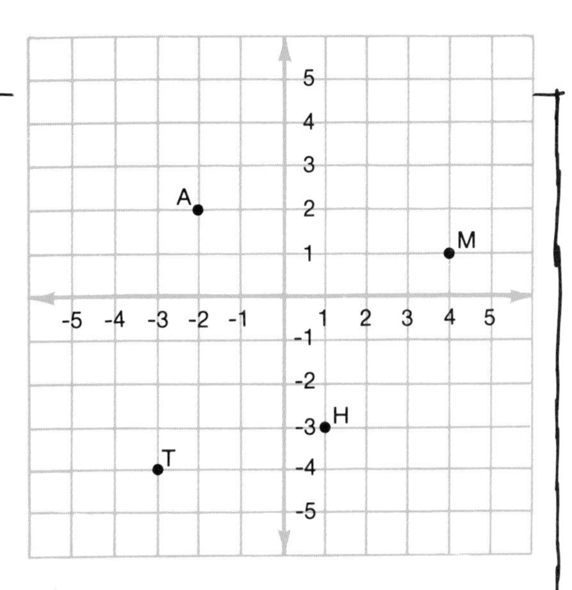

Practice

Graph and label each of the following points.

1. S (2, 5)
2. T (-1, 4)
3. U (-3, -2)
4. D (4, -1)
5. Y (0, -3)
6. I (-4, 0)
7. N (-5, -5)
8. G (-5, 3)

Write the ordered pair for each of the lettered points.

9. A _____
10. B _____
11. C _____
12. D _____
13. E _____
14. F _____
15. G _____
16. H _____
17. I _____
18. J _____
19. K _____
20. L _____
21. M _____
22. N _____
23. O _____
24. P _____

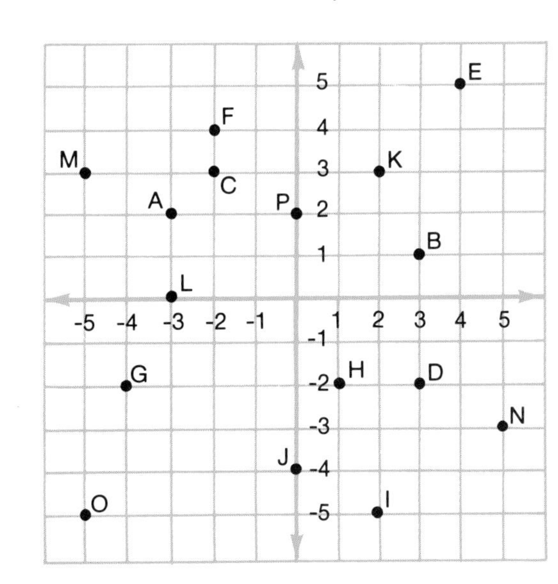

Unit Review

Give the opposite of each of these integers.

1. -8 **2.** 9 **3.** 21 **4.** -17 **5.** -86

Give the absolute value of each of these integers.

6. $|-5|$ **7.** $|11|$ **8.** $|-33|$ **9.** $|25|$ **10.** $|-118|$

Find each sum.

11. -6 + 3 =
12. 8 + 5 =
13. -9 + (-7) =
14. 12 + (-4) =
15. -15 + 6 =
16. -22 + (-14) =

Find each difference.

17. -12 - 4 =
18. -8 - (-3) =
19. 18 - 9 =
20. 15 - (-5) =
21. -7 - (-7) =
22. 10 - 18 =

Find each product.

23. -8 × 4 =
24. 9 × 7 =
25. 5 × (-6) =
26. -3 × (-10) =
27. -12 × 5 =
28. -14 × (-4) =

Find each quotient.

29. -56 ÷ 8 =
30. -55 ÷ (-5) =
31. 21 ÷ (-7) =
32. 44 ÷ 11 =
33. -39 ÷ (-13) =
34. -64 ÷ 16 =

Solve these problems.

35. -15 + (-4 + 2) =
36. 37 - (-12 + 15) =
37. -8 × (4 - 7) =
38. (-15 - 1) ÷ (-8 + 4) =
39. (3 × 4) - (-2 × 1) =
40. (6 - 10) × (-4 + 10) =

Write the ordered pair for each of the lettered points.

41. F _____
42. A _____
43. I _____
44. T _____
45. H _____

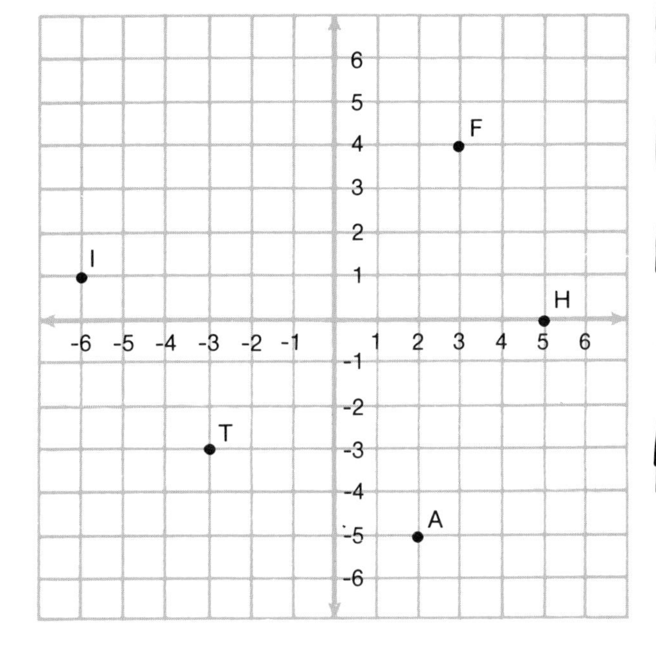

Graph and label each of the following points.

46. G (3,0) **47.** R (-6,-2) **48.** A (-3,4) **49.** D (5,-1) **50.** E (0,-4)

MIND BOGGLER

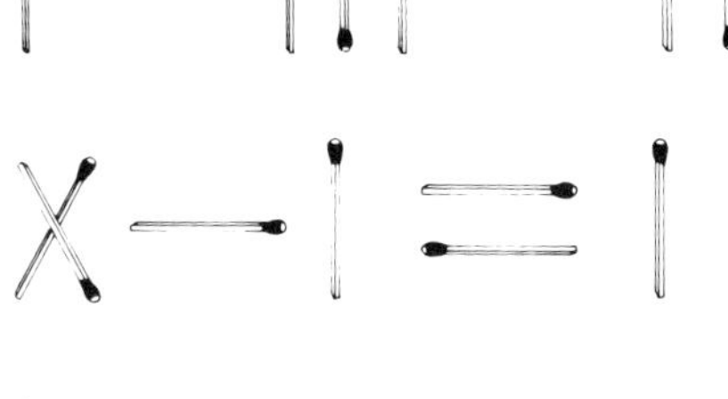

Each of these rows of matches is a puzzle in roman numerals. All the equations are false as they stand, but you can make each true by moving only one match.

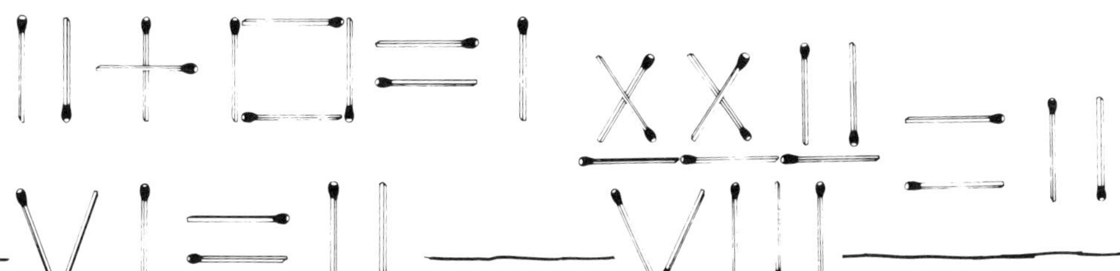

Skills Checkup

1. 5,231,619 + 823,819 + 654,006 + 9,819,016 + 2,347,116

2. 8,000,000 - 5,295,789
3. 51,008 - 12,416
4. 3,860 - 2,049
5. 837 × 89
6. 5,615 × 37
7. 56,489 × 345
8. 756 ÷ 21
9. 33,726 ÷ 231
10. 5,202 ÷ 51

11. $\frac{7}{8} + \frac{2}{3}$
12. $2\frac{3}{5} + 4\frac{7}{10}$
13. $8\frac{3}{4} + 3\frac{5}{6}$
14. $\frac{5}{8} - \frac{1}{6}$
15. $7 - 2\frac{3}{4}$
16. $8\frac{1}{4} - 3\frac{2}{5}$
17. $7 \times \frac{2}{3}$
18. $1\frac{1}{2} \times \frac{5}{6}$
19. $2\frac{3}{4} \times 1\frac{7}{8}$
20. $3\frac{1}{2} \div 2$
21. $\frac{5}{8} \div 2\frac{1}{3}$
22. $2\frac{5}{6} \div 1\frac{2}{5}$

23. 16.3579 + 9 + 18.351
24. 35.4179 + 8.3 + 6.5
25. 9.253 + 6.82
26. 3.14 - 1.936
27. 5 - 0.1467
28. 8.34567 - 1.3
29. 3.486 × 3.5
30. 15.764 × 0.08
31. 2.354 × 1.7569
32. $893.84 - $2.56
33. 31.2 ÷ 24
34. 239.56 ÷ 4.52

35. Joel and Chris were playing a game of darts. Joel had these scores: -50, +20, -15, -20, and +25. Chris had these scores: +50, -25, -10, +20, and -15. What was Joel's final score? his average score? What was Chris's final score? his average score?
36. Mt. McKinley has an elevation of 6,194 meters; Death Valley is 86 meters below sea level. How many meters are between the two extremes? What would be the elevation of a point whose elevation was halfway between Mt. McKinley and Death Valley?
37. At 2:00 A.M. the temperature was -5° C. At noon it was 5° C. How much had the temperature risen? What was the average rise per hour during the period?
38. A jet plane climbs at the rate of 1,075 meters per minute. How many minutes would it take the plane to climb to an altitude of 6.45 kilometers? How far will it have climbed after an hour?

1. 3,251,176 + 76,450 + 341,210 + 12 + 4,158,260 + 345 + 4,578

2. 32,451 - 16,763
3. 2,152 - 1,047
4. 8,761 - 5,456
5. 450,837 × 25
6. 60,437 × 17
7. 5,162 × 5,893
8. 5,202 ÷ 51
9. 1,814 ÷ 32
10. 59,500 ÷ 700

11. $2\frac{1}{5} + 4\frac{3}{7}$
12. $56\frac{4}{7} + 3\frac{7}{9}$
13. $35\frac{6}{13} + 25\frac{2}{3}$
14. $7\frac{1}{6} - 2\frac{5}{8}$
15. $78\frac{3}{14} - 56\frac{1}{3}$
16. $37 - 19\frac{3}{7}$
17. $5\frac{2}{5} \times 3\frac{1}{2}$
18. $7\frac{3}{4} \times 6\frac{1}{6}$
19. $5\frac{3}{7} \times 12\frac{4}{5}$
20. $3\frac{3}{4} \div 1\frac{7}{8}$
21. $6\frac{2}{5} \div 3\frac{1}{2}$
22. $7\frac{2}{3} \div 1\frac{2}{7}$

23. 81.7 + 6 + 0.83 + 25.67
24. 9.5 + 0.7 + 3
25. 7.83 + 9.2 + 0.645
26. 8.34 - 7.0234
27. 2,378.45 - 238.008
28. 908.304 - 2.05
29. 2.357 × 1.74
30. 89.12 × 345.907
31. 617.01 × 3.782
32. $1,955.77 ÷ $257
33. 239.56 ÷ 4.52
34. 1.6856 ÷ 6.02

35. Mr. Damigo is a door-to-door salesman. He spent one day making calls on one street. He started at Central Park and traveled 6 blocks north, then 8 blocks south, then 5 blocks south, then 3 blocks north, and then 7 blocks south. How far was he from Central Park when he finished his calls for the day?
36. Mr. O'Hare earns $350 a week at his job. Mrs. O'Hare spends $87.50 every week on groceries for their family. What part of Mr. O'Hare's income is spent on groceries? If Mr. O'Hare earns $1,500 per month and spends $\frac{1}{3}$ of it on the house payment, what is the O'Hare's monthly house payment?
37. The average number of seventh-grade students who are absent each day is about 1.3. How many were absent over a 20-day period? a 30-day period? a school year of 180 days?
38. If a realtor sold a home and made $1,250 as a 5% commission, what was the selling price of the home? What would have been the amount of his commission if the rate had been 8%?

Glossary

A

absolute value The number of units an integer is from 0, regardless of the direction.

acute angle An angle that measures less than 90°.

acute triangle A triangle with only acute angles.

adjacent angles Two angles that have a common vertex and a common ray between them.

angle (∠) The union of two rays that have a common endpoint, called a vertex.

area The amount of surface in a closed region; measured in square units.

associative property The idea that addends or factors can be grouped in different ways without changing the sum or product; $(a + b) + c = a + (b + c)$.

B

base The number that is used as a factor in exponential notation; in 3^4, 3 is the base; $3^4 = 3 \cdot 3 \cdot 3 \cdot 3$, or 81.

bases The parallel faces of a prism.

binary operation The combining of two numbers mathematically.

bisect To cut into two equal parts.

C

canceling The procedure used to simplify multiplication of fractions by dividing out common factors before the operation is performed.

circle A set of all the points that are equidistant from a given center point.

circumference The distance around a circle.

commutative property The idea that the order of addends or factors can be changed without changing the sum or product; $a + b = b + a$.

complementary angles Two angles, the sum of whose measures is 90°.

composite number A number that has more than two factors.

congruent (≅) The same in size and shape.

cross-product multiplication Multiplying the numerator of a fraction by the denominator of another fraction and multiplying the denominator of the first fraction by the numerator of the second fraction to determine the relationship between the two fractions.

D

degree (°) The unit used for measuring angles.

denominator The bottom number in a fraction; tells the name and number of parts in the whole.

diameter A line segment that goes through the center point of a circle and has its endpoints on the circle.

digits Symbols used to write numbers in standard form; the set of digits = {0,1,2,3,4,5,6,7,8,9}.

disjoint sets Sets whose intersection is the empty set.

distributive property For any numbers a, b, and c, $a(b + c) = ab + ac$.

division property of 0 The idea that 0 divided by any number is equal to 0.

E

edge The line segment where two faces of a polyhedron meet.

elements The objects in a set; also called members.

empty set ($\varnothing$ or { }) A set with no members; also called the null set.

equation A math sentence that states an equality relationship.

equilateral triangle A triangle whose sides are of equal length.

equivalent fractions Fractions that name the same number (have the same value).

estimate To find an approximate answer.

exponent The number that tells how many times a base number is used as a factor; $n^5 = n \cdot n \cdot n \cdot n \cdot n$.

extremes The two middle numbers in a proportion.

F

face A polygonal surface of a polyhedron.

factor (noun) A number that is multiplied by a number or numbers to give a product.
(verb) To find the numbers that have been multiplied to give a product.

finite set A set in which the members can be counted or listed.

fraction Part of a whole object or set; used to express answers to division problems.

fractional form For any two numbers a and b, $\frac{a}{b}$ is fractional form; may represent a fraction, a whole number, or a mixed number.

G

geometry The study of points and the shapes they form.

gram (g) A standard metric unit used to measure weight and mass.

greatest common factor (GCF) The greatest whole number that is a factor of each of two or more numbers being considered.

I

identity element The number that, when applied to a number in an operation, results in that same number. The identity element for addition is 0; the identity element for multiplication is 1.

improper fraction A fractional number whose value is 1 or more; has a numerator greater than or equal to its denominator.

inequality A math sentence that is not an equation.

infinite set A set that is not finite.

integers I = {...-3,-2,-1,0,1,2,3,...}; positive integers = {1,2,3,4,...}; negative integers = {...-4,-3,-2,-1}.

intersecting lines Lines that cross. They have one and only one point in common.

intersection (∩) The set whose members are members of both of two sets being considered.

isosceles triangle A triangle that has at least two sides the same length.

L

least common multiple (LCM) The smallest nonzero number that is a multiple of each of two or more numbers being considered.

line segment Part of a straight line consisting of an infinite set of points between two endpoints.

liter (ℓ) A standard metric unit used to measure liquid volume.

lowest common denominator (LCD) The least common multiple (LCM) of the denominators of each of two or more fractions being considered.

lowest terms The simplest form of a fraction, found when there is no other equivalent fraction with a smaller numerator and denominator.

M

means The two middle numbers in a proportion.

members The objects in a set; also called elements.

meter (m) A standard metric unit used to measure distances.

multiple The product of a whole number and a given number.

multiplicative property of 0 The idea that any number multiplied by 0, or 0 multiplied by any number, is equal to 0.

N

natural numbers N = {1,2,3,4,5,...}.

null set (∅ or { }) A set with no members; also called the empty set.

numerator The top number in a fraction; tells the number of parts being considered.

O

obtuse angle An angle that measures greater than 90° and less than 180°.

obtuse triangle A triangle with one obtuse angle.

open sentence A math sentence that is neither true nor false until more information is given; contains at least one variable.

opposites Numbers that are the same distance from 0 on a number line, but on opposite sides of it.

P

parallel lines (||) Lines that are in the same plane and never intersect.

parallelogram A quadrilateral with opposite sides parallel.

percent (%) The ratio of a given number to 100.

percent change A ratio comparing the amount of change to the original amount; found by determining what percent of the original amount is represented by the amount of change; may be either an increase or a decrease.

perimeter The distance around a figure; the sum of the lengths of the sides of a polygon.

perpendicular bisector A line that intersects a line segment at its middle point and is perpendicular to the line segment.

perpendicular lines (⊥) Intersecting lines that form right angles.

pi **(π)** The number that is the ratio of the circumference of a circle to its diameter; approximately 3.14.

place value The value of a digit's position or place in a numeral.

plane A basic idea in geometry; represented by a set of points extending infinitely in all directions, forming a flat surface; determined by any three points in the plane that are not on the same line.

point A basic idea in geometry; often represented by a dot and named using capital letters.

point of intersection The one and only one point that intersecting lines have in common.

polygon A closed figure made up of line segments; named by using the names of the vertices in order, beginning at any one vertex.

polyhedron A solid figure with flat polygonal faces.

prime factorization The expression of a number as the product of numbers; the fastest and easiest way to find the GCF and LCM of numbers.

prime number A number that has only two factors—1 and itself.

prism A polyhedron with at least two faces that are congruent and parallel.

proper fraction A fractional number whose value is less than 1; has a numerator less than its denominator.

proportion An equation stating that two ratios are equal.

protractor A 180° instrument used to measure and draw angles.

Q

quadrilateral A four-sided polygon. The sum of the measures of the angles is 360°.

R

radius A line segment with one endpoint at the center of a circle and the other endpoint on the circle.

ratio A comparison of two sets, expressed with numbers. The ratio of a to b can be written $a{:}b$ or $\frac{a}{b}$.

ray A part of a straight line consisting of an infinite set of points extending endlessly in one direction from an endpoint.

reciprocals Two numbers whose product is 1.

rectangle A parallelogram with four right angles.

regular polygon A polygon in which all the sides are the same length and all the angles have the same measure.

rename To express a number in another way mathematically.

repeating decimal A nonterminating decimal, one or more of whose digits repeat in a pattern.

rhombus A parallelogram with all four sides the same length.

right angle An angle that measures 90°.

right triangle A triangle with one right angle.

S

scalene triangle A triangle with no two sides the same length.

set A group or collection of objects.

similar (~) The same shape but not necessarily the same size.

solid figure An object that has three dimensions.

solution A number that replaces the variable in a sentence to make the sentence true.

solution set The set of all possible solutions to a given sentence.

square A rectangle with all four sides the same length; a rhombus with four right angles.

straight angle An angle that measures 180°.

straight line A basic idea in geometry; represented by a set of points extending infinitely in opposite directions. A unique line is determined and named by any two points on the line.

subset ($\subseteq$) A set is a subset of another set if all the members of the first set are also members of the second set.

supplementary angles Two angles, the sum of whose measures is 180°.

surface area The total area of the surfaces of a solid.

T

terminating decimal A decimal with a finite number of digits.

transversal A line that intersects two or more lines.

trapezoid A quadrilateral with one pair of opposite sides parallel.

triangle A three-sided polygon. The sum of the measures of its angles is 180°.

U

union ($\cup$) The set found by combining the members of two sets. Each of the members of the union is a member of at least one of the original sets.

V

variable A letter of the alphabet that represents a number.

Venn diagram A diagram used to show relationships among two or more sets.

vertex The point at which two rays or line segments meet; the point where three or more edges meet on a polyhedron (plural: *vertices*).

vertical angles The pairs of opposite angles formed by two intersecting lines.

volume The amount of space in a solid figure; measured in cubic units.

W

whole numbers W = {0,1,2,3,4,...}.

Index

Photo Credits

All photos not otherwise credited are by Unusual Films.

page iv	American Soybean Association
page 5	American Soybean Association
page 12	American Soybean Association
pages 14-15	Richard Peck
page 25	American Soybean Association
page 62	Huffy
page 86	Stewart Custer
page 100	Riegel Corporation
page 102	George Collins
page 114	Southern Railways
page 126	Riegel Corporation
page 130	Rinker Materials Corporation
page 131	Riegel Corporation
page 143	Grace Collins
page 159	George Collins
page 167	Barge Memorial Hospital
page 190	J I Case
page 213	Little League Baseball Headquarters
page 216	Bob Whitmore
page 220	Lockheed California
page 221	Richard Peck
page 222	American Motors Corporation
page 230	Richard Peck
page 238	George Collins
page 245	George Collins
page 250	George Collins
page 265	Piper Aircraft Company
page 270	Rinker Materials Corporation
page 280	Little League Baseball Headquarters
page 299	Bob Whitmore
page 300	Hubbard Scientific Company
page 302	Bob Whitmore
page 310	New York Stock Exchange
page 314	Chicago Board of Trade
page 319	Chicago Board of Trade
page 329	New York Stock Exchange
page 331	George Collins

Unit divider narratives by Sherry Hill and Rita Smith
Project editor, Mary Ann McGilvray